ALIEN GRASSES

OF THE BRITISH ISLES

ALIEN GRASSES

of the

BRITISH ISLES

T. B. RYVES

E. J. CLEMENT

M. C. FOSTER

with guidance on nomenclature by

D. H. KENT

and illustrations by

G.M.S. EASY

Botanical Society of the British Isles
London
1996

Published by the Botanical Society of the British Isles
London

© BSBI 1996

ISBN 0

Camera-ready copy produced by M. C. Foster

Index produced by R. Gwynn Ellis

Printed in Great Britain by The Devonshire Press,
Torquay

The cover illustration shows Greater Quaking-grass (*Briza maxima* L.)
drawn by G. M. S. Easy

CONTENTS

PREFACE

The authors of *Alien plants of the British Isles* (ref.S1) originally intended to include grasses in that work but, because adding the large number of alien grass species would have made the book unwieldy, and because solving numerous problems, particularly of synonymy, would have delayed publication, it was decided to reserve this family for a separate volume.

This decision provided an opportunity to check many details and to increase the amount of information presented. Work already done by the original authors has been brought up to date and greatly extended by T.B.Ryves: the sequence of genera now follows that of *Genera Graminum* (ref.S7); recent proposed changes in the nomenclature of bamboos have been incorporated; instead of a brief selection of herbaria and literature references, as in the earlier volume, no restriction has been put on their number; beneath the generic name notes on the number of species worldwide within the genus, their native areas, their habitats, and particular plants of economic importance have been added; and more information is given about potential grass aliens, most of which have either been found in NW Europe, or have been cultivated from wool waste, bird-seed or other imports.

Two major aids to the identification of specimens have been added: dichotomous keys to the Bambuseae (by D.T.Holyoak) and to some of the larger and more difficult genera (by T.B.R.) have been devised; and more than a hundred illustrations, representative of each non-British genus (excluding bamboos), have been drawn by G.M.S.Easy. These illustrations show not only the whole plant, but also magnifications of the spikelets, florets, ligules and other diagnostic features.

The preparation of this catalogue has revealed various conflicting views among experts about the correct identification of specimens and matters of nomenclature; nor do we three amateurs always fully agree in the conclusions we present. We have had much advice and generous help, but any errors that remain are solely the responsibility of the authors.

T.B.R.
E.J.C.
M.C.F.

Nov. 1995

ACKNOWLEDGEMENTS

During the preparation of this book, we have received much help from numerous botanists, both professional and amateur, most of whose names appear among the personal communications listed in references R1 - R126 or in the list of private herbaria. We especially appreciate receiving from Dr H.J.M.Bowen, Dr E.Chicken, †Mrs C.M.Dony, C.G.Hanson, P.A.Harmes, Dr J.L.Mason, J.R.Palmer, R.M.Payne and Mrs S.Reynolds extensive lists of alien grasses collected since 1950.

We are greatly indebted to D.H.Kent who has checked the nomenclature throughout our book: his knowledge of the relevant botanical literature is invaluable. Dr T.A.Cope of R.B.G., Kew has also taken a great interest in our work and helped in many ways, including the identification and confirmation of difficult species, advice on nomenclature and checking the manuscript. The account of the bamboos, using the most recent nomenclature, has been carefully checked and revised by Dr C.M.A.Stapleton of R.B.G., Kew and D.McClintock, who have also provided determinations for some of the dubious herbarium material of this most difficult tribe. An excellent key of Bambuseae has been provided by Dr D.T.Holyoak. Other valuable advice was also received from Dr A.C.Leslie and Prof. C.A.Stace at an early stage.

Searching for voucher specimens in herbaria is a time-consuming task; this has been undertaken by G.M.S.Easy (CGE), N.Lusmore and M.J.Trotman (BRISTM), Mrs S.Reynolds (DBN), and the late Miss R.Sedergreen (BM). Keepers and staff of several herbaria have been very helpful, namely F.H.Brightman and P.C.Holland (SLBI), Dr J.R.Edmondson (LIV), R.G.Ellis and Dr G.Hutchinson (NMW), Ms Sam Hallett (BRISTM), Dr G.Halliday (LANC), Dr S.L.Jury (RNG), Prof. G.Ll.Lucas (K), Ms S.K.Marner (OXF), Miss C.Taylor (WCR) and A.R.Vickery (BM).

We were very fortunate to obtain the services of G.M.S.Easy: his clear diagnostic drawings should enable the reader to recognize each genus. Almost without exception the drawings are *de novo*, based on herbarium specimens.

We also wish to thank R.G.Ellis for compiling the index, for expert help in editing this work, and for guiding it through publication.

Helpful comments, records of grasses or details of publications were also received from †Mrs E.Bray, R.M.Burton, A.Copping, C.Jenness, J.Killick, L.Margetts, J.Martin, R.C.Palmer, F.Verloove (from Belgium) and B.Wurzell.

One of us (T.B.R.) is especially grateful to the Director and Keeper of the Herbarium at the Royal Botanic Gardens, Kew, and to S.A.Renvoize, the head of the grass section, for permission to use the unrivalled collections and library facilities, without which this Catalogue could not have been prepared.

Ms G.Douglas, the librarian at the Linnean Society of London, has been most helpful and has loaned one of us (E.J.C.) many rare books and journals.

Grateful thanks and recognition must also be given to the late Dr J.G.Dony and J.E.Lousley, who guided us so generously in the early days, especially in introducing us to the delights of wool alien grasses.

Finally, and most of all, we are indebted to the late Dr C.E.Hubbard, who not only devoted much time to naming, both for the authors and for many others, the grasses found - many from remote parts of the world, and often from immature specimens - but who also took the trouble to write long, instructive letters pointing out the important characteristics.

INTRODUCTION

Worldwide, the vast and economically important family of grasses, the Gramineae, now increasingly referred to as the Poaceae, contains a great diversity of structure and habit of growth, from small, creeping species to towering, woody-stemmed bamboos. This diversity has produced innumerable plants of use to mankind.

Foremost in importance are the sources of food for man and his domestic animals and birds: cereals - wheat, maize, rice, barley, oats and rye - cultivated since pre-historic times and now represented by many highly developed selections; sorghums and millets, mostly grown in third world countries; and forage grasses. Species having fibrous leaves or stems, such as the esparto grasses, have been used in the manufacture of cordage, baskets, matting and paper. Grasses with a creeping habit are used to stabilize sand-dunes, mud-flats and embankments. Ornamental kinds, such as the stately bamboos or those having colourful foliage or decorative inflorescences, are used in horticulture.

Representatives of all of these types have for many years been imported into the British Isles and have been found growing wild; other grasses occur as weed species, from impurities in these imports. In addition, many species have been accidentally brought in with other commodities; these are mainly species which have seeds enclosed by husks bearing barbs or bristles - a modification enabling a wide dispersal, especially in imported fleeces.

Among the earliest records of plants growing in the wild in the British Isles are several alien grasses. Some examples quoted by Druce (ref.R126) include

Lolium temulentum, reported without locality by Turner in 1548, the earliest printed record; and

Setaria viridis, 'in a field betwixt Tuddington and Hampton-Court'; and *Echinochloa crus-galli* 'by the heat house garden, Middlesex', both given by Merrett in 1666.

However, in the following catalogue the earliest alien grass records date back only about 200 years, taken from W.Hudson's *Flora Anglica* of 1762 (ref.R97) and J.Sibthorp's *Flora Oxoniensis* of 1794 (ref.R98). Several early grass introductions such as *Spartina alterniflora* dating from 1829, and *Bromus lepidus* dating from 1836, have survived to this day, together with a relatively small number of later introductions. Among these are the hardy bamboos, mostly introduced in the second half of the 19th century, of which *Pseudosasa japonica*, in 1850, is perhaps the earliest of those now having a claim to be wild. Many bamboos are still merely relics of old gardens and estates, not reproducing by seed, but competing successfully with the native vegetation and often long-lived. On the other hand, the great majority of alien grasses are casual, or survive for only a few seasons, unable to withstand our winters. Yet another group, grasses known to be of alien origin but also occurring as native species - perhaps examples of different races - are well represented.

During the 19th century many alien grasses were introduced repeatedly, mainly with ballast and grain, mostly originating from eastern Europe and the Middle East. In those days, when imported grain was heavily contaminated with foreign seeds, alien weeds such as *Anthoxanthum aristatum* and *Bromus arvensis* were commonly found on quaysides, by mills and breweries, and became established. Now that cargoes are no longer unloaded in bulk onto quaysides, but are transported in containers, and grain is cleaned before shipment, these grasses have become rare.

The sources of introduced grasses have also changed in modern times. The preponderance of ballast and grain aliens has largely been replaced by the greatly increased number attributable to wool waste and bird-seed. Others have been introduced with esparto, being found near paper mills; some with oil-milling imports, especially soya bean; and, recently, aliens have been recorded as originating in the grass-seed mixtures now used in quantity on road verges, especially along motorways.

Of all these sources of alien grasses, imported wool is by far the most important. Waste originating from cleaning wool, and shoddy - the fibre from woollen rags - have been used for centuries as soil conditioners. However, the first comprehensive collections of wool aliens were from Montpellier in the south of France, between 1840 and 1880. In Britain the earliest collection that we have located was from Tweedside, between 1872 and 1888, by A.Brotherston (BM). Shortly afterwards J.Fraser published in *Annals of Scottish Natural History* several important papers on alien plants in the Leith area, including some probable wool casuals. *The adventive flora of Tweedside* by I.M.Hayward and G.C.Druce (ref.R4), published in 1919, provides both an account of the wool industry at that time and descriptions of the alien plants found: this book is one of the principal sources of records in our catalogue. R.Probst's *Wolladventivflora Mitteleuropas* (ref.R13), published in 1949, gives a comprehensive summary of all the wool aliens recorded in Europe, and demonstrates the existence of a stable community, in which most species - even some rare endemic species - recur regularly over the years.

Soon after the war there was an enormous upsurge of interest in the study of wool aliens, triggered by Dr J.G.Dony who, in 1946, together with other B.S.B.I. members, found unexpected exotic weeds in old gravel pits and at railway sidings in Bedfordshire. He soon discovered that these alien plants originated from wool waste used by local farmers as a soil conditioner for market-garden crops, and traced its origin to several Yorkshire mills. A detailed account of the resurgence of interest in wool aliens which resulted from this chance finding is given by J.E.Lousley in *A census list of wool aliens found in Britain, 1946-1960* (ref.R1), in which he names the many field botanists involved. The records for N Hampshire were updated (by T.B.R.) in 1974 and 1988 (ref.R2, R3) when many more plants new to Britain were listed. The formidable task of identifying the alien grasses found was undertaken by several specialists, including Dr N.L.Bor of R.B.G., Kew and Dr A.Melderis of the then British Museum (Natural History). But most credit must go to Dr C.E.Hubbard, also of R.B.G., Kew, whose diligence and wide knowledge ensured that the taxonomy of alien grasses in Britain was placed on a sound basis.

The use of wool waste in agriculture, at least in southern England, declined from about 1965, becoming negligible after 1975, owing mainly to the sharp rise in price caused by increases in distribution costs, especially after the closure of many small branch railway lines. The wool industry has also declined, resulting in the closure of many mills, and the wool waste itself now contains far fewer viable seeds. Nevertheless, a few fields containing a good selection of wool aliens are still to be found, at least in Yorkshire, where the earlier work of active botanists such as Mrs F.Houseman, Miss M.McCallum Webster and Miss C.M.Rob is being continued by J.Martin, G.Wilmore and others.

Bird-seed is the second most important source of alien grasses. It has long been realised that many alien grasses found on municipal tips and in gardens originate from bird-seed mixtures. That a large proportion of these plants are grasses was established by the work of C.G.Hanson and Dr J.L.Mason, whose *Bird seed aliens in Britain* (ref.R21) was published in 1985. In addition to listing those species already recorded as bird-seed aliens, they cultivated and identified many more plants from a variety of commercial bird-food mixtures and seed-cleaning waste. This cultivation revealed the source of several surprising aliens found on tips, such as the S American *Brachiaria platyphylla*, and showed that seeds of several potential alien grasses, not yet recorded in the wild, are imported in bird-seed.

Further important publications dealing with other means of introduction include those on the collections of aliens from Bristol and Avonmouth docks by C.I. and N.Y.Sandwith, published in several *Botanical Exchange Club Reports* between about 1930 and 1940; a paper by R.Curtis (1931) on Middle East barley aliens (ref.J1(9:465-469); an account by Miss E.P.Beattie (1962) of esparto grass aliens (ref.J6(4:404-407), amplified by the collections of Miss M.McCallum Webster (ref.R5); and the records of oil-milling or soya bean waste adventives by D.H.Kent and J.E.Lousley (1956) in London (ref.R.20) and by J.R.Palmer (1976) in NW Kent (ref.J41(6:85-90). In addition, many records and descriptions of rare grass species have been published in *B.S.B.I. News*, the *Wild Flower Magazine*, the *London Naturalist* and other local natural history society publications.

It has been possible to examine specimens in only a few herbaria. A number of wrong determinations have come to light: among problems that have been resolved are the true identities of two species supposedly new to science; Dr T.A.Cope has determined that '*Diplachne hackeliana*' is *Eragrostis plana*, and '*Koeleria advena*' is *Trisetaria scabriuscula*. New combinations were required for *Helictotrichon recurvatum* and *Ceratochloa sitchensis* (submitted for publication in *Watsonia*). Unfortunately, many records from published reports and personal communications, even of very rare species, have had to be accepted without examining the voucher specimens.

Two previous comprehensive lists of aliens published this century are S.T.Dunn's *Alien flora of Britain* (ref.R8) and G.C.Druce's *British plant list* (ref.R36). Comparing our catalogue with these earlier lists, and ignoring trivial varieties, the approximate numbers of non-native grasses listed are as follows:

Dunn (1905)	80
Druce (1928)	250
Ryves *et al.* (1996)	580

This catalogue also includes some 50 taxa, known to be of alien origin as well as occurring as natives, and about 80 potential, probably overlooked, or unconfirmed species. Adding these brings the total number of taxa treated to about 710, representing some 7% of the grass flora of the world.

The numbers of grasses attributable to the major means of introduction since 1930 are (roughly):

Wool	430	
Bird-seed	80	
Grain	55	
Horticulture	40	(of which 20 are bamboos)
Esparto	30	
Oil-seed	20	
Grass seed	20	

Of the 580 or so non-native grasses, about 60 have become established (at least for several years), and some 70 have not been recorded since 1930.

PLAN OF THE CATALOGUE

Although this book is essentially a continuation of *Alien plants of the British Isles*, there are several differences in treatment. For that reason a full explanation of a typical entry is given, although much of it is repetition of the earlier work.

In this catalogue we present an annotated list of all alien grass species, arranged in systematic order, which have been reliably recorded as growing wild in the British Isles (including the Channel Islands). The word 'alien' is used in a broad sense: it denotes all plants, whether established or not, that are thought to have arrived as a result of human activities, and includes plants referred to by other authors as 'adventives', 'casuals', 'ephemerals', 'exotics', 'introductions' or 'volunteers'.

In the tradition of British floras, species probably introduced in ancient times with the advent of cultivation are treated as though native. Also, many potential records lacking a reliable name, usually owing to immature material, have had to be excluded.

Emphasis is given in this catalogue to the period since 1930 - a period long enough to put into perspective the 'fashions' in recording, such as the enthusiasm for wool aliens from the 1950s to 1970s and the recent concentration on bird-seed aliens and garden escapes.

For species recorded since 1930, full accounts are given in the following sequence:

> **Scientific name; English name; frequency; status** and **means of introduction; origin; location of voucher specimens; references;** and **synonyms.**

These terms are explained below. For species known before 1930 but not recorded since, shorter accounts are given.

Hybrids are usually mentioned briefly in notes under the parent species; a few important ones receive a full treatment. For some of them more detailed information is readily available in *Hybridization and the flora of the British Isles* (ref.D130).

Entries for taxa recorded in error, or represented only by dubious records, or considered potential aliens (grown from wool waste, bird-seed, etc., but not yet found growing wild), are enclosed in square brackets.

SEQUENCE AND NOMENCLATURE

The circumscription and sequence of tribes and genera basically follow those of *Genera Graminum* (ref.S7) and are numbered to agree with that work. Under the generic headings the number of species worldwide, their native areas and their habitats are given. Within each genus the species are listed alphabetically.

Scientific name   The names of taxa in bold type are those considered to be currently accepted and in accordance with the latest version of the *International code of botanical nomenclature* (ref.S9), the authors' names being abbreviated as in *Authors of plant names* (ref.S2). Names in Roman type are alien taxa; names in italics are taxa which, although native, are also known (or suspected in a few cases) to occur as aliens.

English name   In the interests of standardization, the vernacular names given are those used in *New Flora of the British Isles* (ref.D2).

SUMMARY OF RECORDS

There follows, for species recorded since 1930, a summary of the frequency, status and means of introduction, and where appropriate, notes on distribution, habitat, localities or recent changes of frequency.

Frequency   The system used here to indicate frequency is based on the number of separate localities from which the species has been recorded, in print, on herbarium labels, or privately communicated, represented by bullet symbols as follows:

●	1-4 localities	
●●	5-14 localities	
●●●	15-49 localities	Above 15, the
●●●●	50-499 localities	number of localities
●●●●●	over 500 localities	is an estimate

Status   The categories of permanence are defined as follows:

Casual	Not persisting in a locality for more than two years without re-introduction.
Persistent	Remaining longer than two years but unlikely to be permanent, not reproducing by seed or vigorously spreading vegetatively.
Established	Likely to remain permanently; at least one colony either reproducing by seed or vigorously spreading vegetatively.
Naturalised	Established extensively amongst native vegetation so as to appear native.

Distribution in general terms is given for commonly established species; for other established and persistent species, examples of localities may be mentioned, and for the rarest (•) every locality is named. When known, the locality is followed, in parentheses, by the vice-county name. The vice-county boundaries are shown in the end-papers of *New Flora of the British Isles* (ref.D2); larger-scale versions of this map can be found in *Watsonian vice-counties of Great Britain* (ref.S5) and *Census catalogue of the flora of Ireland* (ref.S6). The advantage of using these old boundaries is that, unlike county boundaries, they remain constant. Dates of records of interest are given, especially for very rare species and recent records.

Means of introduction Grass seeds and propagules coming into the British Isles may be divided into three groups of vectors as follows:

CULTIVATION

Agricultural seed: crop plants growing from spilt or discarded seed, or self-sown, away from cultivated land; plants germinated from seed impurities.

Grass seed: plants originally introduced as either main constituents or accidental impurities of grass seed mixtures and now found wild.

Garden escape: plants discarded, or escaping from gardens.

Relic: cereals persisting in fields; ornamental grasses persisting on sites of former gardens or nursery gardens.

FOODSTUFFS

Grain: cereals found near flour mills, breweries and granaries; cereals from corn fed to domestic fowl and game birds; and weed species from impurities in these.

Bird-seed: grasses germinating, mainly in gardens and on tips, from cage-bird and wild-bird seed mixtures.

Fodder: species found on farms, brought in as, or accidentally with, fodder.

Pet food: grasses found in gardens and on tips from food for hamsters and other small mammals.

OTHER COMMODITIES

Wool: mainly fleeces from Australia, New Zealand and S Africa, but also vicuna and alpaca wools from S America, wool for carpets from central Asia and angora goat hair.

Esparto: various grasses used in the manufacture of high-quality paper.

Cotton.

Where the vector is not known, the habitat is given, e.g. docks, tips.

ADDITIONAL INFORMATION

Origin   The countries, regions or continents mentioned indicate the native area(s) of the species, followed in parentheses by the area(s) in which the species has become naturalised or is cultivated on a large scale.   Although many aliens have come directly from their native areas, others, for example species native in the Mediterranean area, if growing from impurities in wool, will probably have come directly from the southern hemisphere; alien fodder grasses may have been brought in from countries where they are not native. If the species is now widely naturalised, usually in several continents, the term 'widespread' is used.

Location of voucher specimens   Institutional herbaria are abbreviated according to the recommendations given in *British and Irish herbaria* (ref.S8). Privately owned herbaria holding important voucher specimens are sometimes also cited. A list of the herbaria quoted may be found on page xxi. No herbaria are given for the most frequent species (●●●●● and ●●●●), as these are presumed to be represented in all major collections.

References   Literature references are split into four groups: non-serial works giving a *d*escription or illustration (prefix D); serials or *j*ournals (prefix J); non-serial works giving *r*ecords (prefix R); and a *s*upplementary list of miscellaneous works (prefix S).

All books in the list of references are presented in the form used in *Watsonia*, the journal of the Botanical Society of the British Isles; the page number is quoted only if the index is absent or faulty. The abbreviations of journals are those of *B-P-H* (ref.S3, S4); for these references the volume and page number(s) are given, e.g. J23(11:245-247) refers to *Watsonia*, volume 11, pages 245-247.

Illustrations are indicated by an asterisk (*) after the reference number, or after the volume number if more than one volume is quoted. A generous selection of both analytical line drawings and coloured photographs or paintings has, where possible, been chosen to demonstrate all attributes of the plant.

Synonyms   A selected synonymy follows, quoting binomials found in British works and those under which descriptions or illustrations are referenced. Basionyms are given. Additional synonyms, and occasionally homonyms, are sometimes introduced to clarify problems of nomenclature.

ABBREVIATIONS AND SYMBOLS

append.	appendix
auct.	*auctorum*: of authors, but not of the original author
B.S.B.I.	Botanical Society of the British Isles
C	central
c.	*circa*: about
cf.	*confer*: comparable with
cm	centimetre(s)
comp.	compiler; compiled by
cv.	*cultivarietas*: cultivar
dia.	diameter
E	East; eastern
ed.	editor; edition
e.g.	*exempli gratia*: for example
em.	*emendatus:* emended; *emendavit*: he emended
et al.	*et alii*: and others
f.	*filius*: son
fasc.	fascicle(s); part(s)
fig.	figure, illustration
hort.	*hortulanorum*: of gardeners
ht.	height
ined.	*ineditus*: unpublished; not yet published in accordance with the rules of the *International code of botanical nomenclature*
Is	Isle(s); Island(s)
l.c.	*loco citato*: at the place cited
m	metre
MAFF	Ministry of Agriculture, Fisheries and Food
Med.	region centred on the Mediterranean Sea, and typically includes parts of southern Europe, N Africa and SW Asia
mm	millimetre(s)
N	North; northern
NE	northeast
No.	number
nom. illeg.	*nomen illegitimum*: illegitimate name
nom. inval.	*nomen invalidum*: invalid name
nom. superfl.	*nomen superfluum*: name superfluous when published
n.s.	new series (of a periodical)
NW	northwest
p.	page
pp.	pages
q.v.	*quod vide*: which see
R.B.G.	Royal Botanic Gardens
ref.	reference, refer to
rev.	revision; revised by

S	South; southern
SE	southeast
ser.	series
sp.	species (singular)
sphalm.	*sphalmate*: by mistake
subsp.	subspecies (singular)
subspp.	subspecies (plural)
suppl.	supplement
suppls	supplements
SW	southwest
syn.	synonym; synonymy
t.	*tabula*: plate; illustration
transl.	translation; translated by
var.	*varietas*: variety
vol.	volume
W	West; western

*	indicates an illustration (in a referenced work)
†	indicates deceased (before a personal name)
×	indicates a hybrid (before a name) or times (used between measurements in keys)
±	more or less, approximately (used in keys)
[ ]	indicates a taxon recorded in error, a dubious record, or a potential alien

Numbers of post-1930 localities:
● 1-4; ●● 5-14;   ●●● 15-49;   ●●●● 50-499;   ●●●●● over 500.

LIST OF HERBARIA

ABD	Dept. of Botany, University of Aberdeen
BEL	Ulster Museum, Belfast
BM	British Museum (Natural History), London
	(now re-named Natural History Museum)
BMH	Museum of the Bournemouth Natural Science Society
BRISTM	City Museum & Art Gallery, Bristol
CGE	University of Cambridge, Botany School
DBN	National Botanic Gardens, Dublin
DEE	City Museum & Art Gallery, Dundee
E	Royal Botanic Garden, Edinburgh
IPS	Ipswich Museum
K	Royal Botanic Gardens, Kew
LANC	University of Lancaster
LCN	City & County Museum, Lincoln
LIV	Merseyside County Museum, Liverpool
LSR	Leicestershire Museums, Art Galleries & Record Service, Leicester
LTN	Museum & Art Gallery, Luton
LTR	University of Leicester
MANCH	Manchester Museum
MNE	Museum & Art Gallery, Maidstone
NCE	University of Newcastle upon Tyne
NMW	National Museum of Wales, Cardiff
OXF	University of Oxford, Botany School
RAMM	Royal Albert Memorial Museum & Art Gallery, Exeter
RNG	University of Reading, Plant Sciences Laboratories
SLBI	South London Botanical Institute
SWN	Museum, Saffron Walden
TOR	Torquay Natural History Society Museum
WARMS	Warwickshire Museum
WCR	City Museum, Winchester
ZCM	Shetland Museum
HbABMB	Lady Anne B.M.Brewis, Liss, Hampshire
HbCGH	C.G.Hanson, Ware, Hertfordshire
HbDMcC	D.McClintock, Sevenoaks, Kent
HbEJC	E.J.Clement, Gosport, Hampshire
HbHJMB	Dr H.J.M.Bowen, Winterbourne Kingston, Dorset
HbLJM	L.J.Margetts, Honiton, Devon
HbPAH	P.A.Harmes, Portslade, East Sussex
HbRMP	R.M.Payne, King's Lynn, Norfolk
HbRT-A	R.Takagi-Arigho, Exeter, Devon
HbTBR	T.B.Ryves, Kingston Hill, Surrey

BAMBUSEAE

The generic limits have been very uncertain in the past, but they are now beginning to settle down into smaller genera. For example, the genus *Arundinaria* once consisted of 80 species but is now considered to be monotypic. A useful account of garden species is given in ref.J110*(119:262-267). Key on p.107.

YUSHANIA Keng f.   1a

2 species. Himalayas, China into SE Asia.

anceps (Mitford) W.C.Lin   Indian Fountain-bamboo
●●● Established or persistent, forming thickets and sometimes producing seedlings, in a few places in western and southern Britain, Ireland and the Channel Islands; usually in derelict woodland gardens, as at Hengistbury Head, New Forest (S Hants), Borough Green (W Kent), Windlesham (Surrey), Brinton (E Norfolk), Llanybydder (Cards); Murrisk Abbey (W Mayo) and Downpatrick (Co Down); many records from Cornwall in ref.J99*(6:73-91). C & NW Himalayas. BM, K, NMW, RNG, HbDMcC. D1, D2, D47, D73*, J18((388:36), J23(16:196), J26(41:12), J54*(7:t.22), J66*(1:36-37), J110*(108:158), R22, R27, R38, R40, R42, R44, R52, R68. *Arundinaria anceps* Mitford; *A.jaunsarensis* Gamble; *Sinarundinaria anceps* (Mitford) C.S.Chao & Renvoize.

THAMNOCALAMUS Munro   3

c.6 species. Himalayas. The species are clump-forming.

spathiflorus (Trin.) Munro subsp. **spathiflorus**
● Persists in a few woodland places with a mild climate, and covers large areas in Ireland, as at Glanleam, Valencia Island and Rossdohan (both S Kerry). Himalayas. HbDMcC. D47, D129*, D156*, D157*, D158*, J54*(7:t.16, t.17), J66*(1:38-39). *Arundinaria spathiflora* Trin. Includes subsp. *aristatus* (Gamble) D.C.McClint. (*T.aristatus* (Gamble) E.G.Camus; *A.aristata* Gamble).

FARGESIA Franch.   3a

c.40 species. China. The species are clump-forming.

murielae (Gamble) T.P.Yi   Umbrella Bamboo
● Persists in old neglected parks and estates, growing in large clumps; Thursford Wood (W Norfolk) in 1991. W China. HbRMP. D2, D47, D83*, D152*, J66*(14:174-175), R11, R19, R40, R44. *Arundinaria murielae* Gamble; *Sinarundinaria murielae* (Gamble) Nakai; *Thamnocalamus murielae* (Gamble) Demoly. However, *F.spathacea* Franch., which is often treated as a synonym, is considered by C.M.A.Stapleton in ref.J98(21:10-20) to be a distinct species.

spathacea Franch.   Chinese Fountain-bamboo
•• Often grown in gardens; has persisted for over 80 years in a private wood
in Leicestershire where it had been originally planted; established by a stream
at Rusland (Westmorland) in 1964; between Farnborough and Downe (Kent) in
1969; Copthorne Common (E Sussex); Margam Park (Glam) in 1982;
Highmead Mansion near Llanybydder (Cards) in 1985. W China. BM, K,
NMW, RNG. D2, D47, D73*, D74*, D81*, D152*, D159*, D160*,
J23(13:59-61), J66*(14:174-175), J98(21:10-20), R40, R117. *F.nitida* (Mitford
ex Stapf) Keng f.; *Arundinaria nitida* Mitford ex Stapf; *A.spathacea* (Franch.)
D.C.McClint. pro parte; *Sinarundinaria nitida* (Mitford ex Stapf) Nakai (the
type species of *Sinarundinaria*, whose recent flowering has shown it to be a
synonym of *Fargesia*, a genus akin to *Thamnocalamus*, according to
C.M.A.Stapleton in ref.J95(1:6); *Thamnocalamus nitidus* (Mitford ex Stapf)
Demoly; *T.spathaceus* (Franch.) Soderstr. After its very recent flowering
F.nitida has now been shown to be the same species as *F.spathacea* (see
ref.J98(22:17-22).

HIMALAYACALAMUS Keng f.   3b

c.5 species. Himalayas.

[falconeri (Hook.f. ex Munro) Keng f.
A persistent relic of cultivation at Caledonia Nursery, St. Peter Port, Guernsey,
which died after flowering, reported to have set seed. NE Himalayas. D47,
D73*, D156*, D157*, D158*, J54*(7:t.18), J66*(14:171-172), J67*(t.7947),
R11, R40. *Arundinaria falconeri* (Hook.f. ex Munro) Rivière; *A.nobilis*
Mitford; *Thamnocalamus falconeri* Hook.f. ex Munro.]
[hookerianus (Munro) Stapleton
Restricted to the milder parts of Britain, and may regenerate from seedlings in
botanical gardens and greenhouses, as in Edinburgh. E Himalayas. D47,
D80*, D152*, D156*, D157*, J54*(7:t.15), R115. *Arundinaria hookeriana*
Munro; *Chimonobambusa hookeriana* (Munro) Nakai.]

ARUNDINARIA Michx.   10

1 species. Eastern USA. Forming thickets in forest, grassland and inhabited
places.

[gigantea (Walter) Muhl.
On a rubbish dump near Dover's Green (Surrey) in 1964. SE USA. RNG.
D6*, D42*, D141*, D161*, J26(44:15). *A.tecta* (Walter) Muhl.; *Arundo
gigantea* Walter; *A.tecta* Walter. This record needs confirmation.]

PLEIOBLASTUS Nakai   10a

c.25 species. Japan.

auricomus (Mitford) D.C.McClint.

• Persisted on a bomb-site in Chelsea (Middlesex) after the war for a few years; Sark; reported from several other localities. Japan. RNG. D47, D73*, D107*, D152*, J80*(t.2613), R11, R40, R41. *P.viridistriatus* (Siebold ex André) Makino; *Arundinaria auricoma* Mitford; *A.viridistriata* (Siebold ex André) Makino. Most records refer to *Sasaella ramosa*.

chino (Franch. & Sav.) Makino

•• Cultivated and can spread; recorded from many localities, including Barton Wood (Cheshire), Moorland Links Hotel, Yelverton (S Devon), damp woodland along the canal at Send (Surrey), Clandon Park (Surrey), Newtonbarry (Co Wexford), near Western Avenue bridge, Cardiff (Glam) and Southwick Burn (Kirkudbrights); especially large well-established colonies have been recorded from Headington Hill (Oxon) and the RAF sailing club at Medmenham (Bucks). Japan. LIV, NMW, RNG, HbDMcC. D2, D47, D107*, D111*, D114*. *P.maximowiczii* (Rivière) Nakai; *Arundinaria chino* (Franch. & Sav.) Makino; *Bambusa chino* Franch. & Sav.

[**gramineus** (Bean) Nakai

Recorded from Binfield (Berks) in 1964, but comfirmation and details of the status are required. Japan. HbHJMB. D73*, D124*, R39. *Arundinaria hindsii* Munro var. *graminea* Bean; *Thamnocalamus hindsii* (Munro) E.G.Camus var. *gramineus* (Bean) E.G.Camus.]

humilis (Mitford) Nakai

• A relic of cultivation in Guernsey, but now extinct; River Bourne, Virginia Water (Surrey) in 1995; Frensham Hall, Shottermill (Surrey) in 1967; Newtonbarry House, Burclody (Co Wexford) in 1965. Japan. BM, RNG. D2, D47, D107*, D152*, J23(13:59-60), J66*(1:40-41,43), R9, R11. *Arundinaria humilis* Mitford; *Sasa humilis* (Mitford) E.G.Camus.

pygmaeus (Miq.) Nakai var. **distichus** (Mitford) Nakai   Dwarf Bamboo

•• Fairly often persistent in old gardens in the British Isles; Sausmarez Manor, St. Peter Port, Guernsey. Japan. RNG, HbDMcC. D2, D47, D152*, R11, R40. *P.distichus* (Mitford) Muroi & Okamura; *Arundinaria disticha* (Mitford) Pfitzer; *A.pygmaea* (Miq.) Asch. & Graebn. var. *disticha* (Mitford) C.S.Chao & Renvoize; *Bambusa disticha* Mitford; *Sasa disticha* (Mitford) E.G.Camus.

simonii (Carrière) Nakai

•• Rarely persistent in neglected parks and estates; Dulwich Woods, Camberwell (Surrey); derelict bamboo nursery at Lanivet (E Cornwall); well naturalised on stream banks in woodland at Tehidy Country Park (W Cornwall) in 1993; woodland at Rossdohan (S Kerry); Sausmarez Manor, St. Peter Port, Guernsey. Japan. RNG, HbDMcC. D1, D2, D47, D69*, D73*, D107*, D111*, D149*, D151*, D161*, J23(13:59-60), J26(38:90), J67* (t.7146, as var. *variegatus* (Hook.f.) Nakai), J99*(6:73-91), R11, R35, R40, R42.

Arundinaria simonii (Carrière) Rivière & C.Rivière; *Bambusa simonii* Carrière, *Nipponocalamus simonii* (Carrière) Nakai.

SASA Makino & Shibata   14

c.40 species. Mainly Japan, extending to Korea and E China. Woodland and inhabited places. Ref.J100(2:24-38).

palmata (Lat.-Marl. ex Burb.) E.G.Camus   Broad-leaved Bamboo
 ••• Introduced and well established in widely scattered localities; a vast colony at Shandon (Dunbarton); in the wilderness at Brodie Castle (Moray); dominant in damp woodland at Dears Mill, Lindfield (W Sussex) in 1985; edge of Wisley Common and at Shottermill, Haslemere (both Surrey); Gweek Valley (W Cornwall); Co Dublin; Co Down; Co Antrim.   Japan, Sakhalin. BM, CGE, DEE, E, LANC, NMW, OXF, RNG, TCD, HbDMcC. D1, D2, D47, D73*, D84*, D107*, D152*, J16(41:17), J23(13:59-60,149;14:432), J99*(6:73-91), R24, R27, R38, R39, R40, R44, R50, R52, R101, R123. *S.senanensis* auct., non (Franch. & Sav.) Rehder; *Arundinaria palmata* (Lat.-Marl. ex Burb.) Bean; *Bambusa palmata* Lat.-Marl. ex Burb. This species flowers fairly frequently.

veitchii (Carrière) Rehder   Veitch's Bamboo
 •• A persistent relic; Keston Common (E Kent); a large patch by the lake at Cliveden (Bucks); Windlesham (Surrey); Headington Hill (Oxon); a vast colony by the edge of a wood at Grayshott (Surrey); Wooton Fitzpaine (Dorset) in 1983; Offwell woodland reserve (S Devon) in 1992; Church Town cemetery (W Cornwall); Bel Air, Jersey in 1975; Margam Park (Glam) in 1982; a wood at Newtownbarry (Co Wexford). Japan. BM, NMW, RNG. D1, D2, D47, D73*, D107*, D152*, D160*, D161*, J14(125:234), J18(364:29), J99*(6:73-91), R10, R11, R40, R41, R42. *S.albomarginata* (Makino) Makino & Shibata; *Arundinaria veitchii* (Carrière) N.E.Br.; *Bambusa veitchii* Carrière. The record in ref.J26(58:65) is an error for *Sasaella ramosa*.

SASAELLA Makino   14a

c.12 species. Japan. Woodland.

ramosa (Makino) Makino   Hairy Bamboo
 ••• A relic sometimes well established; Esher Common (Surrey); Werescott Farm, Sampford Arundel (N Devon); Tehidy Country Park (W Cornwall); roadsides at Oldbury and Ightham (both W Kent); Fanhams, Ware (Herts); Sonning (Berks); Yate (W Gloucs); Holden Clough, Clitheroe (W Lancs); Rhu (Dunbarton); woodland at Rossdohan (S Kerry). Japan. BM, RNG, HbDMcC, HbHJMB. D1, D2, D47, D107*, D111*, D114*, D152*, J7(38:191-195), J18(364:29), J23(13:59-60), J25(1966:4), J26(44:15), J99*(6:73-91), R9, R11, R38, R39, R44, R45, R46. *Arundinaria vagans* Gamble; *Bambusa ramosa* Makino; *Sasa ramosa* (Makino) Makino & Shibata. The record in J26(58:65) for *Sasa veitchii* is in error for this species.

[senanensis (Franch. & Sav.) Rehder
Reportedly established over a large area at Great Warley (S Essex) in 1964.
Japan. ?CGE, NMW, RNG.   D47, D107*, J26(41:12; 44:15).   *Bambusa*
senanensis Franch. & Sav.   However the records are in error for *Sasa palmata*,
according to ref.R117 and as determined by C.M.A.Stapleton.]

PSEUDOSASA Makino ex Nakai   15

6 species.   Japan, Korea and Taiwan.   Woodland and roadsides.

japonica (Siebold & Zucc. ex Steud.) Makino ex Nakai   **Arrow Bamboo**
••• Persists in the grounds of country houses and garden woodland; long
established in numerous localities, as in an old quarry near Whitehill and the
N side of Titness Park, Sunningdale (both Surrey); woodland at Trawscoed
(Cards); Pendarves Wood, Camborne and St. Nectan's Kieve (both
W Cornwall); Co Down and Co Antrim; according to ref.R27 and J99*(6:73-
91) this is the commonest established bamboo in Surrey and Cornwall
respectively.   Japan, Korea.   BM, NMW, OXF, RNG, HbDMcC, HbHJMB,
HbRMP.   D1, D2, D47, D73*, D111*, D115, D124*, D149*, D159*, D160*,
J23(12:362), J26(44:15), J27(16:217), J66*(1:42-43), R19, R27, R31, R39,
R40, R43, R44, R76, R77, R123.   *Arundinaria japonica* Siebold & Zucc. ex
Steud.; *Bambusa metake* Miq.; *Sasa japonica* (Siebold & Zucc. ex Steud.)
Makino, *Yadakea japonica* (Siebold & Zucc. ex Steud.) Makino.   This species
flowers freely and regularly.

CHIMONOBAMBUSA Makino   20

c.20 species.   China and Japan.   Forest.

marmorea (Mitford) Makino
• A persistent relic of cultivation in Guernsey, now exterminated.   Japan.
D47, D84*, D107*, D111*, R9, R11, R40.   *Arundinaria marmorea* (Mitford)
Makino; *Bambusa marmorea* Mitford.   The plant from Bantry (W Cork) in
RNG was misidentified as this species.

quadrangularis (Franceschi) Makino   **Square-stemmed Bamboo**
•• Naturalised in thickets in SW England and Ireland; Penjerrick (W Cornwall)
in 1993; by the Memorial Gardens at St Just in Roseland (E Cornwall) in 1994;
over a wide area at Fota (E Cork); in woodland on Valencia Island (S Kerry).
China.   HbDMcC.   D2, D47, D73*, D81*, D107*, D111*, D159*, D161*,
D162*, J99*(6:73-91).   *Arundinaria quadrangularis* (Franceschi) Makino;
Bambusa quadrangularis Franceschi.   The culm is supposedly square in cross-
section with rounded corners.

SEMIARUNDINARIA Makino ex Nakai   28

c.10 species.   China and Japan.   Light woodland.

fastuosa (Lat.-Marl.   ex Mitford) Makino ex Nakai   Narihira Bamboo
•• A persistent relic; established on the bank of the Thames at Ham (Surrey)
since 1967; Frensham Hall, Shottermill (Surrey) in 1967; E and W Cornwall;
naturalised at the edge of a damp wood, south side of Dingle Harbour
(Co Kerry) in 1976; forest park (Co Down).   Japan.   BM.   D1, D2, D47,
D73*, D84*, D111*, D114*, D124*, D161*, J23(13:59-60), J99(6:73-91),
R27, R35, R40, R44, R117, R123.   *Arundinaria fastuosa* (Lat.-Marl. ex
Mitford) Houz.; *Bambusa fastuosa* Lat.-Marl. ex Mitford; *Phyllostachys
fastuosa* (Lat.-Marl. ex Mitford) Makino.

PHYLLOSTACHYS Siebold & Zucc.   29

c.80 species.   Himalayas and China.   Woodland.   Contrary to much literature,
the genus is not native to Japan.

aurea (Carrière) Rivière & C.Rivière
• A relic of cultivation; Bagley Wood (Oxon).   China, (USA).   OXF, RNG,
HbHJMB.   D1, D10*, D26*, D47, D56, D73*, D93*, D107*, D124*, D141*,
D151*, D162*, J99(6:73-91), R39.   *P.formosana* Hayata; *Bambusa aurea*
Carrière.

bambusoides Siebold & Zucc.
• Occasionally found in neglected parks and estates; E edge of A393 road at
Ponsanooth (W Cornwall) in 1994.   China.   RNG.   D1, D2, D47, D56, D81*,
D84*, D107*, D111*, D112*(as *P.nigra*), D114*, D115*, D124*, D158*,
D159*, D161*, D162*, J99*(6:73-91), R40.   *P.mazelii* Rivière; *P.quiloi*
(Carrière) Rivière & C.Rivière.

flexuosa (Carrière) Rivière & C.Rivière
• Wooded slopes above Fermain Bay, Guernsey.   China.   OXF.   D47, D99*,
R11.   *Sinarundinaria flexuosa* Carrière.

cf. nigra (G.Lodd.) Munro
• Semi-naturalised in Fairwater Park, Cardiff in 1994; a commonly cultivated
species, but with no other naturalised records.   E China, (Hawaii).   NMW.
D1, D47, D56, D73*, D81*, D93*, D107*, D111*, D115*, D124*, D149*,
D159*, D160*, D161*, J18(361:27), J67*(t.7994), J99(6:73-91), R40, R112.
Bambusa nigra G.Lodd.   Includes *P.henonis* Mitford (*P.nigra* var. *henonis*
(Mitford) Stapf ex Rendle).

viridiglaucescens (Carrière) Rivière & C.Rivière
• Established near Mont Matthieu, St. Ouen, Jersey; Margam Park (Glam) in
1982.   E China.   NMW.   D1, D47, D112*, D161*, D162*, J67a*(t.260),
J99(6:73-91), R40, R42.   *Bambusa viridiglaucescens* Carrière.

ORYZEAE

ORYZA L. 76

c.20 species. Tropics and subtropics. Humid forests and open swamps. *O.sativa* (Rice) is cultivated, usually in small flooded fields, as the cereal which is the basic staple food of much of the world's population. It was domesticated from the wild about 2500 years ago in the Nepal-Yunnan area.

[sativa L. Rice
  Cultivated from bird-seed. Origin obscure, probably SE Asia, (widespread crop). D1, D6, D21*, D26*, D44*, D81*, D93*, R21. It might germinate on tips, but is unlikely to flower in the open in Britain.]

EHRHARTEAE

EHRHARTA Thunb. 89

c.35 species. c.25 species in Southern Africa (one extending to Ethiopia) and the rest from Indonesia to New Zealand. Wet places, forest glades, rocky mountain slopes and coastal dunes. The genus now includes c.10 species previously placed in *Microlaena* R.Br. (see ref.J73(28:181-194).

calycina Sm.
  • A wool casual. Southern Africa, (becoming widespread). BM, CGE, E, K, LIV, RNG. D5*, D6, D8*, D26*, D27*, D44*, D93*, D117*, D118*, R2, R5, R65.

erecta Lam.
  • A wool casual; sometimes escaped in greenhouses and gardens, as at Ware (Herts) and Wolverstone (E Suffolk); probably spread by the exchange of potted plants and may become a serious weed; in an unheated greenhouse at Kingston (Surrey) it has seeded and persisted in quantity for over 20 years, flowering throughout the year. Southern Africa, (becoming widespread). BM, LIV, HbCGH, HbTBR. D5*, D6, D8*, D13*, D24*, D27*, D37*, D44*, D93*, D118, J8*(60:38-40), J8(62:45), R65. According to ref.D115*, J69(34:7), the species naturalised in Italy is the southern African *E.delicatula* Stapf (*E.erecta* Fiori, non Lam.), but the figure is clearly of *E.erecta*. In Sydney this species is now one of the commonest urban weeds.

longiflora Sm.
  •• A wool casual. Southern Africa, (Australia). ABD, BEL, CGE, E, K, RNG. D5*, D8*, D27*, D29*, D44*, D87*, D93*, J60*(43:139-142), R1, R2, R5, R47, R51, R65. *E.longifolia* T.Durand & Schinz pro parte, non Schrad. **Fig.1.**

longifolia Schrad.
  • A wool casual. S Africa. K. D5*, D87, D102, J68(17:51-65), R86.

stipoides Labill.   Weeping-grass
•• A wool casual. Australasia, (becoming widespread). BM, CGE, E, K,
LTN, RNG. D2, D8*, D10*, D16*, D26*, D27*, D44*, D87*, D93*, D116*,
R1, R2, R5, R47. *Microlaena stipoides* (Labill.) R.Br. **Fig.1.**

STIPEAE

STIPA L.   **94**

c.300 species. Temperate and warm temperate regions. Steppes, dry pastures
and rocky slopes. *S.tenacissima* L. (Esparto, Halfa) is used for making paper,
mats and cordage. *S.robusta* (Vasey) Scribn. is said to have a narcotic effect
on cattle. **Key on p.110.**

ambigua Speg.
•• A wool casual. S America. BM, CGE, E, K, LIV, LTN, NMW, OXF,
RNG, SLBI. D12*, D15, D52*, D172*(pp.145,151), D174*, J106*(3:t.23),
R1, R2, R5, R47, R65. *S.dusenii* Hitchc. **Fig.1, 28.**

aristiglumis F.Muell.
•• A wool casual. Australia. BM, E, K, NMW, RNG, SLBI. D2, D7, D8,
D16, D93*, J7*(1921:27), J18(334:22), R3, R38, R47, R65. According to
C.E.Hubbard the wool-alien material may include several unnamed species.
Fig.27.

blackii C.E.Hubb.
• A wool casual. Australia. K. D7, D8, D10*, D93*, J63*(27:569-582), R3.

brachychaeta Godr.
• A wool casual. S America, (Australia). E, RNG. D6, D10, D12*, D15*,
D93*, J22*(16:637-653), J109*(4,22:111), R4, R36. Probably confused with
S.brachychaetoides. **Fig.28.**

brachychaetoides Speg.
• A wool casual. Patagonia. E, K, OXF, RNG, SLBI. D12*, R3, R48.
Fig.28.

cf. **brachyphylla** Hitchc.
Pre-1930 only. A wool casual. S America. E, LIV, OXF. J21*(24:215-289),
J109*(4,22:133), R4, R36. ?*S.leptothera* Speg. was identified with some doubt
by A.Thellung from Galashiels (Selkirks), and A.S.Hitchcock in the reference
cited considered it to be a synonym.

capensis Thunb.   Mediterranean Needle-grass
• A wool casual. Atlantic Is, Med., (widespread). ?E, K, LTN, OXF, RNG.
D1, D2, D5*, D17*, D18*, D25*, D115*, D117*, D119*, D120*, R1, R3,
R5, R47. *S.retorta* Cav., non (Nees ex Steud.) Mez; *S.tortilis* Desf. **Fig.27.**

[**capillata** L.
Pre-1930 only. At a sewage works. S Europe, SW Asia. BM. D1, D18*,
D19*, D25*. Determination very doubtful. **Fig.27.**]

caudata Trin.

Pre-1930 only. A wool casual. S America. E. D12*, D15, D93*, J1(4:28), J22*(16:637-653), R4, R36.

charruana Arechav.

• A wool casual. Argentina, Brazil, Uruguay. RNG. D12*, D15*, D174*, J109*(4,22:64). **Fig.27.**

dregeana Steud.

• A wool casual. Tropical and S Africa. BM, RNG, HbCGH. D5*, D13*, D37*, J68*(8:213,235), R65. Includes var.*elongata* (Nees) Stapf (*S.elongata* (Nees) Steud.; *Lasiagrostis elongata* Nees). **Fig.28.**

filiculmis Delile

• A wool casual. S America. K, RNG. D12*, D15*, D52*, D174*, R2. **Fig.27.**

formicarum Delile

•• A wool casual. S America, (N America). BM, K, LIV, LTN, OXF, RNG, SLBI. D2, D12*, D118, J1(5:311-312), J58*(111:151-163), R1, R2, R36, R48, R65. *Nassella formicarum* (Delile) Barkworth. **Fig.28.**

[**gigantea** Link

A garden relic in Waltham Abbey Gardens (N Essex). SW Europe, NW Africa. BM. D1, D20*, D21*, D117*, R24. *Macrochloa arenaria* (Brot.) Kunth; *M.gigantea* (Link) Hack. **Fig.27.**]

hyalina Nees

• A wool and dock casual. Temperate S America. BRISTM, E, K, LTN, RNG. D12*, D15*, D75*, D93*, J1(8:640; 10:360), R1, R2, R3, R5, R47. *Nassella hyalina* (Nees) Barkworth. **Fig.28.**

[cf. **joannis** Čelak.

A garden escape at Baragill (Caithness) pre-1950. Europe. BM. D1. D164a*, D182*, D183*. Confirmation needed of determination and status. **Fig.27.**]

juergensii Hack.

• A wool casual. S America. K, RNG. D15*, D174*, R3, R48. **Fig.28.**

neesiana Trin. & Rupr.   American Needle-grass

•• A wool casual, which may persist for several years. S America, (widespread). BM, E, K, LIV, LTN, NMW, OXF, RNG, SLBI. D2, D6, D10*, D12*, D15*, D75*, D93*, D115*, J1(8:764), J33(18:43), J70(109:254), R2, R4, R5, R8, R36, R38, R47, R65, R86. *S.eminens* Nees, non Cav.; *S.intricata* Godr.; *S.setigera* auct., non J.Presl; *Nassella neesiana* (Trin. & Rupr.) Barkworth. **Fig.1, 27.**

nitida Summerh. & C.E.Hubb.

• A wool casual. Australia. BM, K. D7, D93*, R3. **Fig.28.**

pampeana Speg.

• A wool casual. S America. K. D10, D12*, D26*, J107*(12:138), J109*(4,22:148), R2. **Fig.28.**

papposa Nees
- A wool casual; also cultivated in R.B.G., Kew (Surrey). S America, (?SE Spain). K, HbTBR. D12*, D15*, D52*, D174*, J64*(16:161-164), R2. **Fig.27.**

[**pennata** L.

An ornamental garden grass whose status as an alien is doubtful and uncertain; there is a very early (1840) record apparently from ballast in Fife. Eurasia, N Africa. BM, CGE, LCN, LIV, OXF, RNG. D1, D6, D20*, D21*, D22*, D25*, D115*, J1(5:793; 6:321), R8, R36, R49, ?R107. **Fig.27.**]

philippii Steud.
- A wool casual. S America. K, OXF, RNG, SLBI. D12*, D15*, D174*, R2, R48, R65. **Fig.28.**

poeppigiana Trin. & Rupr.

Pre-1930 only. A wool casual. Argentina, Chile. E. D12*, D15*, J1(4:27), R4, R36.

cf. **richardsonii** Link
- A wool casual. Western N America. RNG. D6*, D23*, R3.

scabra Lindl. subsp. **falcata** (Hughes) Vickery, S.W.L.Jacobs & Everett
- A wool casual. Australia. BM, E, K, NMW, RNG. D7, D10, D93*, J63(27:569-582), R2, R3, R5, R48, R51. *S.falcata* Hughes. Probably confused with *S.variabilis*. **Fig.28.**

scabra Lindl. subsp. **scabra**
- A wool casual. Australia. RNG. D7. Almost indistinguishable from subsp. *falcata*, and needs confirmation.

[**tenacissima** L.   Esparto

The main component of imported 'esparto grass', but there are no records of germination of seeds. SW Europe, NW Africa. D1, D6, D20*, D119*. *Macrochloa tenacissima* (L.) Kunth. **Fig.27.**]

tenuis Phil.
- A wool casual. S America. E, K, LTN. D12*, J106*(3:39), J107*(12:144), J109*(4,22:78), R3, R5. *S.papillosa* (Hack.) Hitchc.

tenuissima Trin.
- A wool casual. SW USA, Mexico, Argentina. K, RNG. D6*, D12*, D41*, D75*, D174*. **Fig.28.**

variabilis Hughes
- • A wool casual. Australia. BM, K, RNG, SLBI. D7, R1, R2, R5, R50. *S.incurva* Hughes. Treated in ref.D44* as a synonym of *S.nodosa* S.T.Blake. **Fig.27.**

verticillata Nees ex Spreng.
- • A wool casual. Australia. BEL, BM, CGE, E, K, LTN, NMW, RNG, SLBI. D7, D8, D16*, D93*, R1, R2, R5, R38, R47. **Fig.28.**

ANEMANTHELE Veldkamp   94a

1 species. New Zealand. Edges of streamlets. Differs from *Stipa* in morphological characters of leaf and embryo, with a 3-nerved (not 5-nerved) lemma and an obtuse conical calus, as discussed in ref.J97(34:105-109).

[lessoniana (Steud.) Veldkamp
Rarely grown in gardens in southern England and Ireland; reported to seed prolifically at Lucyswood, Bunclody (Co Carlow) and on a stone garden wall in Trengwainton National Trust (W Cornwall) in 1974; also cultivated in botanical gardens. New Zealand. BRISTM(?cultivated), K(cultivated). D79*, D155*, J8(29:13), J63*(27:569-582), R5(cultivated). *Agrostis lessoniana* Steud.; *A.procera* A.Rich., non Retz.; *A.rigida* A.Rich.; *Apera arundinacea* Hook.f.; *A.purpurascens* Colenso; *Oryzopsis lessoniana* (Steud.) Veldkamp; *O.rigida* (A.Rich.) Zotov; *Stipa arundinacea* (Hook.f.) Benth. All records from eastern Australia are in error. **Fig.12, 29.**]

NASSELLA (Trin.) E.Desv.   95

15 species. S America, mainly in the Andes. Hillsides. *N.trichotoma* is widely established as a noxious weed. Recent work by M.E.Barkworth in ref.J52(39:597-614) has suggested that several species referred to *Stipa* in the present work should be placed in *Nassella*.

caespitosa Griseb. var. **peruviana** (Ball) Hack.
Pre-1930 only. S America. E, OXF. J1(4:28-29), J109*(4,22:117), R4, R5, R36. *N.peruviana* Hack.; *Stipa caespitosa* (Griseb.) Speg.

chilensis (Trin.) E.Desv.
• A wool casual. S America, (USA). E. D6, D52*, J22*(7:386), R2. *N.major* (Trin. & Rupr.) E.Desv.; *Urachne chilensis* Trin.

flaccidula Hack. var. **glomerata** Hack.
Pre-1930 only. A wool casual. Bolivia. E, OXF. J1(3:344; 4:28), R4*, R36. Originally misnamed as *Stipa inconspicua*.

[multiflora (P.Beauv.) Druce, nom. inval.
Pre-1930 only. ?Chile. R36. The true identity of this species is dubious since no description was given by G.C.Druce; however according to ref.S12 the name was probably based on *Piptatherum multiflorum* (Cav.) P.Beauv. which is a synonym for *P.miliaceum*.]

trichotoma (Nees) Hack. ex Arechav.
•• A wool casual; also cultivated in R.B.G., Kew (Surrey). Temperate S America, (widespread). BEL, BM, CGE, E, K, LTN, NMW, OXF, RNG. D12*, D15*, D24*, D75*, D93*, D115*, J71*(25:679-680), R1, R2, R5, R36, R47. *Stipa trichotoma* Nees. A frequent wool casual, caespitose with short spiny leaves but often not flowering. **Fig.2, 29.**

ORYZOPSIS Michx.   97

35 species. N temperate and subtropical regions, especially the Middle East. Dry mountain slopes and woodland. Awn usually short, straight and deciduous, unlike most *Stipa* species. *Piptatherum* P.Beauv. is a later name which has been used to distinguish the Eurasian species from most of those in N America.

miliacea (L.) Benth. & Hook. ex Asch. & Schweinf.   Smilo-grass
•• A casual of wool, tips, wasteland, docks and bird-seed; possibly a garden escape, well established in the grounds of Highlands College, Jersey. Atlantic Is, Med., (widespread). BEL, BM, BRISTM, E, K, LTN, NMW, OXF, RNG. D1, D2*, D4, D6*, D12*, D17*, D20*, D75*, D89*, D93*, D115*, J10(38:45), J26(57:71), R1, R3, R5, R21, R23, R36, R38, R40, R42, R47, R52, R65, R86. *O.multiflora* (Cav.) Druce; *Agrostis miliacea* L.; *Piptatherum miliaceum* (L.) Coss. Fig.17, 29.

thomasii (Duby) P.Silva
• A casual on a tip at Stone (W Kent) in 1974. S and SW Europe, Turkey. BM. D1, D18, D117*. *O. miliacea* var. *thomasii* (Duby) Boiss.; *Milium thomasii* Duby; *Piptatherum thomasii* (Duby) Kunth. Very close to *O.miliacea*, but differs in having 20-50 (not less than 20) short branches at the lowest node which are sterile or bear only one spikelet.]

[**virescens** (Trin.) Beck
1930 only. A casual in Jersey. S Europe, Turkey, Caucasus, Iran. D1, D18, D25*, D115*, R40. *Piptatherum virescens* (Trin.) Boiss.; *Urachne virescens* Trin. This record is an error according to ref.R11.]

PIPTOCHAETIUM J.Presl   100

30 species. USA to Argentina. Distinguished from *Stipa* and *Nassella* by its grooved palea. For an account of the genus see ref.J72(6:213-310).

bicolor (Vahl) E.Desv.
• A wool casual. Temperate S America. E, K, RNG, HbCGH. D12*, D15*, R2, R5, R65. *Stipa bicolor* Vahl. Fig.2, 29.

montevidense (Spreng.) Parodi
• A wool casual. Bolivia, Brazil, temperate S America. K, RNG. D12*, D15*, D75*, D172*, R2. *Caryochloa montevidense* Spreng. Fig.29.

ORTACHNE Steud.   101

3 species. Costa Rica to Peru, Patagonia. Open places in stunted montane woodland. Related to *Stipa*, but with glumes much shorter than (not ± equal to) the floret.

rariflora (Hook.f.) Hughes
• A wool alien at Kirkheaton (SW Yorks) in 1959. Argentina. D72, R86. *Muhlenbergia rariflora* Hook.f.; *Stipa retorta* (Nees ex Steud.) Mez, non Cav. The location of the specimen is unknown.

POEAE

FESTUCA L.   104

c.450 species. Temperate regions and tropical mountains. Hills, plains and meadows. Some of the illustrations quoted below refer solely to drawings of the all-important cross-section of the leaves. See ref.D1, D2, D154.

altissima All.   *Wood Fescue*
- Cliveden (Bucks) c.1970, probably introduced for ornament, but only once found in a woodland ride; a rare native woodland grass. Temperate Europe and W Asia. K. D1, D2, D3*, D4.

arundinacea Schreb.   *Tall Fescue*
●●● A wool alien, which may persist; also a very common native pasture grass; also cultivated from wool. Temperate Eurasia, N Africa, (widespread). E, K. D1, D2, D3*, D4, J12(38:359), R2, R5, R65. Many different strains of this most important pasture grass occur. A hybrid with *Lolium multiflorum* has been found. Considered by many botanists (e.g. ref.D177) synonymous with *F.elatior* L.

[arvernensis Auquier, Kerguélen & Markgr.-Dann.
Mountains of southern France. D1, R11. *F.glauca* Lam., non Vill. In error for the native *F.longifolia* Thuill. according to ref.D2.]

brevipila Tracey   *Hard Fescue*
●● Introduced and established on roadsides and railway banks, mainly in southern and eastern England; on dunes NE of La Carrière Quarry, St. Ouen's Bay, Jersey; waste ground, Newport docks (Mons) in 1977. C Europe extending to Belgium and perhaps to S Sweden. BM, K, NMW, TOR, HbLJM. D1, D2*, D14, J11(23:432-433), J14(121:217, 123:244), J20*(106:347-397), J23(16:451; 17:289-299), J29(22:59-61), R11, R16, R24, R27, R39, R41, R54, R55, R56, R57, R58, R59, R60. *F.longifolia* auct. pro parte, non Thuill.; *F.trachyphylla* (Hack.) Krajina, non Hack. ex Druce. According to ref.D2 most records for *F.longifolia* Thuill. and *F.guestfalica* Boenn. ex Rchb. refer to this species.

buchtienii Hack.
Pre-1930 only. A wool casual from Galashiels (Selkirks). ?Bolivia. OXF. J1(9:286). Probably best considered as a form of *F.dolichophylla* J.Presl sensu lato, which is very common in Bolivia, Ecuador and Peru (see ref.D172*, D175).

caprina Nees
- A wool casual. Tropical Africa to the Cape, N Yemen. BM, E, K, RNG. D5*, D13, D68*, R5. *F.nubigena* Jungh. subsp. *caprina* (Nees) St.-Yves. Originally determined as cf. *F.glauca* Lam.

diffusa Dumort.
●● A grass seed alien previously overlooked but recently recorded from many localities and probably established; e.g. Scalloway (Shetland), Shiels (Lanarks),

Cardiff and Newport (Mons) and Les Dicqs, Guernsey. C Europe. BM, E, K, NMW, WARMS, ZCM.   D1, D2*, D115*, J14(118:234; 121:216-217; 123:248), J23(15:141; 16:451; 17:197), J28(21:506), R11, R17, R23, R53. *F.megastachys* (Gaudin) Hegetschw. & Heer; *F.multiflora* Hoffm., non Walter; *F.rubra* L. var. *grandiflora* (Hack.) Howarth; *F.rubra* subsp. *megastachys* Gaudin; *F.rubra* subsp. *multiflora* (Hoffm.) Jirásek.

gautieri (Hack.) K.Richt. subsp. **scoparia** (A.Kerner & Hack.) Kerguélen
 • Road embankment at Exeter (S Devon) in 1992 (confirmed C.A.Stace, T.A.Cope); well established in a quarry near York in 1993 (determined C.A.Stace), probably a garden outcast or introduced with a planted *Hypericum*; this or a similar species was cultivated as an ornamental grass outside a new office building at Teddington (Middlesex) c.1985-1990; cultivated in R.B.G., Kew (Surrey).   SW France, NE Spain.   HbEJC, HbRMP, HbRT-A.   D1, D154*, R7, R10, R19, J14(125:234).   *F.scoparia* (A.Kerner & Hack.) Nyman, non Hook.; *F.varia* Haenke subsp. *scoparia* A.Kerner & Hack.   A tufted grass with short ± glaucous or green pungent or spiny leaves, now widely available from specialist nurseries as an ornamental.

[glauca Vill.
  Grown for ornament in gardens.   S France.   D1, J20*(106:347-397). According to ref.D2 all records refer to *F.brevipila*, or the native *F.lemanii* Bastard and *F.longifolia* Thuill.]

heterophylla Lam.   **Various-leaved Fescue**
 •• Probably introduced in woods as a fodder or landscaping plant, especially in southern England, but extending as far as Scotland; in Ireland in mixed woodland near Grange (Co Limerick).   C and S Europe, SW Asia.   BM, E, LTN, NMW, OXF, RNG, TOR.   D1, D2*, D3*, D4, D18*, D19*, D75, D115*, J9(24:243-244), R17, R18, R113.   *Festuca rubra* subsp. *heterophylla* (Lam.) Hack.   Surprisingly, regarded by ref.D1 as native in Britain.

[indigesta Boiss. subsp. molinieri (Litard.) Kerguélen
  Pyrenees.   The records from Bally Burren (W Galway) and Corrofin (Co Clare) are erroneous according to ref.J20(106:351) and D2, as is the Irish distribution given in ref.D1.   *F.niphobia* (St.-Yves) Kerguélen; *F.ovina* L. var. *niphobia* St.-Yves.]

nigrescens Lam.   *Chewing's Fescue*
 •• A native species also extensively used as a sown grass.   Europe.   BM. D2*, D3*.   *F.rubra* subsp. *commutata* Gaudin (subsp. *caespitosa* Hack.; var. *fallax* sensu Tutin).

rupicola Heuff.
  Pre-1930 only.   SE Europe.   D1, D14, D115*, D180*, J1(8:322; 9:693). *F.hirsuta* Host, nom. illeg.; *F.ovina* subsp. *sulcata* Hack.; *F.sulcata* (Hack.) Nyman.

trachylepis Hack. ex Druce
  Pre-1930 only.   S America.   E.   J1(4:29-30), R4*, R36.   ?*F.dumetorum* Phil., non L.

LOLIUM L.   109

8 species. Temperate Eurasia and N Africa, introduced elsewhere. Meadows, pastures and weedy places. *L.perenne* (Perennial Rye-grass) is one of the best pasture grasses. Several species hybridize readily with some *Festuca* species, forming × *Festulolium*. Ref.J101(1392:1-65).

multiflorum Lam.   Italian Rye-grass

●●●●● An established escape from cultivation naturalised on roadsides etc. in many places throughout the British Isles; also a casual of wool and bird-seed. Europe, Med., (widespread). D1, D2, D3*, D4, D6*, D12*, D75*, D115*, R8, R21. *L.aristatum* Lag.; *L.compositum* Thuill.; *L.italicum* A.Braun; *L.siculum* Parl. Fertile hybrids have been recorded with *L.perenne* (*L.* × *boucheanum* Kunth, very common on wasteland, roadsides. BRISTM, K, NMW. D130), *L.temulentum* (*L.* × *hybridum* Hausskn., on tips or in wool. E, K, NMW. D130, J23(9:390), R5) and *L.rigidum* (*L.* × *hubbardii* Jansen & Wacht. ex B.K.Simon, rare in wool and on tips. BM, K, NMW, RNG. D190, J23(8:299)). Some of these may be casual introductions while others have occurred naturally.

[*perenne* L.   *Perennial Rye-grass*

Cultivated from bird-seed, wool and soya; a very common native grass. Temperate Eurasia, N Africa, (widespread). D1, D2, D3*, D4, D75*, R21, R65.]

persicum Boiss. & Hohen. ex Boiss.

●● A casual of grain, docks and tips; also an impurity in wheat (ref.D3). SW Asia, (N America). BRISTM, K, LTN, RNG. D17*, D18, D22*, D28*, D89*, J10(29:107), R61, R62.

remotum Schrank   Flaxfield Rye-grass

●● A casual of wool, cultivated land, grain and tips; also cultivated from bird-seed; formerly a weed in flax, now a decreasing species. Origin obscure, (Eurasia, N America). BM, K, LCN, NMW, OXF, RNG. D1, D2, D4, D19*, D20*, D75*, D89*, D115*, J1(5:135,409; 8:767; 9:757), J18(385:35), R21, R36, R49, R63, R64, R86, R107, R123. *L.linicola* A.Braun.

rigidum Gaudin   Mediterranean Rye-grass

●●● A casual of wool, esparto, grain, soya, wasteland, docks and bird-seed. Atlantic Is, Med., SW Asia, (widespread). BEL, BM, BRISTM, CGE, E, K, LTN, NMW, RNG, SLBI. D1, D2, D6*, D17*, D18, D19*, D20*, D24*, D48*, D75*, D89*, D115*, D117*, J1(11:48), J23(2:357), R1, R2, R4, R5, R21, R24, R36, R40, R47, R55, R59, R61, R62, R65, R66, R86. Includes *L.loliaceum* (Bory & Chaub. ex Fauché) Hand.-Mazz.; *L.parabolicae* Sennen ex Samp.; *L.strictum* C.Presl; *L.subulatum* Vis.

temulentum L.   Darnel

●●●● A casual of tips, bird-seed, grain and wool; formerly a frequent weed in cornfields, but now very rare. Med., (widespread). D1, D2, D3*, D4, D6*, D17*, D19*, D75*, D89*, D115*, D117*, R8, R21. *L.arvense* With. The grain is sometimes infected with a very poisonous fungus (ergot). A hybrid with *L.rigidum* has occurred as a wool alien in several places. CGE, E, K, RNG. D130, R5, R49.

MICROPYRUM (Gaudin) Link   **111**

    3 species. S Europe, Med. Dry open spaces.

tenellum (L.) Link
- An esparto casual. S Europe, Med. RNG. D1, D18, D20*, D25*, D115*, D117*. *Catapodium tenellum* (L.) Trab.; *Festuca festucoides* (Bertol.) Becherer; *Nardurus lachenalii* (C.C.Gmel.) Godr.; *N.tenellus* (L.) Duval-Jouve, non Rchb. ex Godr.; *Triticum tenellum* L. **Fig.9.**

VULPIA C.C.Gmel.   **112**

    22 species. N temperate and subtropical regions, introduced to the southern hemisphere; a few endemics also occur in S America. Dry open places.

alopecuros (Schousb.) Dumort.
- A wool casual. W Med. BM, RNG. D1, D20*, D75*, D115*, D117*, R1. *Festuca alopecuros* Schousb.

australis (Nees ex Steud.) Blom
- A wool and dock casual. Eastern S America. BM, K, RNG. D12*, D15*, D174*, J23(14:77-78), R1. *Festuca australis* Nees ex Steud. The records in ref.J6(3:289-290) and R47 refer to *V.muralis* with which this species has been confused (see ref.J23(11:72).

bromoides (L.) Gray   *Squirreltail Fescue*
- ••••• An alien of wool, docks and tips; also an abundant native weed of waste places, dry hills, roadsides, etc. Europe, Med., mountains of Africa, (widespread). D1, D2, D3*, D4, R1, R2, R4, R5. *V.myuros* subsp. *sciuroides* (Roth) Rouy; *V.sciuroides* (Roth) C.C.Gmel.; *Festuca bromoides* L.; *F.sciuroides* Roth.

ciliata Dumort. subsp. **ambigua** (Le Gall) Stace & Auquier
Pre-1930 only. Recorded as a wool alien from Gala (Selkirks) in 1873; the specimen collected from Blackmoor (N Hants) in 1969 (ref.R2, R3, R6) is now regarded as an extreme variant of *V.myuros*. A rare native grass of southern England, the Channel Islands, Belgium and NW France. D1, D2, D3*, D4, R4, R86. *V.ambigua* (Le Gall) A.G.More; *Festuca ambigua* Le Gall.

ciliata Dumort. subsp. **ciliata**
- A grain and wool casual, also on reclaimed land; occasionally persistent for a few years in southern England, as at Ardingly Station (E Sussex) in 1967, when it survived for 5 years. Med. BM, K, OXF, RNG. D1, D2, D18*, D20*, D30*, D75*, D115*, D117*, J1(8:766; 9:146), J6(7:566), J26(57:71), R1, R37, R67. *V.aetnensis* Tineo; *V.danthonii* (Asch. & Graebn.) Volkart; *Festuca ciliata* Danthoine ex DC., non Gouan; *F.danthonii* Asch. & Graebn.

cynosuroides (Desf.) Parl.
- An esparto casual. N Africa. K, OXF, RNG. D1, D20*, D31, J1(4:509), J74*(21:372), R5, R36. *V.gypsophila* (Hack.) Nyman; *Ctenopsis cynosuroides* (Desf.) Paunero; *Festuca cynosuroides* Desf.; *Nardurus cynosuroides* (Desf.) Trab.

geniculata (L.) Link
- •• A casual of wool, docks, grain, tips and bird-seed. W Med. BEL, BM, CGE, K, LIV, LTN, NMW, RNG. D1, D20*, D30*, D31*, D75*, D117*, J1(4:509), J18(382:25), R1, R3, R23, R44, R61. *Bromus geniculatus* L.; *Festuca geniculata* (L.) Willd. The specimen in ref.J1(8:211,284) was originally determined as *V.ligustica*.

ligustica (All.) Link
- A casual in a flower-bed in Brighton (E Sussex) in 1992; Exmouth docks (S Devon) in 1994, probably introduced from small boats; otherwise pre-1930 only as an alien of grain, docks and wasteland. Med. BM, K, NMW, RNG, SLBI, HbPAH. D1, D18*, D20*, D31, D75*, D115*, J1(7:1027; 8:142), R10, R36, R52, R55. *Bromus ligusticus* All.; *Festuca ligustica* (All.) Bertol.

membranacea (L.) Dumort.
- A wool casual. W Europe, NW Africa. E, RNG. D1, D25*, D117*, R5. *V.longiseta* (Brot.) Hack.; *Stipa membranacea* L. The Blackmoor (N Hants) record in HbTBR is now considered to be an extreme form of *V.myuros*. This name has unfortunately been widely misapplied (e.g. ref.D3, D4) to our native *V.fasciculata* (Forssk.) Samp. (*V.membranacea* auct., non (L.) Dumort.; *V.uniglumis* Dumort.), see ref.J23(11:117-123). The exact identity of *Festuca membranacea* Druce, non Kit., recorded from Galashiels (Selkirks) about 1870 is unclear.

muralis (Kunth) Nees
- •• A casual of wool and docks; also cultivated from wool; a bulb-field weed in the Isles of Scilly. Atlantic Is, Med., Arabia, (S America). E, ?K, RNG. D1, D2, D17*, D18*, J23(11:72), R3, R4, R36, R52, R61, R65. *V.australis* auct., non Blom; *V.bromoides* var. *microstachys* (Nutt.) Jansen & Weevers; *V.broteri* Boiss. & Reut.; *Festuca bromoides* L. var. *tenella* (Boiss.) Druce; *F.microstachys* Nutt.; *F.muralis* Kunth.

myuros (L.) C.C.Gmel. forma **megalura** (Nutt.) Stace & R.Cotton Foxtail Fescue
- •• A casual of wool and agricultural seed; established in the Isle of Grain (W Kent). Europe, (widespread). BM, CGE, E, K, LIV, LTN, RNG, SLBI. D1, D2, D6*, D10*, D12*, D18*, J1(13:375), J6(1:67), J8(34:22), J23(10:434; 11:72), R1, R2, R5, R24, R27, R54, R58, R65. *V.megalura* (Nutt.) Rydb.; *Festuca megalura* Nutt. Several London records were originally misnamed as *V.ciliata* subsp. *ciliata* according to ref.R45.

myuros (L.) C.C.Gmel. forma *myuros*   Rat's-tail Fescue
- ••• An alien of wool, docks and tips; also a native weed of wasteland, arable land, dry walls, etc., in southern England, but probably introduced further north. C and S Europe, Med., SW Asia, (widespread). E, K, LTN, RNG, SLBI, WCR. D1, D2, D3*, D4, R1, R2, R4, R5. *Festuca myuros* L.

[cf. octoflora (Walter) Rydb.
A wool casual from Blackmoor (N Hants) in 1970, but very immature so that
the determination is dubious; also cultivated from wool. N and S America.
BM, HbTBR. D6*, D41*, D75*, D118*, R3, R6. *Festuca octoflora* Walter.]
sicula (C.Presl) Link
Pre-1930 only. A casual in Leith docks (Midlothian) in 1904. Med. K, RNG.
D1, D20*, D31, D115*, R36. *Festuca sicula* C.Presl; includes *V.setacea* Parl.

WANGENHEIMIA Moench   113

2 species. Spain and NW Africa. Dry open places.

lima (L.) Trin.
• A casual of esparto, docks and a sewage works. W Med. BM, CGE, E, K,
LIV, RNG. D1, D20*, D31*, R5, R36. *W.disticha* Moench; *Cynosurus
lima* L. Very close to *Ctenopsis pectinella* (Delile) De Not. (*Vulpiella
pectinella* (Delile) Boiss.), which has the lower glume reduced to a short scale
(not ± equal to the upper glume). **Fig.2.**

CASTELLIA Tineo   115

1 species. Canary Islands, Med., Arabia, Sudan, Somalia, Pakistan. Dry open
places. Widespread but very local and rarely collected.

tuberculosa (Moris) Bor
• An esparto casual. Distribution of the genus. RNG. D1, D20*, D30*,
D48, D115*, D117*. *C.tuberculata* Tineo; *Catapodium tuberculosum* Moris;
Desmazeria tuberculosa (Moris) Bonnet, *Festuca tuberculosa* (Moris)
T.Durand; *Nardurus tuberculosus* (Moris) Hayek. **Fig.12.**

PSILURUS Trin.   116

1 species. Med. to Pakistan. Dry places. A very inconspicuous grass, even
when in full flower.

incurvus (Gouan) Schinz & Thell.
• A grain, dock and wool casual; recently found as a weed in gravel at Oxford
in 1975. Med., SW Asia, (Australia). E, K, LIV, OXF, SLBI. D1, D17*,
D18*, D20*, D24*, D25*, D31*, D93*, D115*, J8(13:23), R2, R36, R86.
P.aristatus (L.) Trevis; *P.nardoides* Trin.; *Nardus aristata* L.; *N.incurva*
Gouan. **Fig.3.**

CYNOSURUS L.   117

8 species. Europe, N Africa and the Middle East. Meadows and weedy places.

cristatus L.   *Crested Dog's-tail*
• A wool alien; also cultivated from wool-waste; a common native pasture grass. Atlantic Is, Europe, Middle East, (widespread). RNG, HbTBR. D1, D2, D3*, D4, D89*, R1, R2, R65.

echinatus L.   Rough Dog's-tail
••• A grain, dock and wool casual, also on wasteland and in fields, sometimes in abundance; sometimes established, as in bulb fields in the Isles of Scilly , on the Chesil Beach (Dorset) and in Devon and Cornwall; possibly native in the Channel Islands. Atlantic Is, Med., Middle East, (widespread). BM, BRISTM, CGE, DBN, E, K, LSR, LTR, NMW, RNG, WCR. D1, D2, D3*, D4, D12*, D17*, D20*, D31*, D75*, D89*, J1(10:361), R4, R5, R8, R23, R36, R38, R40, R42, R43, R49, R54, R55, R56, R57, R58, R60, R62, R66, R71, R72, R73, R86, R122. *C.giganteus* Ten.

elegans Desf. sensu lato
Pre-1930 only. A grain casual at Cardiff. Atlantic Is, Med. NMW. D1, D17*, D18, D20*, D31, D48*, D115*, J1(8:37; 10:930), R36. Includes *C.effusus* Link (*C.elegans* subsp. *effusus* (Link) Asch. & Graebn.).

LAMARCKIA Moench   118

1 species. Med., Middle East. Dry places.

aurea (L.) Moench   Golden Dog's-tail
•• A casual of wool, tips and waste ground where it may be a garden escape; often cultivated in gardens as an ornamental grass. Med., Middle East, (widespread). BEL, BM, CGE, E, K, LIV, LTN, RNG. D1, D2, D6*, D12*, D17*, D20*, D30*, D31*, D75*, D89*, D115*, D117*, D118*, J1(8:182,423), J8(28:16-17), J18(388:37), J23(13:148), R1, R2, R5, R36, R38, R40, R47, R51, R69. *Cynosurus aureus* L. **Fig.2.**

PUCCINELLIA Parl.   119

c.80 species. Temperate regions, mainly Asia. Coastal and inland saline or alkaline soils; mountain grassland in the Himalayas. Close to *Poa, Festuca* and *Glyceria*.

distans (Jacq.) Parl.   *Reflexed Saltmarsh-grass*
•• An alien of wool, tips, wasteland and river meadows; also a frequent native grass of salt-marshes. N temperate zone, N Africa, (Australia). K, RNG. D1, D2, D3*, D4, R1, R5, R65. *Atropis distans* (Jacq.) Griseb.; *Glyceria distans* (Jacq.) Wahlenb.; *Poa distans* Jacq. The name *P.distans* L. is a later homonym of *P.distans* Jacq. (see T.A.Cope in ref.D51). The introduced forms differ considerably from our native plants according to ref.R1.

fasciculata (Torr.) E.P.Bicknell var. **caespitosa** Jansen
- A wool casual from Linthwaite (SW Yorks) in 1963. S Africa. CGE, E, K, RNG. D5*, R5, R86. *Poa fasciculata* Torr. This variety is not upheld by ref.D87* and the determination is in doubt.

festuciformis (Host) Parl.
Pre-1930 only. A dock casual. Med. BM, K, ?LANC, ?RNG. D1, D18*, D32*, D117*, J1(10:997), R12, R79. *Glyceria festuciformis* (Host) Heynh. ex Rchb.; *Poa festuciformis* Host. The 1918 record from Wadebridge (E Cornwall) is suspect as the specimens were immature according to ref.R52, R80. In Ireland this name has been misapplied by R.L.Praeger and others to a variant of the native *P.maritima* (Huds.) Parl.

rupestris (With.) Fernald & Weath.   *Stiff Saltmarsh-grass*
Pre-1930 only. A ballast alien from S Fife; native around the coasts of England, Wales and Ireland. Coasts of W Europe from Norway to Spain, (N America). D1, D2, D3*, D4, J2(41:125-137). *Poa rupestris* With.

tenuiflora (Griseb.) Scribn. & Merr.
- A wool casual at East Ardsley (SW Yorks) in 1985. Iran, Kashmir, N and C Asia, China. K, OXF, SLBI, HbTBR. D51, D71, D126*, D184*. *Atropis tenuiflora* Griseb.

BRIZA L.   121

20 species. Temperate Eurasia and S America. Grasslands and open places, dry or moist soils. Some species are very ornamental.

humilis M.Bieb.
- A wool casual. SE Europe, SW Asia. E, K, RNG. D1, D17*, D18, D22*, D33*, D48*, R3, R5.

maxima L.   *Greater Quaking-grass*
●●● A casual of wool, tips, docks, roadsides and esparto; a garden escape sometimes naturalised, as in the Isles of Scilly and the Channel Islands; frequently cultivated as an ornamental grass. Atlantic Is, Med., (widespread). BM, BRISTM, E, K, LTN, NMW, OXF, RNG. D1, D2, D3*, D4, D17*, D19*, D24*, D33*, D75*, D89*, J1(10:361), R5, R8, R24, R36, R39, R40, R43, R49, R55, R58, R59, R66, R86, R123.

minor L.   *Lesser Quaking-grass*
●●● A casual of wool, tips, wasteland, roadsides and arable land, occasionally established for several seasons in southern England, apparently decreasing; established in the Isles of Scilly and the Channel Islands and sometimes claimed as a native there; cultivated from bird-seed and as an ornamental grass. Atlantic Is, Med., (widespread). BM, BRISTM, CGE, E, K, LTN, NMW, OXF, RNG. D1, D2, D3*, D4, D75*, D89*, R3, R5, R8, R21, R86. *B.gracilis* hort.

POA L.   124

c.400 species. Cool temperate regions and mountain tops in the tropics.
Mostly in meadows extending to above the tree-line. Only c.15 species are
annual. *P.pratensis* (Smooth Meadow-grass, Kentucky Blue-grass) is a most
valuable fodder grass, and *P.annua* (Annual Meadow-grass) is probably the
most cosmopolitan of all grasses. **Key on p.113.**

ampla Merr.
• Casual at Windsor (Berks) in 1967. Western USA, (Argentina, Chile). K.
D6*, D52*. According to ref.D118, this taxon is best treated as an ecotype of
P.secunda J.Presl subsp. *juncifolia* (Scribn.) Soreng.

angustifolia L.   *Narrow-leaved Meadow-grass*
• A wool alien; also a frequent native grass. Europe, SW Asia, (N America).
K, HbTBR. D1, D2, D3*, R2.

annua L.   *Annual Meadow-grass*
••••• The commonest wool alien; abundant, especially on paths, waste and
cultivated land; a common weed in lawns; cultivated from bird-seed. All
temperate regions and on tropical mountains. D1, D2, D3*, D4, R21.
Flowers throughout the year.

cf. **balfourii** Parn.   *Glaucous Meadow-grass*
• An alien established in some quantity on an old tip at Lampeter (Cards) in
1994, possibly of garden origin; a rare native mountain grass from N Wales to
Scotland. Iceland, Scandinavia. K, HbRMP, HbTBR. D1, D3*, D4, R19,
R33. *P.glauca* Vahl subsp. *balfourii* (Parn.) Syme. Considered by P.J.O.Trist
in ref.J23(16:37-42) to be the shade form of *P.glauca*.

bulbosa L.   *Bulbous Meadow-grass*
•• A rare introduced grass in a few places inland, such as the Thames tow-path
above and below Hampton Court (Middlesex, Surrey); also a rare and local
native grass of open grassy and sandy places by the sea. W Europe, Med. to
C Asia, (widespread). NMW, HbEJC. D1, D2, D3*, D4, J36(1905:103).

chaixii Vill.   *Broad-leaved Meadow-grass*
••• Introduced and naturalised, usually in woodland, in widely scattered
localities in Britain and Ireland. Europe, SW Asia. BM, CGE, E, K, NMW,
RNG, WCR. D1, D2, D3*, D4, D75*, D180*, R5, R8, R27, R36, R39, R40,
R55, R56, R57, R58, R59, R60, R72, R77, R78, R107, R122. *P.sudetica*
Haenke; *P.sylvatica* Chaix. A hybrid with *P.nemoralis* has been recorded but
seems unlikely.

[cita Edgar
Cultivated in a garden at Epsom (Surrey) for several years c.1912; cultivated
at the Welsh Grass Breeding Station, Aberystwyth (Cards) c.1929, but
apparently not distributed elsewhere. New Zealand. K. D61, J63(24:425-
503). *P.caespitosa* G.Forst. ex Spreng., non Poir.; *P.laevis* R.Br. var. *filifolia*
Hook. This grass is similar to *P.poiformis*.]

compressa L.   *Flattened Meadow-grass*
    ●●● An alien of wool, tips and waste ground; also a frequent native grass,
often growing on old walls. Europe, SW Asia, (widespread). BM, CGE,
DBN, E, K, NMW, RNG, TCD. D1, D2, D3*, D4, R1, R4, R5, R122.
P.polynoda Parn.
costiniana Vickery
    ● A wool casual. Australia. K, HbTBR. D7, D93*, R3.
flabellata (Lam.) Raspail   **Tussac-grass**
    ● Introduced (since 1845) and long established in enclosures in Shetland
(e.g. Dunrossness, Exnavoe), where it is used for basket making; more recently
introduced experimentally on Mull (Mid Ebudes); contrary to ref.D1, D2, there
are no records of definitely wild plants. Southern S America, S Atlantic Is.
K, OXF, RNG. D1, D2*, D52*, D147*, D148*, J4(t.1194, t.1197)*,
J6(3:300), J7(1919:209), J8(32:12), J18(343:28), R53, R74, R75. *P.caespitosa*
auct., non Poir.; *Dactylis caespitosa* G.Forst.; *Festuca flabellata* Lam.;
Parodiochloa flabellata (Lam.) C.E.Hubb.
fordeana F.Muell.
    ● A wool casual. Australia. RNG, HbTBR. D7, D8, D16, D35*, D93*, R2.
[cf. glaucantha Schleich. ex Gould
    A wool alien from Gala (Selkirks) in 1963. Europe, N America. CGE, E, K.
D6*. Re-determined as *P.sterilis*.]
gunnii Vickery
    ● A wool casual. Tasmania. E, K. D7, R5.
imbecilla Spreng. var. **breviglumis** (Hook.f.) Cheeseman
    ● A persistent weed in the rock garden at the Royal Botanic Garden, Edinburgh
for many years. New Zealand. E. D113*, D188*, J63*(24:425-503), R7.
infirma Kunth   *Early Meadow-grass*
    ● A wool casual; a garden weed in Co Londonderry; also cultivated from wool;
a rare or over-looked native grass from the Isles of Scilly to Hampshire and the
Channel Islands. Med. to NW India, (S America, Australasia). RNG. D1,
D2, D3*, D4, R4, R65, R123. *P.annua* var. *exilis* Tomm.; *P.annua* var.
remotiflora Hack.; *P.exilis* (Tomm.) Murb.
labillardierei Steud.
    ●● A wool casual; cultivated at the Royal Horticultural Gardens at Wisley
(Surrey). Australia, (New Zealand). BM, CGE, E, K, NMW, RNG. D7, D8,
D10*, D16, D26*, D29, D93*, J63(24:425-503), R3, R5. *P.australis* R.Br.
var. *laevis* Kirk. It rarely flowers in the field so may be over-looked and
under-recorded.
leptoclada Hochst.
    ● A wool casual. Arabia, tropical Africa. K, HbTBR. D13, D36*, D37*,
R1, R2, R5.
cf. **ligularis** Nees ex Steud.
    ● A wool casual. S America. HbTBR. D12*, D52*, R3. The single
flowering spikelet has been lost.

[*nemoralis* L.   *Wood Meadow-grass*
A possible wool alien, or a natural weed; probably introduced as a component
of grass seed for shady places in Ireland and NW Britain; also a common native
grass. Temperate Eurasia, NE America. HbTBR. D1, D2, D3*, D4, R3.
P.caespitosa Poir., non G.Forst. ex Spreng.]

palustris L.   **Swamp Meadow-grass**
••• A casual of wool and grain, docks, wasteland and tips; originally
introduced as a fodder crop and now naturalised by rivers and ponds in
scattered localities; possibly native in fens in East Anglia. N temperate zone,
(S America). BM, BRISTM, E, K, LTN, LTR, NMW, OXF, RNG. D1, D2,
D3*, D4, D75*, D115*, J1(10:361), R5, R24, R36, R39, R49, R50, R55,
R56, R58, R62, R66, R73, R76, R77, R78, R122. *P.fertilis* Host; *P.serotina*
Ehrh. ex Hoffm.

poiformis (Labill.) Druce
• A wool casual. Australia. BM, CGE, E, K, RNG, SLBI. D7, D8*, D27*,
D29, D38, D93*, J1(4:640), R1, R3, R5. *P.australis* R.Br., nom. illeg.;
P.caespitosa auct., non G.Forst. ex Spreng.; *P.labillardierei* auct., non Steud.;
P.laevis R.Br.; *P.plebeia* R.Br.; *Arundo poiformis* Labill.

[*pratensis* L.   *Smooth Meadow-grass*
A probable wool alien, or a natural weed; also a very common native grass.
Temperate Eurasia, (widespread). HbTBR. D1, D2, D3*, D4.]

[remota Forselles
Cultivated in the R.B.G., Kew (Surrey); very similar to *P.chaixii* and possibly
overlooked. N, C and E Europe. D1, D180*.]

schimperiana Hochst. ex A.Rich.
• A wool casual. N Yemen, tropical Africa, Ethiopia. K. D13, D36*, D37*,
D68*, R48.

sieberiana Spreng. var. **cyanophylla** Vickery
• A wool casual. New South Wales. HbCGH, HbEJC, HbTBR. D7, D10*,
D44*, D93*, J63(24:425-503). *P.australis* auct., non R.Br. Part of the
original plant has grown into a large ornamental tussock, still flowering
profusely in a garden at Kingston-upon-Thames (Surrey) after 20 years.

sterilis M.Bieb. group
• A wool casual. E Europe, W Asia. CGE, E, K, LTN, RNG. D1, D18*,
R5, R48, R51. Includes *P.pannonica* A.Kern. subsp. *scabra* (Asch.
& Graebn.) Soó (*P.scabra* Asch. & Graebn.) and *P.sterilis* M.Bieb., which are
virtually indistinguishable.

trivialis L. subsp. *trivialis*   *Rough Meadow-grass*
••• A wool alien; also cultivated from wool; a very common native grass.
Temperate Eurasia, N Africa, (widespread). HbCGH, HbTBR. D1, D2,
D3*, D4, R2, R65. Much under-collected as an alien. Subsp. *sylvicola*
(Guss.) H.Lindb. (*P.sylvicola* Guss.) may have been overlooked, see ref.D1,
J59*(7:85-91).

DACTYLIS L.   125

1 species. Temperate Eurasia,(including many subspecies endemic around the
Mediterranean and in Macaronesia, with one in the Canary Islands); widely
introduced elsewhere.   Meadows, woods, wasteland and stony hills.
D.glomerata (Cock's-foot) is a very valuable forage grass.

glomerata L. subsp. **aschersoniana** (Graebn.) Thell.   Slender Cock's-foot
• Naturalised on Cliveden Estate (Bucks), in Sherborne Park (Dorset) and
West Horsley Place (Surrey). W and C Europe. BM, CGE, E, K, NMW,
OXF, RNG. D1, D2, D3, D4, D19*, D75*, D115*, J23(1:22; 9:184; 10:187),
R5, R44. *D.aschersoniana* Graebn.; *D.polygama* Horv.

glomerata L. subsp. *glomerata*   *Cock's-foot*
•••• A common wool alien, which may persist; cultivated from bird-seed;
an abundant native pasture grass. Temperate Eurasia, N Africa, (widespread).
D1, D2, D3*, D4, D75*, D115*, R1, R2, R21. Frequently grown from wool-
shoddy cultures.

glomerata L. subsp. **hispanica** (Roth) Nyman
• An alien of docks and esparto; cultivated experimentally. Med., SW Asia.
BEL, CGE, E, K, OXF, RNG, SLBI. D1, D2, D18, D20, D30*, D115*,
J1(9:378), J6(6:52), R5, R36. *D.hispanica* Roth. Claims as a native in
SW Ireland need confirmation.

EREMOPOA Roshev.   137

4 species. E Med. to W China. Similar to the annual species of *Poa*, but with
whorled panicle branches.

persica (Trin.) Roshev.
• A casual of wool, docks and wasteland. SW Asia. BM, BRISTM, K, OXF,
RNG, SLBI. D14, D18*, D22*, D75*, D126*, J1(8:766; 13:111), R36, R62.
Poa persica Trin. **Fig.3.**

SPHENOPUS Trin.   140

2 species. Atlantic Is, Med. to Iran. Saline soils.

divaricatus (Gouan) Rchb.
Pre-1930 only. Leith docks (Midlothian) in 1909. Atlantic Is, Med.,
Middle East. D1, D17*, D18, D20*, D30*, D31*, D115*, J1(9:378,531),
J36(1909:44), R36. *S.gouanii* Trin.; *Poa divaricata* Gouan. The specimen in
LIV was an error for *Cutandia maritima*; an old record from Guernsey was a
misidentification for native *Catapodium rigidum* according to ref.R40.

DESMAZERIA Dumort.   **142**

2 species. Med. Dry sandy places.

sicula (Jacq.) Dumort.
● A casual on a tip at Truro (W Cornwall) in 1940; several much earlier records from Co Kerry, Ireland; cultivated in botanical gardens and occasionally seeding. Med. BM, K, RNG. D1, D14, D20*, D31*, D75*, D115*, J31(10:17-18), R36. *Catapodium siculum* (Jacq.) Link; *Cynosurus siculus* Jacq.

CATAPODIUM Link   **143**

2 species. Europe and N Africa to Iran. Dry places.

rigidum (L.) C.E.Hubb. ex Dony subsp. **hemipoa** (Delile ex Spreng.) Stace
● A casual. Atlantic coasts of SW France, N Spain, Med. RNG. D1, D18*, D20*, D31, D115*, D117*. *C.hemipoa* (Delile ex Spreng.) Lainz; *Desmazeria rigida* (L.) Tutin subsp. *hemipoa* (Delile ex Spreng.) Stace; *Festuca hemipoa* Delile ex Spreng.; *Scleropoa hemipoa* (Delile ex Spreng.) Parl.

SCLEROCHLOA P.Beauv.   **144**

2 species. Europe and N Africa to Iran. Dry places. Very close to *Desmazeria* and *Puccinellia*.

dura (L.) P.Beauv.
● A wool alien at Castleford (SW Yorks) in 1984; pre-1930 a ballast and dock casual; cultivated in botanical gardens. S Europe, N Africa and SW Asia, (USA, Australia, New Zealand). OXF, RNG, SLBI, HbCGH. D1, D6*, D8*, D17*, D18, D20*, D31*, D48*, D51*, D75*, D93*, D115*, D118*, J1(1867:18; 5:135; 8:424), J36(1905:103), R65, R107. *Cynosurus durus* L. **Fig.3.**

CUTANDIA Willk.   **145**

6 species. Med., Middle East. Coastal sands and stony hillsides.

divaricata (Desf.) Asch. ex Barbey
● An esparto casual. W Med. CGE, E, K, RNG. D1, D20*, D31*, D115*, D122*, J6(4:406), R5. *Scleropoa divaricata* (Desf.) Parl.; *Festuca divaricata* Desf. **Fig.15.**

maritima (L.) Barbey
Pre-1930 only. Musselburgh docks (Midlothian). Canary Is, Med., Iberian Peninsula. LIV. D1, D18*, D20*, D115*, D117*, D177*. *Scleropoa maritima* (L.) Parl.; *Triticum maritimum* L.

memphitica (Spreng.) Benth.
● A wool and esparto casual. Med., Middle East. RNG, HbTBR. D1, D17*, D18*, D20*, D39*, D48*, D75*, D122*, D177*, J6(4:406), R2.

C.scleropoides Willk.; *Dactylis memphitica* Spreng.; *Scleropoa memphitica* (Spreng.) Parl.

philistaea (Boiss.) Benth. ex B.D.Jacks.
- An esparto casual. E Med. K. D17*, D20*, J6(4:406), R5. *Desmazeria philistaea* (Boiss.) H.Scholz; *Scleropoa philistaea* Boiss.

VULPIELLA (Batt.& Trab.) Burollet   **146**

1 species. W Med. Dry sandy places.

tenuis (Tineo) Kerguélen
- An esparto casual; also cultivated from wool shoddy collected from Gala (Selkirks) in 1963. W Med. CGE, E, K, RNG. D1, D20*, D31*, J6(4:406), J74*(22:114), R5, R36. *V.incrassata* (Salzm. ex Loisel.) Burollet; *V.stipoides* (L.) Maire; *Bromus tenuis* Tineo; *Cutandia incrassata* (Salzm. ex Loisel.) Benth.; *Vulpia incrassata* (Salzm. ex Loisel.) Parl. **Fig.9.**

AMMOCHLOA Boiss.   **150**

3 species. Med., Middle East. Dry sandy places.

pungens (Schreb.) Boiss.
Pre-1930 only. N Africa. ?BM. D20*, D31*, D75*, D101*, D121, R36. *Dactylis pungens* Schreb.; *Sesleria echinata* Lam. **Fig.6.**

ECHINARIA Desf.   **151**

1 species. Med., Middle East.

capitata (L.) Desf.
- Mostly pre-1930 but one record from Hull docks (SE Yorks) in 1938. A grain casual; cultivated from bird-seed. Med., Middle East. BRISTM, K, RNG, SLBI. D1, D14, D17*, D18, D20*, D31*, D48*, D75*, D115*, D117*, J1(10:361), R8, R12, R21, R36, R68. *Cenchrus capitatus* L.; *Panicastrella capitata* (L.) Moench. Two early wool-alien specimens in BM from Chester in 1872 were in error for *Tribolium echinatum*. **Fig.3.**

HAINARDIEAE

NARDUROIDES Rouy   **152**

1 species. W Med. Dry places. According to C.A.Stace (ref.R6) this genus should be placed in the tribe *POEAE*, but we have followed ref.S7.

salzmannii (Boiss.) Rouy
- An esparto casual. W Med., (Cyprus, Turkey). CGE, RNG. D1, D18, D20*, D31, D117*, D123*, R5, R36. *Catapodium salzmannii* (Boiss.) Boiss.; *Festuca salzmannii* (Boiss.) Boiss.; *Nardurus salzmannii* Boiss. **Fig.16.**

PARAPHOLIS C.E.Hubb.   155

6 species. Middle East and Med., northwards along the Atlantic coast of
Europe to the Baltic; introduced to most other temperate regions. Sandy soils
near the sea and salt marshes. Ref.J65*(115:1-17).

filiformis (Roth) C.E.Hubb.
  • A wool casual (pre-1930); also on the Isle of Grain (W Kent) in 1948. Med.
  ?E, K. D1, D117*, J65*(115:7), J74*(22:201). *Lepturus filiformis* (Roth)
  Trin.; *Pholiurus filiformis* (Roth) Schinz & Thell.; *Rottboellia filiformis* Roth.
  The early record from Galashiels (Selkirks) in ref.R4 is probably correct
  although the geographical range given seems to refer to *P.incurva*. An earlier
  record in 1922 cited in ref.J1(6:753) was an error for *Hainardia cylindrica*
  (specimen at K). Very difficult to differentiate from *P.strigosa*.
incurva (L.) C.E.Hubb.   *Curved Hard-grass*
  •• A casual of wool, ballast and docks; also cultivated from wool; a rare native
  along the S and E coasts of England, S Wales and eastern Ireland. Atlantic Is,
  Med. and coast of W Europe, SW Asia, (widespread). E, K, NMW, RNG.
  D1, D2, D3*, D4, D75*, D115*, D117*, R4, R5, R8, R65. *Aegilops incurva*
  L.; *A.incurvata* L.; *Lepturus incurvatus* (L.) Trin.; *L.incurvus* (L.) Druce;
  Pholiurus incurvus (L.) Schinz & Thell.
pycnantha (Hack. ex Druce) C.E.Hubb.
  Pre-1930 only. Med. ?OXF. D1, D18, D117*, J1(2:99, as 33), J6(5:257),
  R55. *Lepturus filiformis* var. *pycnantha* Hack. ex Druce; *L.pycnantha* Hack.
  ex Druce.
strigosa (Dumort.) C.E.Hubb.   *Hard-grass*
  • Dewsbury tip (SW Yorks) c.1960; also pre-1930 as a casual from Barry
  Docks (Glam); also cultivated from bird-seed; a frequent native grass of salt
  marshes. Coasts of SW Europe, Med., (Australia). NMW. D1, D2, D3*,
  D4, D75*, D115*, R21, R86. *Lepiurus strigosus* Dumort.; *Lepturus filiformis*
  auct., non (Roth) Trin. The NMW specimen was originally misnamed as
  Hainardia cylindrica.

HAINARDIA Greuter   157

1 species. Med. Coastal meadows and roadsides. Easily confused with
Parapholis, but with only 1 (not 2) glumes in each spikelet.

cylindrica (Willd.) Greuter   *One-glumed Hard-grass*
  ••• A casual of wool, grain, ballast, wasteland, sewage works, bird-seed and
  tips. Med., (widespread). BM, BRISTM, CGE, E, K, LTN, NMW, RNG.
  D1, D2*, D5*, D8*, D14, D20*, D26*, D31*, D75*, D115*, D118*,
  J1(7:1027), J10(1941), J18(340:27), J30(92:44), J75(13:122-196), R5, R20,
  R21, R23, R44, R45, R47, R49, R50, R51, R55, R57, R59, R66, R69, R82,
  R86. *Lepturus cylindricus* (Willd.) Trin.; *Monerma cylindrica* (Willd.) Coss.
  & Durieu; *M.subulata* (Savi) P.Beauv.; *Rottboellia cylindrica* Willd. **Fig.16.**

MELICEAE

GLYCERIA R.Br.   **158**

c.40 species. Temperate regions. Wet places and in shallow water.

[australis C.E.Hubb.
A wool casual possibly over-looked as native *G.fluitans*. Australia. D93*, D181*. A synonym is *G.fluitans* sensu J.M.Black, non (L.) R.Br., which is the plant illustrated in ref.D8*.]

declinata Bréb.   *Small Sweet-grass*
• A wool casual; also a frequent native grass in wet muddy places. Atlantic Is, W and C Europe, (USA, Australia). HbCGH, HbTBR. D1, D2, D3*, D117*, R3. Confused with *G.notata*.

fluitans (L.) R.Br.   *Floating Sweet-grass*
• A wool casual; also a common native grass in wet places. Europe, Med., (widespread). SLBI, HbABMB, HbTBR. D1, D2, D3*, D4, D117*, R3. It occurred at Blackmoor (N Hants) as a wool alien in some quantity, but only in 1973. *Festuca fluitans* L.; *Poa fluitans* (L.) Scop.

[grandis S.Watson
A potential alien in Britain, as it is established and spreading in NW Europe and Scandinavia. N America, (Europe). D1, D6*, D118*, J102*(13:109-112), R7.]

maxima (Hartm.) Holmb. var. **variegata** Boom & J.D.Ruys
• In damp roadside hollows, at Westcott Heath (Surrey) in 1965, and Cardiff in 1978 (possibly planted); grown for ornament around ponds and along streams. Of garden origin. NMW, HbEJC. D3, D14, D21*, D21a*, D163. *Molinia maxima* Hartm.

multiflora Steud.
• A wool casual; also cultivated from wool. S America. BM, K, RNG, HbCGH. D12*, D15*, D52*, D151*, D174*, R1, R47, R65.

notata Chevall.   *Plicate Sweet-grass*
• A wool casual; also cultivated from wool; a frequent native grass in wet places. Europe, Med., (S America). E, K, RNG. D1, D2, D3*, D117*, R1, R5, R65. *G.fluitans* var. *plicata* Fr.; *G.plicata* (Fr.) Fr. Probably widely introduced into other countries, but confused with *G.declinata*.

spicata Guss.
• A wool casual. Med. RNG. D1, D20, D31, D115, D117*, R1, R47. *G.fluitans* var. *spicata* (Biv.) Trab. Considered by some as the basionym, *Poa spicata* Biv. is an illegitimate name, being predated by *P.spicata* L.

[striata (Lam.) Hitchc.
A potential alien in Britain, as it is established and spreading in NW Europe and Scandinavia; cultivated regularly in R.B.G., Kew (Surrey). N America, (Europe). D1, D6*, D25*, D40*, D41*, D42*, D118, J49(23:251-255), J51*(5:63-68; 28:29-36), R7. *G.michauxii* Kunth; *G.nervata* (Willd.) Trin.; *Poa nervata* Willd.; *P. striata* Lam.]

MELICA L.   160

c.80 species. Temperate regions (except Australia). Woodland shade to dry stony slopes.

[altissima L.

Sometimes cultivated, but there are no records of it escaping. C and E Europe, temperate Asia. D1, D14, D32*, D75, D164*, D165*.]

ciliata L.

Pre-1930 only. Possibly cultivated, as it is grown as a popular ornamental grass. Europe, SW and C Asia, N Africa. D1, D18, D19*, D20*, D30*, D31, D75*, R36.

violacea Cav.

• A wool casual. Argentina, Chile. BM, K, RNG. D12*, D137*, J53(25:97-160), J82*(29:1-116), J115*(40:41-89), R3.

AVENEAE
including Agrostideae, Phalarideae

HELICTOTRICHON Besser   171

c.100 species. Temperate regions, mainly Eurasia, and tropical mountains. Dry hills, meadows, wood margins, rarely in or near water. Includes the Australian genus *Amphibromus* Nees, which differs in having a glabrous ovary.

bromoides (Gouan) C.E.Hubb.

Pre-1930 only. Leith dock (Midlothian) in 1910. Med. RNG, SLBI. D1, D20*, D31*, R36. *Avena bromoides* Gouan; *Avenula bromoides* (Gouan) H.Scholz.

neesii (Steud.) Stace   **Swamp Wallaby-grass**

•• A wool casual. Australia. BM, E, K, LTN, NMW, OXF, RNG, SLBI. D2, D7, D8, D24*, D26*, D27*, D29*, D44*, D93*, J58*(113:3-13), R1, R2, R5, R47, R65. *Amphibromus neesii* Steud.; *A.nervosus* (Hook.f.) Baill.; *Avena nervosa* R.Br., non Lam.; *Danthonia nervosa* Hook.f.

[planiculme (Schrad.) W.Sauer & Chmelitschek sensu lato

Probably of garden origin. A casual. Mountains of E Europe. LIV. D1, D47, D71, D164a*, D165*. *H.planiculme* (Schrad.) Henrard; *Avena planiculmis* Schrad.; *Avenochloa planiculmis* (Schrad.) Holub. See ref.R107 for comments on several erroneous early Scottish records.]

cf. **recurvatum** (Swallen) Cope & Ryves

• A wool casual. Australia. No specimen. D7, D8*, D38, R2. *Amphibromus recurvatus* Swallen.

[sempervirens (Vill.) Pilg.

A frequent garden plant, which may self-seed. SW Alps. D1, R90. *Avena sempervirens* Vill.]

turgidulum (Stapf) Schweick.
- A wool casual. S Africa. K, LTN, RNG. D5*, D87*, J68*(3:203), R47.
Avena turgidula Stapf; *Avenastrum turgidulum* (Stapf) Stapf.

ARRHENATHERUM P.Beauv.   172

6 species. Europe, Med., Middle East. Weedy places and dry grassland.

album (Vahl) Clayton
- A wool casual. W Med., Cyprus. LTN. D1, D20*, D31, D117*,
J74*(17:365), J108*(6:11), R36, R47. *A.erianthum* Boiss. & Reut.; *Avena
alba* Vahl.

AVENA L.   173

c.25 species. Med., Middle East, extending to N Europe, widely introduced
to other temperate regions; 2 endemic species in Ethiopia. Weedy places and
cultivated land. Includes *A.sativa* subsp. *sativa* (Cultivated Oat), which was
domesticated about 2000 BC.

barbata Pott ex Link   Slender Oat
- •• A wool and grain casual; established in the Channel Islands. Atlantic Is,
Med., (widespread). BM, E, K, LTN, RNG, SLBI. D1, D2, D6*, D8*,
D12*, D20*, D26*, D75*, D89*, D93*, D115*, D117*, D118*, J15(108:34),
J18(379:26), R2, R4, R5, R36, R40, R45, R47, R48, R61, R65, R86, R88.
A.alba auct., non Vahl.   Includes *A.lusitanica* (Tab.Morais) B.R.Baum.
Confused with *A.strigosa*.

brevis Roth
- A wool casual at East Ardsley (SW Yorks) in 1981. Origin obscure,
(cultivated as a cereal in NW Europe and rarely naturalised). D1, D75,
D115*, J15(108:34), R86. *A.strigosa* subsp. *brevis* (Roth) Thell.

byzantina K.Koch   Algerian Oat
- A casual of wheat, roadsides and gravel pits. Origin obscure, (widespread
cereal crop in warm regions); probably derived from *A.sativa* by selection
under cultivation. BM, BRISTM, K. D1, D2, D12*, D18, D20*, D75*,
D93*, D115, D117*, J1(13:279), R55, R59, R61.   *Avena fatua* var.
glabrescens Coss. & Durieu.

fatua L.   Wild-oat
- ••••• A casual of wool and bird-seed; a weed of arable and waste land,
widely naturalised and locally abundant, especially in southern Britain;
increasing. Eurasia, N Africa, (widespread). D1, D2, D3*, D4, R8, R21.
Includes *A.vilis* Wallr. A hybrid with *A.sativa* (*A.* × *marquandii* Druce) has
been recorded. D2, D130, R62.

nuda L.   Naked Oat
Pre-1930 only. Formerly extensively cultivated in Cornwall and the Isles of
Scilly; also more recently grown from bird-seed. Origin obscure, (cultivated

as a cereal on a small scale in central Europe). BM, HbCGH. D19*, D75, D115, R21, R43. *A.sativa* subsp. *nuda* (L.) Rouy.

sativa L. subsp. **praegravis** (Krause) Tab.Morais
• Scattered along the grassy sea wall W of Crayford Ness (W Kent) in 1991. E Europe. D1, J18(425:9). *A.sativa* var. *praegravis* Krause.

sativa L. subsp. **sativa**   Cultivated Oat
●●●●● A casual of bird-seed, tips and wasteland; a common escape or relic of cultivation on arable land. Origin obscure, (widespread). D1, D2, D3*, D4, D75*, D93*, D115*, R21. Includes *A.orientalis* Schreb. A hybrid with *A.fatua* (q.v.) has been recorded.

sterilis L. subsp. **ludoviciana** (Durieu) Gillet & Magne   Winter Wild-oat
●●●● A wool casual; an established weed of arable land, widespread and locally abundant, especially in the southern Midlands; increasing. Med., SW Asia, (widespread). D1, D2, D3*, D4, D75, D93*. *A.ludoviciana* Durieu; *A.persica* Steud.

sterilis L. subsp. **sterilis**   Animated Oat
●● A casual of grain, docks, legume crops and wool; possibly a garden escape. Med., S Asia, (widespread). BM, NMW, OXF, RNG. D1, D2, D12*, D20*, D30*, D31, D75*, D89*, D93*, D115*, D117*, J1(9:377), J6(3:441), J10(29:23), J17(33:51-67), R1, R3, R23, R36, R38, R39, R40, R61, R62, R68. *A.macrocarpa* Moench.

strigosa Schreb.   Bristle Oat
●●● An escape from or relic of cultivation sometimes established in parts of Wales, Scotland and Ireland; a wool and grain casual; now becoming very much rarer than formerly (although there are recent records from Wales and Ireland); also cultivated from bird-seed. Origin obscure, probably Europe. BM, BRISTM, CGE, DBN, E, K, LTN, NMW, RNG, TCD. D1, D2, D3*, D4, D19*, D75*, D89*, D93*, D115*, D117*, J1(7:412; 10:361), J16(55:7-14), R5, R8, R14, R15, R24, R36, R39, R40, R45, R49, R55, R56, R57, R60, R62, R65, R66, R70, R72, R78, R81, R86(1840), R89, R107, R122, R123. *A.agraria* Brot.

GAUDINIA P.Beauv.   174

4 species. Med., Azores. Weedy places and rocky sea cliffs.

fragilis (L.) P.Beauv.   French Oat-grass
●●● A casual of tips, docks, grass seed and agricultural land; in widely scattered localities in southern England, Wales and Ireland; sometimes long established, or possibly native, as in meadows south of Grande Mare in Guernsey (for over 60 years), and near Ryde, Newtown to Whitefield and Ashey on the Isle of Wight (for over 70 years). Europe, Med., (S America, Australia). BM, BRISTM, CGE, DBN, E, K, NMW, OXF, RNG, SLBI, TCD. D1, D2*, D15*, D17*, D19*, D20*, D30*, D31*, D75*, D115*, D117*, D180*, J1(9:760; 10:361; 11:415-416), J6(5:357; 7:257,593), J8(20:10-11; 53:20), J9(14:215; 15:331; 16:53), J19(128:121; 130:206;

131:278), J23(2:59; 13:343), R5, R11, R22, R24, R27, R32, R40, R84, R85, R87, R122. *Avena fragilis* L. **Fig.16.**

DISSANTHELIUM Trin. 176

16 species. Peru and Bolivia to Mexico and California. Mainly in the high Andes. Ref.J62(11:361-376).

calycinum (J.Presl) Hitchc.
Pre-1930 only. A wool casual. Andes of Bolivia and Peru. E, OXF. D78*, D170, D172, J1(5:56), J80*(t.1374), R4, R36. *D.supinum* Trin.; *Brizopyrum calycinum* J.Presl. The Mexican material has been segregated as *D.mathewsii* (Ball) R.C.Foster & L.B.Sm. **Fig.9.**

TRISETUM Pers. 178

c.70 species. Temperate regions except S Africa. Perennials of meadows, mountain slopes and alpine grassland.

spicatum (L.) K.Richt.
• A wool casual. Temperate regions of both hemispheres. E, K. D1, D6*, D16*, D19*, D23*, D24*, D26*, D40*, R3, R5, R51, R107. *Aira spicata* L.

TRISETARIA Forssk. 179

c.15 species. Med. to W Himalayas. Dry open places. Annuals related to *Trisetum*, which is perennial, and to *Rostraria*, but with bisetulate or bicuspidate lemmas.

aurea (Ten.) Pignatti
• Casual in the marshalling yard, St. David's Station, Exeter (S Devon) in 1990. S Europe, Med. RAMM. D1, D18, D115*, J14(124:242), J71*(29:pl.31). *Koeleria aurea* Ten.; *Trisetum aureum* (Ten.) Ten.; *T.condensatum* (Link) C.Presl; *T.noeanum* Boiss.

loeflingiana (L.) Paunero
Pre-1930 only. S Europe, SW and C Asia, N Africa. D1, D20*, D22*, D31, D115*, J76*(9:576-578), R36. *T.cavanillesii* (Trin.) Maire; *Avena loeflingiana* L.; *Trisetum cavanillesii* Trin.; *T.gaudinianum* Boiss.; *T.loeflingianum* (L.) C.Presl.

michelii (Savi) D.Heller
Pre-1930 only. A wool casual; also in Leith docks (Midlothian) in 1911. Med., Atlantic Is, (Australia). E, OXF, RNG. D1, D8*, D17*, D18, D20*, D27*, D31*, R4, R36. *Avellinia michelii* (Savi) Parl.; *Bromus michelii* Savi; *Koeleria michelii* (Savi) Coss. & Durieu; *Vulpia michelii* (Savi) Rchb.

panicea (Lam.) Maire
• A casual of wool, grain, wasteland and tips; most records are pre-1930. Med. BM, E, K, NMW, OXF, RNG. D1, D20*, D30*, D31, D115*, D117*, J1(7:222), R4, R36, R55. *Avena panicea* Lam.; *Koeleria panicea* (Lam.)

Domin; *Trisetum neglectum* (Savi) Roem. & Schult.; *T.paniceum* (Lam.) Pers.
Very easily confused with *Rostraria cristata*. **Fig.9, 22.**
scabriuscula (Lag.) Paunero
Pre-1930 only. An esparto casual at Levenhall near Edinburgh in 1918. Spain,
Portugal. K, OXF, RNG. D1, D117*, J1(5:314), R36. *Avena scabriuscula*
Lag.; *Koeleria scabriuscula* (Lag.) Hack.; *Trisetum scabriusculum* (Lag.) Coss.
ex Willk. This grass was also described as a species new to science, *Koeleria
advena* Stapf ex J.Fraser, in ref.j2(27:302) at K, and has recently been re-
determined by T.A.Cope (ref.R116).

VENTENATA Koeler   **180**

8 species. S Europe to Iran and C Asia. Dry places.

dubia (Leers) Coss. & Durieu
   • A casual of grass seed at Bingley (SW Yorks) in 1972, and at Grays chalk
   quarry (S Essex) in 1986. C Europe, Med., S Russia, SW Asia, (N America).
   K, HbEJC. D1, D18, D31*, D75*, D110*, D115*, D118, D180*,
   J8*(45:1,24-25). *Avena dubia* Leers. **Fig.16.**
macra (Steven ex M.Bieb.) Boiss.
   Pre-1930 only. A casual on a tip at Yiewsley (Middlesex) in 1928. Crimea,
   SW and C Asia. K. D1, D18, D22*, D48*, D71*, D125, J53(26:65-79).
   Avena macra Steven ex M.Bieb.; *Gaudinopsis macra* (Steven ex M.Bieb.) Eig.

ROSTRARIA Trin.   **182**

c.10 species. Med. to Middle East. Dry weedy places. Annual derivatives of
Koeleria Pers. with a better developed awn.

cristata (L.) Tzvelev   **Mediterranean Hair-grass**
   ••• A casual of wool, esparto, docks, tips and bird-seed. Also a weed in bulb
   fields and hops. Atlantic Is, Med., Middle East, (widespread). BM, CGE, E,
   K, LTN, NMW, OXF, RNG, SLBI. D1, D2*, D6*, D12*, D15*, D16*,
   D17*, D20*, D24*, D75*, D89*, D93*, D115*, D117*, D118*, D177*,
   J1(8:454; 10:361), J6(4:327), J8(34:23), J26(41:11), R1, R3, R5, R8, R23,
   R24, R36, R38, R43, R51, R54, R55, R61, R65, R66. *Festuca cristata* L.;
   F.phleoides Vill.; *Koeleria phleoides* (Vill.) Pers.; *Lophochloa cristata* (L.)
   Hyl.; *L.phleoides* (Vill.) Rchb.; *Trisetaria cristata* (L.) Kerguélen. Not to be
   confused with *R.phleoides* (Desf.) Holub (*Koeleria hispida* (Savi) DC.;
   Lophochloa hispida (Savi) Pignatti) of the central Mediterranean. **Fig.6.**
litorea (All.) Holub
   Pre-1930 only. A dock casual at Musselburgh (Midlothian) in 1914. Med.
   RNG. *Alopecurus litoreus* All.; *Lophochloa pubescens* (Lam.) H.Scholz.
pumila (Desf.) Tzvelev
   Pre-1930 only. A grain casual at Leith docks (Midlothian) in 1905.
   Atlantic Is, Med., Middle East, (S Africa, Australia). E, LIV, RNG, SLBI.
   D1, D5*, D8*, D17*, D20*, D22*, D30*, D31, D93*, D117*, D177*, R36.

Avena pumila Desf.; *Lophochloa pumila* (Desf.) Bor; *Trisetaria pumila* (Desf.)
Maire; *Trisetum pumilum* (Desf.) Kunth.

salzmannii (Boiss.) Holub
- A casual of esparto. S Spain, N Africa. CGE, E, K. D1, D20*, D31,
D117*, R5. *Koeleria salzmannii* Boiss.; *Lophochloa salzmannii* (Boiss.)
H.Scholz.

DESCHAMPSIA P.Beauv.   187

c.40 species. Temperate regions. Meadows, moors and woods.

[*caespitosa* (L.) P.Beauv.   *Tufted Hair-grass*
Cultivated from wool and probably a common wool alien; also a common
native grass. Cosmopolitan in cool and cold temperate areas, and on tropical
mountains. D1, D2, D3*, D4, D26*, D93*, R65. *Aira caespitosa* L.
Variants from the southern hemisphere are probably best treated as being
conspecific.]

danthonioides (Trin.) Munro ex Benth.
- A grass seed casual, not lasting more than one season; in sown grass on the
golf course at Galley Hill (Beds); Woburn Park (Beds) in 1977; Ashbourne
(Derbys) in 1977. Western N America, Argentina, Chile. BM, K, LTN,
RNG. D6*, D23*, D43, D118*, D129*, D153*, J8*(17:16-17), J18(385:35),
J23(12:393; 16:169), J56(10:322-324), R25, R65, R91. *Aira danthonioides*
Trin.

HOLCUS L.   188

6 species. Europe, N Africa and Middle East; perhaps S Africa. Grassland,
open woodland and wasteland. *H.lanatus* (Yorkshire-fog) is introduced as a
weed to most temperate regions.

annuus Salzm. ex C.A.Mey.
Pre-1930 only. Leith docks (Midlothian) in 1920. Med., Caucasus,
(Australia). OXF. D1, D17*, D18, D20*, D31, D38, D110*, D115*, D126*,
J1(6:55), J71*(25:183-190), J74*(13:197,217), R36. *H.setiglumis* Boiss.
& Reut.; *H.setosus* Trin., nom. illeg.

lanatus L.   *Yorkshire-fog*
••• A common wool alien which persists; also an abundant native meadow
grass. Temperate Eurasia, NW Africa, (widespread). E, RNG. D1, D2, D3*,
D4, D75*, D115*, R1, R2, R5. Common in cultivation from wool shoddy,
and under-recorded.

mollis L.   *Creeping Soft-grass*
- A wool alien; also a common native grass. Europe, (N America, Australia).
HbTBR. D1, D2, D3*, D4, D75*, D115*, R2.

setiger Nees
- A wool casual. S Africa, (Australia). E, RNG. D5, R5, R51. Probably
conspecific with *H.annuus* (see ref.D38, D71). Not to be confused with

H.setiger De Not. ex Parl. (*H.notarisii* Nyman) of ref.D115*, an endemic of NW Italy.

CORYNEPHORUS P.Beauv. 189

5 species. Europe and Med. to Iran. Sandy places and seaside dunes. The genus is characterised by the extraordinary awns, which are divided into a twisted column and a clavate limb with a ring of hairs at the junction.

canescens (L.) P.Beauv. *Grey Hair-grass*
• Now well established on coastal sand dunes south of Lossiemouth station (Moray) and in Inverness; still persistent on dunes near Morar (Westerness), where it was originally introduced c.1895; a rare but locally abundant native grass of coastal dunes in eastern England and the Channel Islands. Coasts of Scandinavia to the W Med. and inland to Russia. ABD, CGE, E, K, LIV, OXF. D1, D2, D3*, J1(1:501-502), J23(19:192-193), J34(14:13-15), D4, R5. *Aira canescens* L.; *Weingaertneria canescens* Bernh. This grass is very common from Denmark to Belgium, just across the English Channel, and its recent occurrence in Scotland may simply be an extension of its natural range.

AIRA L. 191

8 species. Europe and Med. to Iran, now widespread. Open places on dry sandy soils.

caryophyllea L. subsp. *caryophyllea* *Silver Hair-grass*
•• A wool casual; also a very common native grass. Europe, N Africa, W Asia, (widespread). ABD, CGE, DBN, E, K, LTN, RNG. D1, D2, D3*, D4, D75*, D93*, D115*, D117*, R1, R3, R5.
caryophyllea L. subsp. **multiculmis** (Dumort.) Bonnier & Layens
•• Possibly native; frequent in Scotland, parts of Ireland and SW England but rarer in southern England. SW Europe, NW Africa, (Australia). BM, E, K, NMW, OXF, RNG. D1, D2, D3, D4, D16*, D20*, J6(7:32), J23(10:434; 12:363). *A.caryophyllea* var. *major* Gaudin; *A.multiculmis* Dumort. Recorded in error from Frilford (Berks) according to ref.R39. According to C.A.Stace and T.A.Cope (ref.D2, R116) this subspecies is now regarded as the same as subsp. *caryophyllea* by nearly all taxonomists.
cupaniana Guss.
• A wool casual; also occasionally found on port tips. Med., (widespread). ?E, LTN, OXF, RNG. D1, D5*, D20*, D24*, D26*, D30*, D31, D93*, D115*, D117*, J1(6:55), R1, R36, R51. This was the first wool alien to be found in vc.37 (Worcs), at Moor Farm, Eardiston in 1952, ref.R118.
elegantissima Schur
•• A casual of wool, grass seed and weedy places; in two places near Exeter (S Devon) in 1989, one of which was on a cemetery wall and probably originated from a floral wreath; a weed in a greenhouse pot at Bronnllys (Brecs); Glasgow c.1990; cultivated in R.B.G., Kew (Surrey). Med.,

(widespread). BM, CGE, E, K, OXF, NMW, RNG, SLBI. D1, D6*, D15*, D17*, D20*, D23*, D26*, D31, D41*, D75*, D93*, D115*, D118*, J14(123:249), R1, R3, R4, R5, R36, R51. *A.capillaris* Host, non Savi; *A.elegans* Willd. ex Gaudin, nom. illeg.

praecox L.   Early Hair-grass
   • A wool casual; also a very common native grass. Europe, Caucasus, Ethiopia, (widespread). E. D1, D2, D3*, D4, D75*, D93*, D115*, R5.
provincialis Jord.
   • A casual of wool, docks and tips. SE France, Corsica, (Australia). BM, E, OXF, RNG, SLBI. D1, D14, D29, D44*, D93*, D115*, J1(6:55), R1, R5, R36, R66.

ANTHOXANTHUM L.   195

   c.18 species. Temperate Eurasia and Africa including the tropical mountains, and in C America; introduced to other temperate regions. Meadows and dry places.

aristatum Boiss.   Annual Vernal-grass
   •• A casual of cereal crops, waste ground, paper mills, docks, and weedy places; formerly widespread but now very rare; occasionally persistent for a few years, as in sandy fields in Surrey and E Suffolk (where last seen in 1970); introduced with grass seed at Wavenden Heath (Beds) in 1982. S Europe, N Africa, (N America). BM, BRISTM, DBN, K, LTN, NMW, OXF, RNG, TOR. D1, D2, D3*, D4, D18, D20, D75*, D89*, D115*, D117*, D118*, R8, R86(1899), R118. *A.odoratum* subsp. *aristatum* (Boiss.) Trab.; *A.puelii* Lecoq & Lamotte.

odoratum L.   Sweet Vernal-grass
   •• A wool alien, capable of persisting; also cultivated from wool; a very common native pasture grass. Temperate Eurasia, (widespread). E. D1, D2, D3*, D4, D75*, D89*, D115*, R5, R65. Almost certainly under-recorded as a wool alien.

ovatum Lag.
   • A casual garden weed, probably from bird-seed, at Petersham (Surrey) in 1966; also cultivated at the Welsh Plant Breeding Station. Med. K. D1, D20, D115*, D117*, D129*. *A.odoratum* subsp. *ovatum* (Lag.) Trab.

PHALARIS L.   196

   15 species. N temperate region, mainly Med., California; S America; widely introduced throughout the world. Dry or damp weedy places. *P.canariensis* (Canary-grass) is widely cultivated for bird-seed. An account of the genus has been given by D.E.Anderson in ref.J92(16:1-96).

angusta Nees ex Trin.
   •• A casual of wool, docks, wasteland and animal feed, decreasing; occasionally cultivated. N and S America, (S Africa, Australia). BM,

BRISTM, E, K, LTN, NMW, OXF, RNG, SLBI. D5, D6*, D10*, D12*, D15*, D27*, D41*, D75*, D93*, D118, D129*, J1(4:508; 5:407; 7:220; 8:454; 9:676; 10:360; 12:83), J8(39:8), J18(376:25), R1, R2, R4, R23, R36, R39, R48, R52, R55, R57. *P.angustata* sphalm.; *P.chilensis* J.Presl.

.aquatica L.   **Bulbous Canary-grass**
●●● A persistent escape or relic, sown for pheasant food and cover, sometimes abundant, mainly in East Anglia and Kent; a casual of wool, esparto, wasteland and wheat; cultivated from bird-seed; possibly a casual of grass and clover seed; also cultivated for forage. Med., (widespread). BM, BRISTM, CGE, E, K, LTN, OXF, RNG, SLBI. D1, D2*, D16*, D20*, D22*, D23*, D26* D30, D31, D75*, D89*, D93*, D115*, D117*, J1(8:764; 9;468); J6(4:406); J8(27:15; 30*:12-13; 39*:1,8), J23(13:149,169), R1, R2, R21, R36, R38, R47, R54, R85, R86, R118. *P.bulbosa* L.(1759), non L.(1755); *P.nodosa* Murray; *P.tuberosa* L. A hybrid with native *P.arundinacea* (*P.* × *monspeliensis* Daveau) is cultivated abroad and may have been overlooked (ref.D13, J8(27:15), J78(161:1).

arundinacea L. var. picta L.   **Gardener's Garters**
●● A garden outcast persistent on tips and roadsides in widely scattered localities. Of garden origin. BM, E, NMW. D3, D75, D93*, J10(38:45), R5, R24, R65, R86. A common ornamental grass with the leaves striped green and cream.

brachystachys Link   **Confused Canary-grass**
●● A casual of wool, esparto, ballast, docks, wasteland, grain and bird-seed. Med., SW Asia, (N America). BM, BRISTM, K, OXF, RNG, SLBI. D1, D2, D6*, D17*, D18, D20*, D22*, D30*, D31, D75, D89*, D115*, D117*, D129*, J1(8:422; 10:360; 12:64,302), J23(2:209), R1, R2, R5, R21, R36, R47, R57, R61, R66. *P.nitida* C.Presl; *P.quadrivalvis* Lag. The hybrid with *P.aquatica* at K, from wool, needs confirmation.

canariensis L.   **Canary-grass**
●●●●● A casual of bird-seed, grain, tips and possibly wool; possibly an escape from cultivation, sometimes persistent for a few years, mainly in the south. Med., (widespread). D1, D2, D3*, D4, D12*, D17*, D75*, D89*, D93*, D115*, D117*, J8*(30:13; 39:1), R8, R21. *P.ovatus* Moench.

caroliniana Walter
Pre-1930 only. A grain casual at Bristol; Leith docks (Midlothian) in 1907; Eltham Green (W Kent) in 1917. N America. BM, SLBI. D6*, D23*, D40*, D41*, D118, R8. *P.intermedia* Bosc.

coerulescens Desf.
●● A casual of docks, ballast and tips; persisted in a railway yard at Par (E Cornwall) for several years; last record 1934; occasionally cultivated. Med. BM, BRISTM, K, NMW, RNG, SLBI. D1, D10*, D18, D20*, D27*, D31, D75*, D93*, D115*, D177*, J1(7:1025; 8:764; 10:359), R8, R23, R36, R55, R71, R92. *P.aquatica* auct., non L.; *P.bulbosa* Cav., non L.; *P.paradoxa* var. *coerulescens* (Desf.) Paunero

lemmonii Vasey
Pre-1930 only. Thetford (W Norfolk) in 1916. California, (Australia). OXF.
D6*, D43, D118*, D185, J1(5:54), R36.

minor Retz.   Lesser Canary-grass
●●● A casual of grain, docks, bird-seed, wool and esparto; sometimes well
established on cultivated land, as in bulb fields in the Isles of Scilly and carrot
fields in East Anglia; possibly native in the Channel Islands, where it is locally
frequent. Med., SW Asia, (widespread). BEL, BM, BRISTM, CGE, E, K,
LTN, NMW, RNG, TOR. D1, D2, D3*, D4, D6*, D15*, D20*, D30*,
D75*, D89*, D93*, D115*, D117*, D118*, J1(4:77; 6:157; 9:468), R1, R2,
R5, R8, R21, R22, R24, R27, R36, R39, R40, R43, R49, R54, R55, R57,
R58, R62, R66, R86. *P.gracilis* Parl.

paradoxa L.   Awned Canary-grass
●●● A casual of grain, bird-seed, wool, esparto and wasteland; recently well
established as a weed of arable land and cereals in several places in the south
and east. Med., (widespread). BEL, BM, BRISTM, CGE, DBN, E, K, LTN,
NMW, RNG, SLBI. D1, D2, D6*, D15*, D20*, D23*, D30*, D31, D75*,
D89*, D93*, D115*, D117*, J1(4:77; 5:133; 6:405,752; 9:468,530; 10:360;
12:819), J10(38:45), J18(403:39), R1, R2, R5, R8, R9, R16, R20, R21, R24,
R27, R36, R39, R40, R49, R54, R55, R57, R58, R60, R62, R66, R86, R123.
Includes *P.appendiculata* Schult.; *P.praemorsa* Lam.

truncata Guss. ex Bertol.
Pre-1930 only. Leith and Slateford docks (Midlothian) in 1906; Batley
(SW Yorks) in 1913; Glasgow in 1921. Med. BM, OXF, SLBI. D1, D20*,
D75, D115*, J77*(32:137).

AGROSTIS L.   197

c.200 species. Temperate regions and on tropical mountains. Open places,
grassland and light shade. **Key on p.116.**

aemula R.Br.
● A wool casual. Australia. E, K, RNG. D7, D8, D16, D24, D27, D29,
D45*, D46*, D93*, J48*(2:t. opp. p.309), R1, R3, R5, R51. *Lachnagrostis
aemula* (R.Br.) Nees ex Hook.f. Confused with *A.avenacea* in ref.R4.

avenacea J.F.Gmel.   Blown-grass
●●● A casual of wool and esparto. Australia, New Zealand, (widespread).
BEL, BM, CGE, E, K, LTN, NMW, RNG, SLBI. D2*, D6*, D12*, D16*,
D24*, D26*, D75*, D87*, D116*, D118, J1(11:461), R1, R2, R4*, R5, R23,
R36, R38, R50, R51, R54, R56, R65, R66, R77, R86, R88, R93.
A.retrofracta Willd.; *Calamagrostis retrofracta* (Willd.) Link ex Steud.;
Deyeuxia retrofracta (Willd.) Kunth; *Lachnagrostis avenacea* (J.F.Gmel.)
Veldkamp; *L.filiformis* (G.Forst.) Trin. According to ref.D2 this species is
established in Britain, but this is a mistake, because the plants were
misidentifications of *A.scabra* (e.g. see RNG).

billardierei R.Br. var. **filifolia** Vickery
- A wool casual on Linthwaite tip (SW Yorks) in 1963. Australia. BM. D7, D8*.

capillaris L.   **Common Bent**
- ●●● A wool alien; also cultivated from wool; widely used for fine lawns; also a very common native grass. Temperate Eurasia, (widespread). HbCGH, HbTBR. D1, D2, D3*, D4, R2, R65. *A.tenuis* Sibth.; *A.vulgaris* With. Hybrids with several other *Agrostis* species occur, but have probably arisen naturally.

castellana Boiss. & Reut.   **Highland Bent**
- ●●● A casual of wool and grass seed; now widespread as a major component in grass mixtures. Atlantic Is, Med., (widespread). BM, K, LTN, NMW, RNG. D1, D2, D3, D18, D19*, D20, D31, D75*, D89, D115*, D117*, D180*, J8(10:16); J18(403:39), J33(31:28), R3, R48, R52, R55, R59, R62. Includes *A.hispanica* Boiss. & Reut.; *A.olivetorum* Godr. Probable hybrids occur with *A.capillaris* (*A.* × *fouilladei* P.Fourn.), *A.gigantea* and *A.stolonifera* L. (See ref.D1, D2).

[*curtisii* Kerguélen   **Bristle Bent**
Pre-1930 only, as an alien in Ireland; native in S and SW England, S Wales, locally abundant on heaths. W Europe. DBN. D1, D2, D3*, D4, R113. *A.setacea* Curtis. This record needs confirmation.]

diegoensis Vasey
- A casual at Avonmouth docks (W Gloucs) in 1964. Western N America. RNG. D6*, D78*, D185.

eriantha Hack.
- A wool casual at Bradford (SW Yorks) in 1920 and Linthwaite (SW Yorks) in 1963. S Africa. E. D5*, D87*, J1(6:54), R5, R36. *A.suavis* Stapf. This species is difficult to distinguish from *A.avenacea* without the root.

exarata Trin.   **Spike Bent**
- A grass seed component or casual. Kamchatka, Kurils, Western N America. LTN, HbEJC. D2, D6*, D41, D118*, D129*, R48. Probably overlooked; the Woburn Sands (Beds) plant, found in 1981, resembled native *Apera interrupta*, but is a perennial which could persist. A very variable species.

gigantea Roth   **Black Bent**
- ●● A wool alien; also cultivated from wool and bird-seed; a common native grass and weed. Temperate Eurasia, (N America, Australia). HbCGH, HbTBR. D1, D2, D3*, D4, R2, R65.

hyemalis (Walter) Britton, Sterns & Poggenb.   **Small Bent**
- A casual of wool and wasteland. N America. D2*, D6*, D41*, D75*, R1, R20. *Cornucopiae hyemalis* Walter. Most records probably refer to the closely related *A.scabra* which may be separated by the key given in ref.D2. Often misspelt as *A.hiemalis*.

lachnantha Nees   **African Bent**
- •• A wool casual. Arabia, Sudan and Ethiopia to S Africa. BEL, BM, BRISTM, CGE, E, K, LTN, NMW, OXF, RNG, SLBI. D2, D5*, D75*, J1(11:461), R1, R2, R4, R36, R51, R54, R66, R86, R93.

nebulosa Boiss. & Reut.
- • In gardens, perhaps always cultivated as an ornamental grass and capable of seeding. Spain, Portugal, Morocco. BM, K, LIV, OXF, RNG. D1, D20*, D47, D75*, D117*, J1(11:461), R36, R40, R42. The SLBI specimen was in error for ?*A.scabra*.

cf. **parviflora** R.Br.
- • A wool casual at Kirkheaton (SW Yorks) in 1958. SE Australia. RNG. D7, D38, D93*.

pourretii Willd.
- Pre-1930 only; a casual at Leith docks (Midlothian) in 1920. W Med., Portugal. ?BM, OXF, RNG. D1, D20*, D31, D117*, J1(6:54; 11:461), R36. *A.muelleri* C.Presl; *A.pallida* DC., non With.; *A.salmantica* (Lag.) Kunth.

cf. **preissii** (Nees) Vickery
- • A wool casual from Blackmoor (N Hants) in 1966. Australia. D7, R3, R94. *Lachnagrostis preissii* Nees. Determined by C.E.Hubbard, but unfortunately the voucher specimen has been lost. The nerves of the lemma and palea were shortly excurrent, and he could not match the specimen with any named species, so that it was probably new to science.

scabra Willd.   **Rough Bent**
- ••• A casual of wool, grain, tips, docks, and timber yards; occasionally established by railways, as at Nine Elms (Surrey), Bordon (N Hants), Hull (SE Yorks) and Glasgow. N America, NE Asia, Greenland, (Europe). BM, CGE, E, K, LIV, LTN, NMW, OXF, RNG, SLBI. D1, D2, D6*, D19*, D23*, D41*, D42*, D43, D118*, J1(10:360; 11:461), J8*(27:1,18-20), J15(106:39), J23(1:59; 9:391; 10:434; 13:149,343; 14:433), J26(60:88), J28(19:431), J34(10:8), J35(65:198), R3, R5, R8, R12, R20, R26, R27, R36, R38, R48, R51, R55, R62, R86. *A.hyemalis* auct., non (Walter) Britton, Sterns & Poggenb.

tenerrima Trin.
- Pre-1930 only. W Med. D1, D14, D20*, D31, D129*, J39*(2:207), J76*(7:611-612), R36. *A.elegans* Thore ex Loisel., non (Walter) Salisb.

× **AGROPOGON** P.Fourn.   **197×212**

2 nothospecies. Hybrids between species of *Agrostis* and *Polypogon* which are partially fertile. They are difficult to separate on taxonomic criteria. Damp open grassy places.

littoralis (Sm.) C.E.Hubb.   *Perennial Beard-grass*
- •• Occasionally found as an alien of wool, tips and docks; a rare native grass in southern England. S and W Europe, Turkey, (widespread). BM, E, K, NMW. D1, D2, D3*, D4, D18, D75*, D93*, D115*, J20(51:73-151),

J81*(17:1-112), R4, R36, R40.   × *A. elongatus* (Lag.) C.E.Hubb. ined.;
× *A. lutosus* auct., non (Poir.) P.Fourn.; *Agrostis* × *littoralis* sensu Sm., non
With.; *Agrostis stolonifera* L.   × *Polypogon monspeliensis*; *Polypogon elongatus*
Lag.; *P. littoralis* Sm.
[*robinsonii* (Druce) Melderis & D.C.McClint.
Recorded from Guernsey in ref.D2, D130.   *Agrostis* × *robinsonii* Druce;
A. stolonifera × *Polypogon viridis*.   A naturally occurring hybrid, not
introduced, and hence best regarded as native.]

CALAMAGROSTIS Adans.   198

c.270 species. Temperate regions and on tropical mountains. Mainly damp
places, also in woods, heaths and mountain grassland. Includes the genus
Deyeuxia P.Beauv.

[argentea DC.
Grown as an ornamental grass; it self-seeds readily in Europe and may have
been overlooked. S and C Europe. D1, D25*, D115*, D180*. *Achnatherum
calamagrostis* (L.) P.Beauv.; *Agrostis calamagrostis* L.; *Lasiagrostis
calamagrostis* (L.) Link; *Stipa calamagrostis* (L.) Wahlenb. It usually appears
in plant catalogues, incorrectly, under the more attractive name of *C. splendens*
Trin., a closely related species from Russia, N and C Asia (ref.D1, D184*).
An anomalous species, now placed in the genus *Achnatherum* P.Beauv. in
ref.D1.]
[arundinacea (L.) Roth
Pre-1930 only. Recorded as a garden escape. Europe, SW Asia. D1, D166,
D167, D180*, R8, R36. *C. sylvatica* (Schrad.) Besser, non Host; *Agrostis
arundinacea* L.; *Arundo sylvatica* Schrad. Contrary to ref.R8, we cannot trace
this plant in gardening literature.]

AMMOPHILA Host   199

2 species. Europe, N Africa and eastern N America; introduced worldwide in
temperate regions. Coastal and lacustrine sand dunes. Widely planted as a
sand binder.

arenaria (L.) Link   *Marram*
• Sandy roadside at Wrotham Heath (W Kent), known since 1982 but not
flowering; occasionally planted on inland golf courses; a common native grass
on coastal sand dunes. Coast of W Europe, (Arabia, Egypt, N America,
Australia). D1, D2, D3*, D4, D6*, D75*, R41. *Arundo arenaria* L.
breviligulata Fernald   **American Marram**
• Introduced in the late 1950s and established in one small area on sand dunes
at Newborough Warren (Anglesey) but possibly now extinct (ref.R19). Eastern
N America. D2, D6*, D185. *A. arenaria* subsp. *breviligulata* (Fernald) Maire
& Weiller.

ECHINOPOGON P.Beauv.   202

7 species. New Guinea, Australia and New Zealand. Open woodland.

ovatus (G.Forst.) P.Beauv.   Hedgehog-grass
  • A wool casual. Australia, New Zealand. CGE, E, K, RNG. D7, D8*,
D16*, D24, D27*, D29, D44*, D75*, D93*, R3, R5. *Agrostis ovata* G.Forst.
Fig.10.

DICHELACHNE Endl.   204

5 species. New Guinea, Australia and New Zealand. Forest clearings,
subalpine grassland. Ref.J73(22:5-12).

crinita (L.f.) Hook.f.
Pre-1930 only. A wool casual. Australia, New Zealand. OXF. D7, D8*,
D16*, D27*, D29, J1(6:55), R4, R36. *Anthoxanthum crinitum* L.f.
micrantha (Cav.) Domin
  • A wool casual. Australia. RNG. D7, D8, D16, D24*, D26*, D27, D29,
D137*. *D.sciurea* (R.Br.) Hook.f.; *Stipa micrantha* Cav. **Fig.5.**

TRIPLACHNE Link   205

1 species. Med. Open places by the sea.

nitens (Guss.) Link
Pre-1930 only. Par harbour (E Cornwall) in 1927. Atlantic Is, Med. D1.
D17*, D18, D20*, D31*, D117*, J1(8:322), R36. *Agrostis nitens* Guss.;
Gastridium nitens (Guss.) Coss. & Durieu; *G.triaristatum* Durieu. **Fig.6.**

GASTRIDIUM P.Beauv.   206

2 species. Europe to Iran. Broken ground and arable land.

phleoides (Nees & Meyen) C.E.Hubb.   Eastern Nit-grass
  •• A casual of wool, tips, fields and docks. NE Africa, SW Asia,
(widespread). CGE, E, K, LTN, RNG. D1, D2, D3, D5*, D8*, D13*, D18,
D20*, D27*, D37*, D48*, D93*, D117*, R1, R3, R5, R47, R51.
G.ventricosum subsp. *phleoides* (Nees & Meyen) Tzvelev; *Lachnagrostis
phleoides* Nees & Meyen. Probably it was this species that was cultivated from
bird-seed in ref.R21 rather than *G.ventricosum*, as the two are readily confused.
ventricosum (Gouan) Schinz & Thell.   Nit-grass
  •• A casual in England, S Wales and ?Ireland; formerly frequent as a corn
field weed in SE England, now very rare (ref.D2); a very rare native grass in
SW England and the Channel Islands. Atlantic Is, S and W Europe, N Africa,
SW Asia, (widespread). ?DBN, NMW. D1, D2, D3*, D4, D18, D75*,
D115*, D117*, J23(16:43-54), R8, R113. *G.australe* P.Beauv.; *G.lendigerum*
(L.) Desv.; *Agrostis ventricosa* Gouan; *Milium lendigerum* L.   Includes
G.laxum Boiss. & Reut. According to many authors (e.g. D18, D20*, D110*,

D115*) a third species, *G.scabrum* C.Presl (*G.muticum* Günther), is recognized, but the diagnostic characters are not reliable.

LAGURUS L.   **207**

1 species. Med. Maritime sands. Widely cultivated as an ornamental grass.

ovatus L.   Hare's-tail

••• A casual of wool, grain and tips; probably originally introduced in the Channel Islands and long naturalised there in abundance; occasionally naturalised on maritime sand in southern England, as at Dawlish (S Devon) and Littlehampton (W Sussex); also in Ireland at Rosslare Harbour (Co Wexford). Cultivated from bird-seed; a popular ornamental grass in gardens, which may escape. Atlantic Is, Med., (widespread). BM, BRISTM, DBN, K, LCN, NMW, OXF, RNG, TCD, TOR. D1, D2, D3*, D4, D75*, D89*, D115*, J9(24:515-517), R2, R8, R21, R24, R36, R38, R40, R49, R55, R59, R62, R64, R66, R113. **Fig.24.**

APERA Adans.   **208**

3 species. Europe to Afghanistan. Dry sandy soils and as a weed of arable land.

intermedia Hack.

• A wool casual; plants growing in Slateford and Leith docks (Midlothian) in 1906 set abundant viable seed which was successfully cultivated the following year. SW Asia. BM, K, RNG, SLBI. D1, D18, D22*, D48*, D75*, J1(4:508), J17(34:43-45), R1, R3, R5, R36, R38, R62, R95.

interrupta (L.) P.Beauv.   *Dense Silky-bent*

• A very rare dock alien; a grass seed impurity (with *Ventenata* at Grays chalk Quarry (S Essex) in 1986); by a disused railway at Henlow (Beds) in 1973; also a rare and local native grass in the Breckland and a few widely scattered places in England, possibly increasing according to ref.R19. W, S and C Europe, (N America). BM, LTN, NMW. D1, D2, D3*, D4, D75*, D115*, J1(10:361), J59*(15:141-148), R8, R39, R49, R66, R118. *Agrostis interrupta* L. The wool-alien record from Blackmoor (N Hants) in 1968 (ref.R65) needs confirmation.

spica-venti (L.) P.Beauv.   Loose Silky-bent

••• A casual probably introduced with grain and clover, now well established and widely distributed as an agricultural weed and on waste ground, mostly in southern England, but extending into Wales and Scotland; recorded as a dock alien from Dublin in 1994; also a rare wool alien; dubiously native in some localities; also cultivated from bird-seed. Temperate Eurasia, (N America). ABD, BRISTM, DBN, E, NMW, RNG, TCD. D1, D2, D3*, D4, D75*, D89*, D115*, R1, R4, R5, R8, R21, R86, R113. *Agrostis spica-venti* L.

ZINGERIA P.A.Smirn.   **210**

4 species. Romania and Turkey to S Russia, Palestine and Iran. Meadows and
stream sides.

biebersteiniana (Claus) P.A.Smirn.
 • A wool casual from Galashiels (Selkirks) in c.1983. Crimea, SE Russia,
Caucasus, SW Asia. D1, D71, D126*, R119. *Agrostis biebersteiniana* Claus.
pisidica (Boiss.) Tutin
 • A casual at Bristol docks in 1939. Romania, Turkey, Caucasus, SW Asia.
BRISTM. D1, D18, D50*, D71, J1(12:303), J59(7:85-91), R88. *Agrostis
pisidica* Boiss.; *A.trichoclada* Griseb. var. *pisidica* (Boiss.) Boiss. **Fig.5.**

MIBORA Adans.   **211**

2 species. W Europe and NW Africa. Damp sandy soils.

minima (L.) Desv.   *Early Sand-grass*
 •• Accidentally introduced into several nurseries and gardens, e.g. Ferndown
(Dorset) where it flourished as a weed for many years but is probably now
gone, Woodbridge (E Suffolk) and as a garden weed at Flitwick (Beds),
(ref.R118); ?native on dunes in S Wales, Anglesey, E Lothian and the Channel
Islands (where it is abundant). W Europe, NW Africa, (Australia, USA). BM,
BRISTM, K, NMW, RNG. D1, D2, D3*, D4, D75*, D115*, D117*,
J59*(13:252-258). *Agrostis minima* L.

POLYPOGON Desf.   **212**

18 species. Warm temperate regions and on tropical mountains. Damp places.
Key on p.118.

[**aegypticum** ined.
 A wool casual, exhibited at the B.S.B.I. Exhibition Meeting in 1963. Origin
and authority untraced. J6(5:378). Perhaps a form of *P.monspeliensis* or
P.maritimus.]
australis Brongn.
 Pre-1930 only. A dock alien at Bristol in 1918. Temperate S America,
(N America). BM. D6*, D23, D118, D185, J1(5:407), R36, R62. *P.crinitus*
Trin., non Nutt. **Fig.29.**
elongatus Kunth
 •• A wool casual. Arizona, Mexico, C and S America, (N America). BM,
E, K, OXF, RNG. D6*, D12, D15*, D43, D52*, D75*, D118, D174*,
J58*(111:151-163), R1, R5, R36, R51, R86. **Fig.29.**
fugax Nees ex Steud.
 • A wool casual; also cultivated in R.B.G., Kew (Surrey). Seashore,
Co Wicklow in 1858. Atlantic Is, NE Africa, Asia. BM, DBN, K, RNG.
D14, D22*, D37*, D48, D49, D75*, D92*, D124*, D126*, D127,

J58*(111:151-163), R113. *P.demissus* Steud.; *P.littoralis* auct., non Sm.
Close to *P.elongatus*. **Fig.29.**
[interruptus Kunth
Possibly overlooked as *P.elongatus*. S America, (N America). D6*, D41,
D75*, D118, D128, D153*.]
linearis Trin.
• A casual of wool and waste ground. Chile. BM, E, OXF, RNG. D15,
D46*, J1(2:420; 9:377), R4*, R86. *P.longiflorus* Nees ex Steud. **Fig.29.**
maritimus Willd.
•• A casual of wool and docks. Atlantic Is, Med., Asia, (Australia,
N America). BM, E, K, LIV, LTN, OXF, RNG, SLBI. D1, D2, D6*, D15*,
D17*, D18, D19*, D20*, D22*, D30*, D31, D75*, D115*, D117*, D118*,
J23(1:59), R1, R2, R4, R5, R20, R23, R36, R38, R51, R54. *P.monspeliensis*
var. *maritimus* (Willd.) Coss. & Durieu. Some specimens are incorrectly
determined, and should be *P.monspeliensis*. **Fig.29.**
monspeliensis (L.) Desf.   **Annual Beard-grass**
••• A casual of wool, bird-seed, esparto, waste land and docks; cultivated in
gardens; a rare native round the coast of southern England and in the Channel
Islands. Europe, Med., NE tropical and S Africa, Asia, (widespread). BEL,
BM, CGE, DBN, E, K, LTN, NMW, RNG, SLBI. D1, D2, D3*, D4, D22*,
D75*, D89*, D93*, D115*, D117*, D118*, R1, R2, R4, R8, R21, R86, R113.
Alopecurus monspeliensis L. Wool-alien variants with small spikelets have been
separated by C.E.Hubbard as *P.paniceus* (L.) Lag. (*P.monspeliensis* var.
paniceus (L.) Gray), but they are not clearly differentiated (RNG, HbEJC,
HbTBR. D34*, R2). See × *Agropogon* for hybrids with *Agrostis* species.
A hybrid with *P.viridis* (q.v.) has also been recorded. **Fig.29.**
[pumilus E.D.Clarke
A wool alien. Egypt. J6(6:52-53), J8(42:22), J18(340:27), R86.
P.monspeliensis var. *pumilus* (E.D.Clarke) Melderis. Apparently a dwarf form
of *P.monspeliensis* (not *P.maritimus* as stated in *Index Kewensis*).]
[tenellus R.Br.
Cultivated from wool shoddy. SW Australia. K. D7, D27, D59*, R1.
Fig.29.]
viridis (Gouan) Breistr.   **Water Bent**
••• A casual of wool, waste land and tips in many places in Britain;
naturalised and increasing in the Channel Islands, and occasionally established
in damp spots in England. Atlantic Is, Med., SW Asia, (widespread). BEL,
BM, BRISTM, CGE, E, K, LTN, NMW, RNG. D1, D2, D3*, D4, D6*,
D17*, D19*, D39*, D75*, D89*, D93*, D115*, D117*, J58*(111:151-163),
R1, R3, R36, R47, R65. *P.semiverticillata* (Forssk.) Hyl.; *Agrostis*
semiverticillata (Forssk.) C.Chr.; *A.verticillata* Vill.; *A.viridis* Gouan.
A hybrid with *P.monspeliensis* has been recorded. See also the entry for
× *Agropogon*. **Fig.29.**

CHAETOPOGON Janch.   213

1 species. Med. Sandy places.

[fasciculatus (Link) Hayek
  Pre-1930. A casual; occasionally cultivated in botanic gardens. Med.
  K(cultivated), OXF. D1, D20*, D115*. *Chaeturus fasciculatus* Link.
  The status and identification of the specimen from Slinfold (W Sussex)
  in ref.R92 needs confirmation. Another old record reported in ref.J1(3:343)
  was shown in the later ref.J1(5:148) to be a viviparous form of *Poa pratensis*.
  Fig.5.]

ALOPECURUS L.   219

36 species. N temperate regions and S America. Damp meadows to stony
slopes.

[*bulbosus* Gouan   *Bulbous Foxtail*
  Pre-1930 on waste ground in Co Dublin, but needs confirmation; possibly a
  wool alien at Blackmoor (N Hants) in 1967; also a rare native grass. Coasts of
  W Europe and Med. DBN, E. D1, D2, D3*, R2, R5, R113. An unlikely
  wool alien, which may have been confused with material from another locality.]
geniculatus L.   *Marsh Foxtail*
  •• A wool alien; also a common native grass growing in wet places.
  N temperate zone, (Australia). CGE, E, K, RNG. D1, D2, D3*, D4, D75*,
  R1, R2, R5.
macrostachyos Poir.
  Pre-1930 only. An esparto casual from Leith docks (Midlothian) in 1921.
  NW Africa. D20*, D31, D75*, J1(6:321), R36. *A.bulbosus* Gouan var.
  macrostachyos (Poir.) Trab.
magellanicus Lam.
  • A wool casual. Southern S America. K, HbEJC, HbTBR. D12*, D52*,
  J1(5:311), R2, R4, R36, R48. *A.antarcticus* Vahl. Probably the grass
  described as *A.alpinus* Sm. var. *robustus* Druce from Tweedside in ref.R4.
myosuroides Huds.   *Black-grass*
  ••••• A common weed and probable native of arable land and waste places;
  a wool casual; cultivated from bird-seed. Europe, temperate Asia,
  (widespread). D1, D2, D3*, D4, D75*, R8, R65. *A.agrestis* L.
pratensis L.   *Meadow Foxtail*
  • A wool alien; also a very common native grass. Europe, N Asia,
  (widespread). RNG. D1, D2, D3*, D4, R1.
rendlei Eig
  • A casual of docks and waste land ; a nursery weed (among Italian plants) at
  Windlesham (Surrey) in 1988. S Europe, NW Turkey, (?NW Africa). BM,
  K, NMW, HbCGH. D1, D18, D20*, D75*, D89*, D115*, D129*, D180*,
  J1(7:1025), J24(Feb.1989), R8, R23, R65. *A.utriculatus* (L.) Pers., non
  Banks & Sol.

setarioides Gren.
Pre-1930 only. Introduced with hay near Oxford in 1895. Yugoslavia, Greece, W Turkey. BRISTM, K, LIV, NMW. D1, D18, D75*.
utriculatus (L.) Banks & Sol.
• A grain casual from Felixstowe docks (Essex) in 1939. Greece, SW Asia. D1, D17*, D18, D20*, D22*, D31*, D48, D75*, J23(1:58), R36. *A.anthoxanthoides* Boiss.; *Phalaris utriculata* L. Specimens in NMW of *A.rendlei* and *A.setarioides* were wrongly identified as this species.

CORNUCOPIAE L.   220

2 species. E Med. to Iraq. Ditches and wet places.

cucullatum L.
Pre-1930 only; a grain casual found in docks and wasteland. E Med., SW Asia. BM, K, OXF, RNG. D1, D17*, D18, D22*, D33*, D75*, D115*, R36, R44, R96. **Fig.5.**

BECKMANNIA Host   221

2 species. N temperate zone. Meadows and damp places.

eruciformis (L.) Host   **European Slough-grass**
• Possibly a hay casual at Claygate (Surrey) in 1916; tip at Kew (Surrey); the record from Sharpness docks (W Gloucs) in 1986 needs confirmation; occasionally cultivated. Eurasia. BM, BRISTM, K, OXF, RNG. D1, D2, D14, D17*, D18, D75*, D115*, J1(4:508; 6:752; 7:1025; 8:140; 10:359), J12(37:188), J59*(3:209-211), R23, R36, R62, R78. *Phalaris eruciformis* L. Much confused with *B.syzigachne*, so that most of the records are probably wrong (e.g. see ref.J8(41:14; 47:34). The differences between the two species are given in ref.D1 and D2.
syzigachne (Steud.) Fernald   **American Slough-grass**
•• A casual of bird-seed, grain and docks; abundant and persistent at Avonmouth (W Gloucs), where it was originally named in error as *B.eruciformis*; cultivated from USA rye-grass mixture. N America, Asia, (Europe). BM, BRISTM, NMW. D1, D2*, D6*, D14, D23*, D40*, D42*, D81*, D118*, J8(29*:10-11; 41:14; 47:34), J59*(3:209-211), R20, R21, R23, R59, R62, R65, R88. *B.eruciformis* auct., non (L.) Host; *Panicum syzigachne* Steud. **Fig.17.**

PHLEUM L.   222

15 species. N temperate zone and S America. Meadows and dry grassland.

alpinum L.   **Alpine Cat's-tail**
• A wool casual; a rare native alpine of northern Britain. Mountains of Eurasia, N and S America. BM, CGE, E, K, RNG. D1, D2, D3*, D4, R5. *P.commutatum* Gaudin.

echinatum Host
   Pre-1930 only. Med. D1, D18, D75*, D115*, D129*, J36(1905:103), R36.
exaratum Griseb.
   • A dock, grain and tip casual; no record since 1933 near Bristol. SE Europe,
   SW Asia. BM, BRISTM, K, LIV, OXF, RNG, SLBI. D1, D3, D17*, D18,
   D22*, D75*, D115*, J1(6:157; 10:360,549), J3(21:27), J36(1905:103), R8,
   R36, R57. *P.graecum* Boiss. & Heldr. subsp. *graecum*. The records from
   Swanage (Dorset) in 1915 in ref.J1(5:133), R28 in BMH are errors for the
   perennial *P.pratense* subsp. *serotinum* according to ref.R9.
hirsutum Honck.
   Pre-1930 only. Central S Europe. BM, OXF, RNG. D1, D115*, D180*,
   J1(5:407; 8:423; 10:360), J71*(29:259-260), R29, R36. *P.michelii* All.
   The very early record in ref.R107 is an error.
paniculatum Huds.
   • An casual of wasteland and docks. Med. BM, BRISTM, K, LIV, OXF,
   RNG(?cultivated), SLBI, SWN. D1, D3, D6, D14, D18, D75*, D81*, D115*,
   J1(5:270,407,688; 6:157; 10:360), J36(1905:103), R8, R36, R57, R62, R71,
   R84, R97, R98, R107. *P.asperum* Jacq. The earliest records date back to
   before 1762 when it was wrongly described as native by W.Hudson in ref.R97.
pratense L. subsp. *pratense*   *Timothy*
   •• A wool alien; also cultivated from bird-seed; a common native grass.
   Eurasia, (widespread). RNG, HbCGH, HbTBR. D1, D2, D3*, D4, D75*,
   R1, R3, R21. *P.nodosum* L.
pratense L. subsp. *serotinum* (Jord.) Berher   *Smaller Cat's-tail*
   • A wool and tip casual; also a common native grass. Europe, SW Asia,
   N Africa. BMH, E. D1, D2, D3*, D4, D115*, J1(5:133), R3, R9, R28.
   P.bertolonii DC.; *P.nodosum* auct., non L.; *P.pratense* subsp. *bertolonii* (DC.)
   Bornm.; *P.serotinum* Jord. See the comment given for *P.exaratum*.
subulatum (Savi) Asch. & Graebn.
   •• A casual of waste ground, docks and grain. Med., Syria to Arabia. BM,
   BRISTM, K, OXF, RNG, SLBI. D1, D3, D6, D17*, D18, D20*, D31, D75*,
   D115*, J1(5:688; 7:220; 8:423,764; 10:360; 13:111), J36(1905:103), R8, R24,
   R36, R49, R55, R88, R107. Includes subsp. *ciliatum* (Boiss.) Humphries
   which is not worthy of subspecific rank. *P.bellardii* Willk.; *P.tenue* (Host)
   Schrad.; *Phalaris cylindrica* DC.; *P.subulata* Savi.

BROMEAE

BROMUS L.   225

   c.45 species. Temperate regions, mostly Eurasian. Open grassland and ruderal
   habitats. We have followed ref.D2 in splitting *Bromus* L. sensu lato into four
   segregate genera: however this is at variance with other modern treatments
   which either prefer the split genera at a lower rank (e.g. Hitchcock in ref.D6

and Clayton & Renvoize in ref.S7 who opt for sections of *Bromus*) or do not
recognize them as distinct at all (Watson & Dallwitz in ref.S10). *Bromus* sensu
stricto are annual species with scarcely compressed spikelets and broad elliptic
or oblong glumes and lemmas.

[adoensis Steud.
　　Pre-1930 only. Ethiopia. R36. As *B.advensis* in ref.R36. This species is now
　　considered conspecific with *B.pectinatus* (see ref.D13, D51, D177).]
alopecuros Poir.
　　•• A wool casual. Med., SW Asia, (N America). BM, E, K, LIV, LTN,
　　OXF, RNG. D1, D17*, D18, D20*, D27*, D31, D93*, D115*, D118, R1,
　　R2, R3, R5, R36, R50, R51, R86. *B.alopecuroides* Poir.; *B.contortus* Desf.
arduennensis Dumort.
　　Pre-1930 only. A casual at Penzance (W Cornwall). Formerly endemic in the
　　Ardennes in Belgium and France in *Triticum* crops, now extinct except in a few
　　botanic gardens. K. D1, D25*, D186*, R8, R36. *Bromus bromoides* (Lej.)
　　Crép. is an invalid (tentative) name.
[arenarius Labill.
　　A rare wool casual. Australia, (N America, Mexico). BM, CGE, E, K, OXF,
　　RNG. D6*, D8*, D10*, D27*, D38, D78, D93*, J1(9:286), R1, R3, R4, R5,
　　R51. *B.australis* R.Br.; *Serrafalcus arenarius* (Labill.) C.A.Gardner. Treated
　　here as conspecific with *B.pectinatus*, and not to be confused with *B.arenarius*
　　Pourr. Probably introduced to these countries with live sheep.]
arvensis L.   Field Brome
　　••• A grain, agricultural seed and wool alien, sometimes persistent; previously
　　frequent but now rare and decreasing; cultivated from bird-seed. Eurasia,
　　(N America). BEL, BM, BRISTM, CGE, E, K, LTN, NMW, RNG, SLBI,
　　TOR. D1, D2, D3*, D4, D75*, D89*, D115*, J1(10:362), R4, R8, R21, R24,
　　R27, R36, R39, R40, R48, R49, R54, R55, R56, R57, R58, R60, R62, R66,
　　R71, R72, R76, R81, R86, R107, R124. *Serrafalcus arvensis* (L.) Godr.
brachystachys Hornung
　　• A wool casual at Bentley Station (N Hants) in 1960; also pre-1930 as a grain
　　alien. E Med., SW Asia. K, RNG. D1, D17*, D18, D22*, D180*,
　　J1(7:906), R8, R36, R44, R88, R96. *B.aegyptiacus* Tausch subsp. *palaestinus*
　　Melderis; *B.palaestinus* (Melderis) Melderis; *B.pseudobrachystachys* H.Scholz;
　　B.tigridis Boiss. & Noë.
briziformis Fisch. & C.A.Mey.
　　•• A casual of waste ground and grass seed, as on new sports fields, etc.;
　　also grown as an ornamental grass. SW and C Asia, (Europe, N America).
　　BM, K, NMW, OXF, RNG, SLBI. D1, D3, D6*, D22*, D23*, D40*, D48*,
　　D75*, D118, J1(8:767; 10:362), J8(9:15), R20, R23, R36, R55, R65.
commutatus Schrad.   Meadow Brome
　　• A probable dock and wool alien; also a frequent and widespread native
　　meadow grass. Europe, N Africa, W Asia, (N America). HbTBR. D1, D2,
　　D3*, D4, R3, R4, R65. *B.pratensis* Ehrh. ex Hoffm.

danthoniae Trin.
- A casual in docks; cultivated at R.B.G., Kew (Surrey). SW and C Asia. BRISTM, K, SLBI. D17*, D18, D22*, D48*, D75*, D129*, J1(9:679; 11:520), R61, R62. *B.lanceolatus* var. *danthoniae* (Trin.) Dinsm.; *B.macrostachys* Desf. subsp. *danthoniae* (Trin.) Asch. & Graebn.; *B.macrostachys* var. *triaristatus* Hack. ex Druce.

grossus Desf. ex DC.
- A grain casual. Europe. BM, BRISTM, NMW, RNG. D1, D19, D75*, D115*, J23*(9:319-332), J79(48:170-173), R36, R84. *B.secalinus* var. *grossus* (Desf. ex DC.) Koch. Apparently known only from cultivated fields; it may have originated as a derivative of the Mediterranean *B.neglectus* (Parl.) Nyman. A full account of the origin and taxonomy is given in ref.J116(38:295-380).

hordeaceus L. subsp. **divaricatus** (Bonnier & Layens) Kerguélen
- •• A wool and grain casual. Med., (N America). BM, CGE, E, K, LTN, OXF, RNG. D1, D3, D6*, D10*, D20*, D31, J1(10:362; 11:520; 12:819; 13:112), J3(4:150), J6(3:300), J8(23:8), R1, R2, R4, R5, R51, R54, R65, R86. *B.hordeaceus* subsp. *molliformis* (Lloyd) Maire & Weiller; *B.lloydianus* Nyman; *B.molliformis* Lloyd. Some early records of *B.molliformis*, e.g. in ref.R36, refer to the native subsp. *ferronii*.

[*hordeaceus* L. subsp. *ferronii* (Mabille) P.M.Sm.
A wool alien; a rare native grass of cliff tops. W Europe. LTN. D1, D2, D3, D187*, R1. *B.ferronii* Mabille. Almost certainly an error.]

hordeaceus L. subsp. *hordeaceus*　　　　　　　　　　　　　　**Soft Brome**
- •••• A very common alien of wool, docks and tips; also an abundant native weed on waste ground, cultivated land, roadsides, etc. throughout Britain. Europe, Med., W Asia, (widespread). D1, D2, D3*, D4, R4, R5. *B.mollis* L. The form with hairless spikelets, var. *leiostachys* Hartm., has been found as a wool casual (specimen in K).

intermedius Guss.
- A wool casual. Med. BM, E, K, NMW, RNG. D1, D18*, D20*, D22, D30, D31, D115*, D117*, R1, R5, R86. *Serrafalcus intermedius* (Guss.) Parl. Probably most records are in error for *B.hordeaceus* subsp. *divaricatus*.

[*interruptus* (Hack.) Druce　　　　　　　　　　　　　　　*Interrupted Brome*
Accepted with reservations as native. Apparently endemic in S and C England, (Netherlands). RNG. D2, D3*, D75*. Once frequent to locally abundant in fields of sainfoin, rye-grass and clovers, its seed being distributed with the seeds of these fodder plants. First collected in 1849, it became extinct in the wild in 1972 but is still grown annually in a few botanical gardens, e.g. R.B.G., Kew (Surrey). *B.mollis* var. *interruptus* Hack. A very distinct species, distinguished by its split palea from all other species of *Bromus*.]

japonicus Thunb.　　　　　　　　　　　　　　　　　　**Thunberg's Brome**
- ••• A casual of wool, grain, docks, wasteland and bird-seed. Warm temperate Eurasia, (widespread). BM, BRISTM, E, K, LTN, NMW, OXF, RNG, SLBI, TOR. D1, D2*, D6*, D12*, D17*, D18*, D19*, D41*, D75*, D89*, D115*,

J1(9:679; 10:362; 13:112), J23(2:356), J26(55:45), R1, R2, R4, R5, R8, R21, R36, R39, R47, R49, R55, R62, R65, R84, R107.   *B.patulus* Mert. & W.D.J.Koch; *Serrafalcus patulus* (Mert. & W.D.J.Koch) Parl.   Most of the wool-alien records are referrable to *B.pectinatus* according to C.E.Hubbard (see ref.R3).

lanceolatus Roth   **Large-headed Brome**

•• A wool, esparto and bird-seed casual; a garden escape. Med., SW Asia, (Australia). BM, CGE, E, K, LANC, NMW, OXF, RNG, SLBI. D1, D2*, D17*, D18, D20*, D22*, D30*, D31*, D75*, D89*, D115*, J1(7:223; 8:182,767; 9:379), J8*(26:15), J23(13:148), R1, R2, R4, R5, R8, R21, R23, R36, R40, R48, R50, R57, R65, R68, R86, R88. *B.divaricatus* Rhode ex Loisel.; *B.macrostachys* Desf.; *Serrafalcus macrostachys* (Desf.) Parl. Includes *B.lanuginosus* Poir.

lepidus Holmb.   **Slender Soft-brome**

•••• Widespread in cultivated grassland, cornfields, waste land and road sides; introduced with grass seed, especially *Lolium* species; possibly native in some localities. Origin obscure, probably NW and C Europe, (Australia). D1, D2, D3*, D4, D75*, D115*. *B.brachystachys* auct. brit., non Hornung; *B.britannicus* I.A.Williams. It has been known in Britain since 1836 according to ref.D3.

pectinatus Thunb.

•• A wool casual. S and NE Africa, SW Asia, India, China, (Europe, N America, Australia). BM, E, K, OXF, RNG. D5, D13, D37*, D51, D75*, J73(4:502), R2, R5, R65. *B.adoensis* Steud.; *B.arenarius* Labill., non Pourr.; *B.japonicus* Thunb. var. *pectinatus* (Thunb.) Asch. & Graebn.; *B.japonicus* Thunb. var. *velutinus* (Nocca) Asch. & Graebn.; *B.pectinatus* Thunb. var. *vestitus* (Schrad.) Pénzes; *B.vestitus* Schrad. Formerly much confused in wool with *B.japonicus*.

[*pseudosecalinus* P.M.Sm.   *Smith's Brome*

Accepted with reservations as native. DBN. J53*(77:63), R122. Treated by ref.D1, D3 as an endemic of Britain and Ireland, but by ref.D2 as introduced.]

scoparius L.

•• A casual of wool and grain. Med., SW Asia. BM, BRISTM, E, K, LCN, LTN, OXF, RNG, SLBI. D1, D17*, D18*, D20*, D31*, D75*, D115*, D117*, J1(9:693; 11:520; 12:305), R1, R3, R4, R5, R8, R36, R47, R49, R55, R62. *B.rigens* L.; *Serrafalcus cavanillesii* Willk.

secalinus L.   **Rye Brome**

••• A wool and dock casual; in grain once common in the south as an established weed in arable land, now scarce and usually as a casual in winter wheat; still occasionally locally abundant, as at the edge of a field on the Theobald's Estate, Cheshunt (Herts) in 1993, and at Hooperton (S Devon) in 1994. Europe, N Africa, W Asia, (N America). BM, BRISTM, DBN, E, K, LSR, LTR, MANCH, NMW, OXF, RNG. D1, D2, D3*, D4, D75*, D89*, D115*, J15(116:141), J23*(9:319-322), J26(73:194), R1, R5, R8, R122.

Serrafalcus secalinus (L.) Bab. Includes *B.billotii* F.W.Schultz; *B.multiflorus* Sm., non Weigel.

squarrosus L.

•• A casual of wool, docks, arable land and railways. Eurasia, N Africa. BM, BRISTM, K, LCN, LIV, NMW, OXF, RNG, SLBI. D1, D6*, D18*, D19*, D30*, D40*, D75*, D115*, J1(4:510; 8:322,767; 9:469,693; 10:362), J23(2:59), R2, R4, R8, R23, R36, R39, R49, R54, R55, R56, R57, R62, R88, ?R107. *B.wolgensis* Fisch. ex Jacq.

trinii E.Desv.

• A wool casual. Argentina, Chile, (Western USA). K. D6*, D23*, D52*, D153*, D172*, R1, R118. *B.berterianus* Colla.

ANISANTHA K.Koch   225a

12 species. N and S temperate regions. Open grassland and ruderal habitats. Tufted annuals with compressed spikelets, narrow long-awned (at least 1.5cm long) glumes and lemmas, and bifid lemmas with hyaline teeth 2-5mm long.

diandra (Roth) Tutin ex Tzvelev   Great Brome

••• A grain and wool alien, naturalised and locally abundant in the south, especially East Anglia and the Isles of Scilly; possibly native on dunes in the Channel Islands; recorded from sandy beaches at Rush (Co Dublin) and Rosslare (Co Wexford) in Ireland; increasing; also cultivated from bird-seed. Atlantic Is, Med., SW Asia, (widespread). BM, BRISTM, CGE, E, K, LTN, NMW, OXF, RNG, SLBI, TCD. D1, D2, D3*, D4, D75*, D89*, D115*, J1(6:159; 9:469; 10:362), J23(1:58), J33(18:43), R1, R2, R4, R5, R24, R27, R39, R40, R43, R49, R54, R55, R57, R58, R59, R60, R62, R65, R71, R86, R113. *A.gussonei* (Parl.) Nevski; *Bromus diandrus* Roth; *B.gussonei* Parl.; *B.maximus* auct., non Desf.; *B.oxyodon* Schrank; *B.rigens* auct., non L.

fasciculata (C.Presl) Nevski

• A casual. Med. ?LTN, HbHJMB. D1, D17*, D20*, D22* D39*, D115*, D117*, R47, R118. *Bromus fasciculatus* C.Presl.

madritensis (L.) Nevski   Compact Brome

••• A casual of wool, esparto, tips, docks, wasteland and cultivated ground; possibly native in a very few localities, as on the carboniferous limestone near Bristol; established elsewhere on old walls and ruins; also cultivated from bird-seed. Atlantic Is, Med., (widespread). BM, BRISTM, CGE, DBN, E, K, LIV, LTN, NMW, OXF, WRC. D1, D2, D3*, D4, D75*, D115*, D117*, J33(18:43), R1, R2, R4, R5, R8, R21, R86, R122. *Bromus madritensis* L. The var. *ciliata* (Guss.) Tzvelev with hairy spikelets is a rare grain casual (LTN, RNG. ref.J8*(53:37-38), R118; also from Guernsey in 1992, ref.R19).

rigida (Roth) Hyl.   Ripgut Brome

•• A casual of wool, grain, agricultural seed and ballast, sometimes persistent, especially on sand by the sea; possibly native in the Channel Islands. Med., SW Asia. BRISTM, ?DBN, IPS, K, LTN, NMW, OXF, RNG. D1, D2, D6*, D12*, D17*, D19*, D20*, D75*, D89*, D115*, J1(10:362), R1, R5, R8, R11,

R19, R24, R27, R36, R40, R42, R49, R55, R56, R57, R59, R86, R113.
Bromus maximus Desf., non Gilib.; *B.rigidus* Roth; *B.villosus* Forssk., non
Scop. Difficult to separate from *A.diandra*, and dubiously distinct; perhaps
better treated as *A.diandra* var. *rigida* (Roth) Sales (see ref.J20(115:197-210).
The Surrey record in ref.R27 is an error for *A.diandra* according to ref.R44.

rubens (L.) Nevski   **Foxtail Brome**
••• A casual of wool, grain and esparto. Med., (N America, Argentina,
Australia). BM, BRISTM, CGE, E, K, LTN, NMW, RNG, SLBI. D1, D2,
D6*, D17*, D18, D20*, D30*, D75*, D89*, D115*, J1(8:424; 9:469; 10:362;
11:47; 12:511), J6(4:406), J10(28:386), J15(108:33), R1, R2, R4, R5, R24,
R36, R38, R40, R50, R51, R54, R61, R86, R93, R100, R101. *Bromus*
madritensis subsp. *rubens* (L.) Domin; *B.rubens* L.

sterilis (L.) Nevski   *Barren Brome*
•••• A frequent wool alien; also a very common lowland weed. Europe,
Med., SW Asia, (widespread). D1, D2, D3*, D4, D89*, R1, R3, R4, R8.
Bromus sterilis L. The seeds have been found in wool waste.

tectorum (L.) Nevski   **Drooping Brome**
••• A casual of wool, grain and grass seed established in a few localities;
naturalised and locally abundant in Breckland (W Norfolk, W Suffolk); only old
records from Ireland; also cultivated from bird-seed. Eurasia, N Africa,
(widespread). BM, BRISTM, CGE, DBN, E, LTN, NMW, OXF, RNG,
WRC. D1, D2, D3*, D4, D6*, D17*, D75*, D89*, D115*, D117*, J1(9:469;
10:362), J33(18:43), R1, R3, R4, R5, R8, R21, R36, R38, R39, R40, R49,
R54, R55, R57, R58, R62, R71, R113. *Bromus tectorum* L.

BROMOPSIS (Dumort.) Fourr.   **225b**

c.70 species. Temperate regions. Woodland and meadows. Perennial grasses
with subterete elongate spikelets with closely over-lapping florets.

ciliata (L.) Holub
Pre-1930 only. Leith docks (Midlothian) in 1909; banks of the River Dee,
Chester (Cheshire) in 1924. N America. SLBI. D6*, D23*, D40*, D42*,
J1(7:604), R36. *Bromus ciliatus* L.

erecta (Huds.) Fourr.   *Upright Brome*
•• Probably introduced in Ireland; a common native grass on chalk and
limestone in southern England, rarer in Wales and southern Scotland, also
frequent on roadsides and wasteland. Europe, SW Asia, NW Africa, (N and
S America). D1, D2, D3*, D4, R122. *Bromus erectus* Huds.; *Zerna erecta*
(Huds.) Gray.

inermis (Leyss.) Holub   **Hungarian Brome**
••• Cultivated for fodder and pheasant food, and escaped or introduced and
naturalised on sandy soils in widely scattered localities; a casual of wool;
increasingly introduced with grass seed; cultivated in R.B.G., Kew (Surrey),
where it spreads rapidly by rhizomes and is difficult to control. Europe, Asia,
(widespread). BM, BRISTM, CGE, E, K, NMW, OXF, RNG, SLBI. D1,

D2, D6*, D18*, D19*, D23*, D40*, D75*, D89*, D93*, D115*, D118, J1(10:362; 11:519), R1, R5, R24, R27, R36, R39, R40, R49, R55, R56, R57, R58, R59, R62, R65, R66, R71, R86. *Bromus inermis* Leyss.; *Zerna inermis* (Leyss.) Lindm. This species may be the *Bromus erectus* recorded in ref.R4.

[**pumpelliana** (Scribn.) Holub
Possibly introduced with grass seed; recorded from the banks of a reservoir at Walthamstow (S Essex) in 1967, on a bank at Barnehurst (W Kent) in 1984 and near Exeter (S Devon) in 1992, but probably only forms of *B.inermis*, or the hybrid which is very common in western N America. NW America, E Asia. BM. D2, D6*, J26(53:84; 64:115), J59(14:95-96), R24. *Bromus inermis* subsp. *pumpellianus* (Scribn.) Wagnon; *B.pumpellianus* Scribn.]

CERATOCHLOA DC. & P.Beauv.   225c

c.20 species. N and S America. Open woodland and meadows. Grasses with large strongly compressed spikelets and keeled glumes and lemmas.

brevis (Nees ex Steud.) B.D.Jacks.   Patagonian Brome
•• A casual of wool, tips, waste ground, and sewage works; established for a few years from 1972 in a sandy car park by the sea at Pagham (W Sussex). S America, (Australia). BM, E, K, LTN, RNG. D2, D12*, D52*, D93*, R1, R2, R5, R67, R86, R99. *Bromus brevis* Nees ex Steud.

carinata (Hook. & Arn.) Tutin   California Brome
••• An escape from cultivation both as a silage crop and as a botanic garden plant, now well naturalised in some localities, abundantly so by the Thames in the Kew-Richmond-Hammersmith area (Surrey and Middlesex); first recorded from Ireland at Dublin Port in 1987; a casual of wool, docks and tips; increasing. Western N and S America. BEL, BM, BRISTM, CGE, DBN, E, K, NMW, RNG, SLBI, TCD. D1, D2, D6*, D19*, D23, D42*, D75, D118, D143, J1(11:672; 12:66), J8*(28:12-14), J12(40:44-45), R1, R2, R4, R5, R20, R24, R27, R39, R55, R56, R66, R68, R71, R77, R113. *Bromus carinatus* Hook. & Arn.; *B.laciniatus* Beal; *B.pendulinus* Sessé ex Lag., non Schrad. The record from Rickmansworth Aquadrome (Herts) in ref.R57 is an error for *C.marginata*.

cathartica (Vahl) Herter   Rescue Brome
••• A casual of wool, grain and bird-seed; an escape from or relic of cultivation sometimes established and locally abundant as a weed of arable land in the south, especially in the Isles of Scilly and the Channel Islands. S America, (widespread). BM, BRISTM, DBN, E, K, LIV, LTN, NMW, RNG, SLBI, WRC. D1, D2, D6*, D8*, D12*, D19*, D26*, D75*, D89*, D115*, J1(7:413; 10:362; 12:819), J33(18:43), R1, R2, R4, R5, R8, R21, R27, R36, R39, R40, R43, R49, R54, R55, R56, R58, R59, R62, R66, R71, R81, R86, R113. *C.unioloides* (Willd.) P.Beauv.; *Bromus catharticus* Vahl; *B.schraderi* Kunth; *B.unioloides* Kunth ; *B.willdenowii* Kunth; *Festuca unioloides* Willd.

marginata (Nees ex Steud.) B.D.Jacks.   **Western Brome**
•• A casual of wool and docks; ?established at Rickmansworth Aquadrome
(Herts) in 1961. N America. BM, E, K.   D2, D6*, D75*, J1(9:146),
J6(7:392), R1, R2, R4, R36, R57.   *Bromus marginatus* Nees ex Steud.
Possibly only a hairy form of *C.carinata*.

[**sitchensis** (Trin.) Cope & Ryves
Cultivated by MAFF at Starcross (S Devon) in 1985 as a possible fodder grass,
and may have been introduced on farms. N America. D6*. *Bromus sitchensis*
Trin. The determination is doubtful according to ref.R19, as it is similar to
C.carinata.]

staminea (E.Desv.) Stace   **Southern Brome**
• A casual of tips and wasteland; persisted at the sewage works at Lindfield (W
Sussex) from 1958 until 1965 when the habitat was lost; Littlehampton
(W Sussex) in 1988; it readily self-seeds when grown in gardens. Southern
S America, (N America). K, OXF, HbRMP, HbTBR. D2, D52*, D93, D118,
J23(18:413), R5, R19, R37. *Bromus cebadilla* Steud.; *B.stamineus* E.Desv.;
B.valdivianus Phil. Possibly confused with *B.lithobius* Trin. (*B.fonkii* Phil.),
also from southern S America, see ref.D52*, which is an alien in SE Australia.
The Lindfield plant was wrongly named as *B.marginatus* in ref.J6(4:172).
According to ref.D179 the correct basionym for this taxon is *B.cebadilla*,
because it was published slightly earlier, but the evidence for this is
inconclusive.

BOISSIERA Hochst. ex Steud.   **226**
1 species. Turkey to Pakistan. Dry stony open places.

squarrosa (Banks & Sol.) Nevski
Pre-1930 only. A dock casual. SW Asia. K. D17*, D18, D22*, D48*,
D51*, J1(8:641). *B.bromoides* Hochst. ex Steud., nom. illeg.; *Bromus pumilio*
(Trin.) P.M.Sm.; *Pappophorum squarrosum* Banks & Sol. **Fig.13.**

TRITICEAE
including Brachypodieae

BRACHYPODIUM P.Beauv.   **227**

16 species. Temperate Eurasia, NW Africa, Arabia, mountains of tropical and
southern Africa; Mexico to Bolivia. Woodland, grassland and open ground.
According to C.A.Stace, in ref.R6, this genus should be placed in a separate
tribe BRACHYPODIEAE.

distachyon (L.) P.Beauv.   **Stiff Brome**
••• A casual of wool, docks, wasteland, grain, esparto and bird-seed.
Atlantic Is, Med., W Asia, (widespread). BM, BRISTM, CGE, E, K, LIV,
LTN, RNG, SLBI. D1, D2*, D6*, D17*, D20*, D22*, D23*, D31*, D48*,

D75*, D89*, D115*, D117*, D118*, J1(8:424; 11:520; 12:205,819), J6(3:442; 4:406), J8*(22:1,14), J10(30:112), J18(382:25), J23(1:300), R1, R2, R4, R5, R21, R27, R36, R49, R54, R55, R61, R62, R101, R102. *Bromus distachyos* L.; *Trachynia distachya* (L.) Link.

retusum (Pers.) P.Beauv.

Pre-1930 only. A dock casual. Med., Arabia. RNG. D1, D18, D20*, D31, D115*, D117*, R36. *B.ramosum* Roem. & Schult.; *Bromus ramosus* L., non Huds.; *B.retusus* Pers.

sylvaticum (Huds.) P.Beauv.   *False Brome*
• An alien on tips; cultivated from bird-seed; a common native grass of shady places. Temperate Eurasia, NW Africa. HbCGH. D1, D2, D3*, D4, R21. *Festuca sylvatica* Huds.

ELYMUS L.   228

c.150 species. N and S temperate regions, especially in Asia. Occuring in meadows, woodland, upland and steppe regions, and on dunes. Closely related to *Leymus*. Many of the species were formerly in *Agropyron*. Recently many species have been placed in the genus *Elytrigia* Desv., characterised by having long rhizomes and short awns, but further work is needed to clarify the situation.

antarcticus Hook.f.
• A wool casual at Evesham (Worcs) in 1958. Temperate S America. K. D52*. *E.albowianus* Kurtz; *E.latiglumis* Phil.

[**breviaristatus** (Hitchc.) Á.Löve subsp. scabrifolius (Döll) Á.Löve
Grown from a mixture of Uruguayan wool from Bradford (SW Yorks) in c.1960. Uruguay, Argentina. BM, K, NMW, RNG. D12*, D15*, D52*, D72, R1. *Agropyron attenuatum* (Kunth) Roem. & Schult. var. *platense* Parodi; *A.repens* (L.) P.Beauv. var. *scabrifolium* (Döll) Arechav.; *A.scabrifolium* (Döll) Parodi; *Elytrigia scabrifolia* (Döll) Á.Löve; *Triticum repens* L. var. *scabrifolium* Döll. See the entry under *Agropyron attenuatum* for further comments.]

canadensis L.
•• A wool and dock alien; established for some years on waste ground at Yiewsley (Middlesex); only two old records from Ireland. Temperate Asia, N America. BRISTM, DBN, E, K, OXF, NMW, RNG, SLBI. D2, D6*, D40*, D41*, D42*, D53*, D75*, D76, D118, J1(8:425; 10:363), R3, R36, R55, R61, R100, R113. *Clinelymus canadensis* (L.) Nevski. Listed as *Elymus* sp. in ref.R2.

[**elongatus** (Host) Runemark subsp. ponticus (Podp.) Melderis
This grass has been sown along motorways in the Palatine lowlands of SW Germany, and has spread into adjacent natural vegetation to become widespread. It is likely to occur in Britain. SE Europe, Turkey, Egypt, Arabia, (Australia, N America). D1, D18, D118, J46(24:75), J51(27:22-24). *Elytrigia pontica* (Podp.) Holub; *Triticum obtusiflorum* DC.; *T.ponticum* Podp.

This or a closely similar grass is now widely sown as cv. 'Tyrrell' in Australia (ref.D44*).]

[interruptus Buckley

Cultivated in gardens and botanical gardens. N America. K. D6*. *E.diversiglumis* Scribn. & Ball.]

nutans Griseb.

• A wool casual found at East Ardsley (SW Yorks) in 1981. Temperate Asia. K, HbCGH, HbTBR. D126*. *Clinelymus nutans* (Griseb.) Nevski.

scabrus (R.Br.) Á.Löve   **Australian Couch**

•• A wool casual. Australia, New Zealand. BEL, BM, CGE, E, K, LIV, LTN, NMW, RNG. D2, D7, D8*, D16*, D24*, D26*, D29, D44*, D93*, R1, R2, R5, R47, R65, R66, R86. *Agropyron scabrum* (R.Br.) P.Beauv.; *Festuca scabra* Labill., non Vahl; *Triticum scabrum* R.Br.

sibiricus L.

Pre-1930 only. On ballast at Kinghorn (Fife) in 1904; Coatbridge (Lanarks) in 1925; on Tees-side under Barnard Castle walls (Co Durham) in 1924. Temperate Asia, (E and EC Europe). OXF, SLBI. D1, D71, D126*, D184*, J1(7:604,907), J36(1905:103), J50(5:141), R36, R100. *Clinelymus sibiricus* (L.) Nevski. Sometimes confused with *Agropyron sibiricum* (Willd.) P.Beauv.

[smithii (Rydb.) Gould

Reported as a wool casual at Blackmoor (N Hants) in 1972. N America. HbCGH, HbTBR. D6*, D41*, D153*, R3. *Agropyron smithii* Rydb.; *Elytrigia smithii* (Rydb.) Nevski. The specimens have been re-determined as a form of the native *E.repens* (L.) Gould (*Elytrigia repens* (L.) Nevski).]

subsecundus (Link) Á.& D.Löve

Pre-1930 only. A casual on waste ground. N America. BM, K, NMW. D6*, D118. *E.trachycaulus* subsp. *subsecundus* (Link) Gould; *Agropyron subsecundum* (Link) Hitchc.; *Triticum subsecundum* Link. Originally determined in error as *A.caninum* (L.) P.Beauv. from Eurasia by American botanists.

trachycaulus (Link) Gould ex Shinners

Pre-1930 only. A fodder casual found at Avonmouth docks (W Gloucs). N America. BRISTM. D1, D6*, D23*, D40*, D42*, D53*, D118*, J1(10:41,363). *Agropyron pauciflorum* (Schwein.) Hitchc., non Schur; *A.tenerum* Vasey; *A.trachycaulum* (Link) Malte; *Triticum trachycaulum* Link.

virginicus L.

• A casual of wool, wasteland, docks and sewage works; also cultivated in gardens. No records since 1960. N America. BM, E, K, NMW, OXF. D6*, D40*, D41*, D42*, D53*, D75*(var. *muticus* Hook.), J1(8:323), R1, R5, R36, R55.

HYSTRIX Moench   **229**

9 species.   N America, temperate Asia, New Zealand.   Woodland and meadows.

patula Moench   Bottle-brush-grass
Pre-1930 only.   Waste ground at Oxford in 1924; occasionally grown in botanical gardens.   Eastern N America.   OXF.   D6*, D40*, D53*, D54*, J1(7:457), R36.   *Asperella hystrix* (L.) Humb.; *Elymus hystrix* L.   **Fig.4.**

LEYMUS Hochst.   **231**

c.40 species.   N temperate zone, 1 species in Argentina.   Steppes, often adapted to saline, alkaline or dune habitats.   Close to *Elymus*.

arenarius (L.) Hochst.   *Lyme-grass*
•• A garden escape (ref.D2); planted on dunes as a sand binder; a frequent native grass of maritime sand dunes.   N and NW Europe, (Australia, Argentina).   R86.   *Elymus arenarius* L.
karelinii (Turcz.) Tzvelev
• A wool casual at Wakefield (SW Yorks) in 1981.   Siberia, C Asia, S Urals.   HbTBR.   D71, D126*.   *Elymus karelinii* Turcz.; *E.kopetdaghensis* Roshev.
paboanus (Claus) Pilg.
• A wool casual at Wakefield (SW Yorks) in 1981.   Siberia, C Asia, S Urals.   HbTBR.   D71.   *Elymus paboanus* Claus.
secalinus (Georgi) Tzvelev
• A wool casual at Wakefield (SW Yorks) in 1981.   Siberia, C Asia, Tibet, W China, Japan.   HbTBR.   D71.   *Triticum secalinum* Georgi.

TAENIATHERUM Nevski   **234**

1 species.   Med. to Pakistan, C Asia.   Dry grassy slopes.

caput-medusae (L.) Nevski
•• A casual of wool, grain, tips and docks; sometimes cultivated.   Med., SW and C Asia, (Australia, N America).   BM, BRISTM, K, LCN, OXF, RNG.   D1, D6*, D17*, D18, D20*, D22*, D31*, D75*, D117*, D118*, J1(8:768; 9:760; 10:363; 11:522; 12:305), J3(21:29), J15(112:28), R1, R8, R36, R44, R49, R61, R86.   *T.asperum* (Simonk.) Nevski; *T.crinitum* (Schreb.) Nevski; *Elymus caput-medusae* L.; *Hordeum asperum* (Simonk.) Degen ex Hayek; *H.caput-medusae* (L.) Coss. & Durieu; *H.crinitum* (Schreb.) Desf. Often treated as two distinct species, but the characters are not reliable (see ref.J20(76:340-344).   **Fig.4.**

CRITHOPSIS Jaub. & Spach   **235**

1 species.   Crete and Libya to Iran.   Dry grassland.   The 2-flowered spikelets are paired on a fragile hairy rhachis.

delileana (Schult.) Roshev.
- A wool casual. Crete, Libya to Iran. BRISTM, K, LTN, RNG. D1, D17*, D18, D20*, D22*, J1(10:363; 11:522), R1, R2, R62. *Elymus delileanus* Schult. **Fig.4.**

HORDEUM L.   237

c.40 species. Temperate regions throughout the world, but only introduced in Australasia, in open weedy or grassy places. It has been claimed that some form of *Hordeum* (Barley) is the oldest of all cultivated plants. Modern forms of *H.vulgare* (Six-rowed Barley and Four-rowed Barley) are most important cereals. The nomenclature of the South American species is taken from ref.D72. The identification of much of the material needs careful revision which must await the publication of an up-to-date account of the genus.

bogdanii Wilensky
- A wool casual found at East Ardsley (SW Yorks) in 1981. Russia, N Iran and C Asia. BM, K, HbCGH, HbTBR. D1, J114*(40:248), R86.

brachyantherum Nevski
- A wool casual; also a casual on Hanwell tip (Middlesex) in 1953. Western N America. BEL, CGE, E, RNG. D6*, D23*, D42*, D43*, D53*, D118*, R3, R5, R55, R86. *H.californicum* Covas & Stebbins. One specimen was originally wrongly determined as *H.procerum*.

brevisubulatum (Trin.) Link subsp. **brevisubulatum**
Pre-1930 only. A casual on waste ground; sometimes sown in grass seed mixtures. E Europe, Asia. K. D1, D81*, D129*, D184*, J1(6:327,638), R36, R55. *H.nodosum* L. var. *brevisubulatum* (Trin.) Thell.; *H.pratense* Huds. var. *brevisubulatum* (Trin.) Thell.; *H.secalinum* Schreb. var. *brevisubulatum* Trin.

chilense Roem. & Schult.
- A wool casual. S America. BM, RNG, HbCGH. D52*, D75*, J18(376:25), J65*(133:539-554), R2.

comosum J.Presl
- A wool casual. S America. K, LIV, NMW, RNG. D52*, D75*, J1(5:584), R2.

[**compressum** Griseb.
A wool casual. S America. RNG. D5, D12*, J1(10:363), R1, R3, R62. According to ref.D72 this name can refer to either *H.cordobense* or *H.stenostachys*, depending on which var. is intended, so that early records are indeterminate without re-examination. The specimen collected from Blackmoor (N Hants) in 1965 was re-determined as *H.muticum* according to ref.R5. According to ref.D5 this species is native in S Africa, but it must have been either mis-identified or introduced with sheep.]

cordobense Bothmer, N.Jacobsen & Nicora
- • A casual at Avonmouth docks (W Gloucs) in 1930; also probably a wool alien. S America. K. D72, J65*(133:539-554). *H.compressum* var. *tenuispicatum* Hack. & Stuck.

distichon L.   Two-rowed Barley
- • • • A casual escape or relic of cultivation, sometimes persistent; a casual of wool, docks and bird-seed; also cultivated from bird-seed. Origin obscure, probably SW Asia, (widespread). BM, BRISTM, E, K, NMW, OXF, RNG, WRC. D1, D3*, D14, D18, D19*, D75, D93*, D115*, J1(9:469; 10:363), R5, R21, R36, R40, R55, R59, R62, R76, R86, R113.

euclaston Steud.   Argentine Barley
- • • A wool casual. S America. BM, K, LTN, ?NMW, RNG, SLBI. D12*, D15, D75, R1, R2. *H.pusillum* subsp. *euclaston* (Steud.) Covas.

flexuosum Nees ex Steud.
- • A wool casual. S America. K, LTN, RNG. D12, R1, R5, R47, R50. *H.pusillum* Nutt. subsp. *flexuosum* (Nees ex Steud.) Cabrera.

geniculatum All.   Mediterranean Barley
- • • • A casual of wool, grain, esparto, tips and grass seed; cultivated from fenugreek seed in 1985 (ref.R65). Atlantic Is, Med., SW and C Asia, (N America, Australasia). BEL, BM, BRISTM, CGE, E, K, LTN, NMW, RNG, WCR. D1, D2, D3, D6*, D17*, D20*, D23*, D31, D93*, D115*, D117*, J1(10:363; 11:48), R1, R2, R5, R36, R40, R54, R55, R57, R62, R66, R86. *H.gussoneanum* Parl.; *H.hystrix* Roth; *H.marinum* subsp. *gussoneanum* (Parl.) Thell.; *H.maritimum* With. subsp. *gussoneanum* (Parl.) Asch. & Graebn.

halophilum Griseb.
- • A wool casual. S America. K, NMW, HbTBR. D52*, D72, D172, J103(14:117-136). *H.pubiflorum* subsp. *halophilum* (Griseb.) Baden & Bothmer.

jubatum L.   Foxtail Barley
- • • • A casual of wool, docks, grain, bird-seed, oil-seed and grass seed, sometimes briefly persistent; a garden escape; occasionally naturalised briefly on the verges of trunk roads in England, e.g. Wimbledon Common (Surrey). NE Asia, N and S America, (widespread). BM, BRISTM, CGE, DBN, E, LTN, NMW, OXF, RNG, SLBI. D1, D2*, D3, D6*, D12*, D19*, D23*, D40*, D75*, D89*, D118*, J1(6:161; 9:846; 10:363), J8(24:24), J26(63:70), R1, R2, R5, R8, R20, R21, R24, R30, R36, R39, R49, R54, R55, R57, R58, R59, R60, R66, R71, R76, R77, R86, R123. *H.caespitosum* Scribn. ex Parn.; *H.pampeanum* (Hauman) Herter (*H.jubatum* var. *pampeanum* Hauman), which has been wrongly equated with both *H.lechleri* and *H.pubiflorum*.

lechleri (Steud.) Schenck
- • A wool casual at Idle (SW Yorks) in 1957. S America. K, RNG. D52*, R5. *H.pubiflorum* var. *intermedia* (Hauman) Melderis; *Elymus lechleri* Steud. Confused with *H.comosum*, *H.jubatum* and *H.pubiflorum*.

[*marinum* Huds.   *Sea Barley*
    Possibly a wool casual; native on the coast of Britain. Atlantic Is, Med.,
    W Europe coasts, SW Asia, (N America, Australia).   E, K, LTN, HbCGH.
    D1, D2, D3*, D4, D22*, J33(18:43), R1, R3, R4, R5(cultivated), ?R86.
    Confused with *H.geniculatum*.]
murinum L. subsp. **glaucum** (Steud.) Tzvelev
    ••• A wool and esparto alien; established at Haven Banks, Exeter (S Devon)
    in 1994, perhaps introduced from over-wintering small yachts.   Med.,
    SW Asia, (widespread). BM, CGE, E, K, LTN, NMW, OXF, RNG. D1, D2,
    D6*, D12*, D17*, D23*, D43, D93*, J6(1:323-324,583-584), J15(108:34),
    J20(72:158), J23(14:433), R1, R2, R5, R38, R47, R50, R51, R66, R86, R88,
    R93. *H.glaucum* Steud.; *H.stebbinsii* Covas.
murinum L. subsp. **leporinum** (Link) Arcang.
    ••• A casual of wool and esparto. Atlantic Is, Med., Asia, (widespread).
    BM, CGE, E, K, LTN, NMW, RNG, SLBI. D1, D2, D3, D6*, D12*, D15*,
    D16*, D23*, D26*, D75*, D89*, D93*, D115*, D117*, J6(1:323), J8(18:10),
    J26(57:72; 60:91), J33(18:43), J34(14:16-17), R1, R2, R5, R38, R54, R55,
    R66, R86. *H.leporinum* Link.
murinum L. subsp. *murinum*   *Wall Barley*
    ••• A common alien of waste places and wool; also cultivated from wool;
    a common native or long-established introduced grass. Europe, SW Asia,
    (widespread). HbCGH. D1, D2, D3*, D4, D75*, D115*, J34(14:16-17),
    R65, R122.
muticum J.Presl
    • A wool casual. S America. BM, CGE, E, RNG. D172*, J65*(133:539-
    554), R1, R3, R4, R5, R36. Includes *H.andicola* Griseb.; *H.chilense* Brongn.
    var. *muticum* (J.Presl) Hauman. Originally determined as *H.compressum*.
parodii Covas
    • A wool casual. S America. K. D52*, J113*(18:74-77).
procerum Nevski
    • A wool casual. S America. BM, E, K, ?LTN, RNG. D12*, D52*, R3,
    R47. *H.hexaploidum* Covas. Confused with *H.brachyantherum*.
pubiflorum Hook. f.   *Antarctic Barley*
    •• A wool casual, established in an apple orchard at Barming (W Kent),
    probably now gone. Southern S America. BM, CGE, E, K, LTN, NMW,
    RNG, SLBI. D2, D52*, D75*, J10(32:21), J18(361:27), J33(18:43), R1, R2,
    R5, R38, R47, R51, R65, R86, R88. *H.comosum* var. *pubiflorum* (Hook.f.)
    Thell.; *H.secalinum* Schreb. var. *pubiflorum* (Hook.f.) Hauman. Confused with
    H.lechleri and *H.violaceum*.
pusillum Nutt.   *Little Barley*
    •• A wool casual. N America. BM, E, K, LTN, RNG, SLBI. D2, D6*,
    D15*, D40*, D41*, D42*, D43, D53, D75*, R1, R2, R3, R5, R38, R50, R65,
    R86, R93. Close to *H.euclaston*: a useful key is given in ref.D2 to separate the
    two species.

stenostachys Godr.
  • A wool and dock casual. S America, (S Africa). K, RNG. D12*, D15*, D52*, D151*, D174*, J65*(133:539-554), R3, R5, R103. *H.compressum* var. *superatum* Hack.; *Critesion stenostachys* (Godr.) Á.Löve.
violaceum Boiss. & Hohen.
  • A wool casual; also recorded from Hayling beach (S Hants) in 1920. SW Asia. BM, E. D18, D75*, D81*, J1(5:410; 6:161), R1, R3, R5, R30, R36. *H.brevisubulatum* subsp. *violaceum* (Boiss. & Hohen.) Tzvelev. Confused with *H.pubiflorum*.
vulgare L.   Six-rowed Barley
  •••• A bird-seed casual; an escape from or relic of cultivation on arable land. Origin obscure, probably SW Asia, (widespread). D1, D2, D3*, D4, D6*, D18*, R8, R21. Includes *H.hexastichon* L.; *H.sativum* Pers.; *H.trifurcatum* Jacq. ex Baill.

AGROPYRON Gaertn.   238

  c.15 species.   Med., through the Middle East to China, Australia and New Zealand.   The genus is restricted to species with keeled glumes and somewhat pectinate racemes, most other former species now being in *Elymus*. Apparent hybrids between *A.cristatum*, *A.desertorum* and *A.sibiricum* are planted for erosion control and may be widespread (ref.D118).

[**attenuatum** sensu Lousley, non (Kunth) Roem. & Schult.
  Grown from Uruguayan wool and recorded by J.E.Lousley in ref.R1.   We assume that he meant *A.attenuatum* (Kunth) Roem. & Schult. var. *platense* Parodi, a native of Uruguay and Argentina, rather than var. *attenuatum* which is native in the mountains of W tropical S America.   These two varieties are very similar taxonomically, and may only be separated on their geographical ranges.   See the entry under *Elymus breviaristatus* subsp. *scabrifolius*.]
cristatum (L.) Gaertn.
  • A casual; Montrose (Angus) in c.1853; Avonmouth docks (W Gloucs) in 1962; also perhaps from grass seed at Cambridge in 1972 and on a roadside at Exeter (S Devon) in 1989. Eurasia, N Africa, (N America). BM, E, K, LIV, OXF, RAMM, RNG. D1, D6, D18, D20*, D22*, D23*, D42*, D75*, D81*, D89*, D115*, J18(367:29-30), R36, R107. *Bromus cristatus* L.; *Eremopyrum cristatum* (L.) Willk.; *Triticum cristatum* (L.) Schreb.   Includes subsp. *pectinatum* (M.Bieb.) Tzvelev; *A.pectiniforme* Roem. & Schult.   The records given in ref. J18(337:30; 340:26) almost certainly refer to the closely similar *A.desertorum* found at the same locality, as given in ref.R55. **Fig.21.**
desertorum (Fisch. ex Link) Schult.
  • A casual at Hyde Park Corner (Middlesex) in 1962. E Europe, Asia, (N America). BM, RNG. D1, D6*, D42*, D118*, R55. *Triticum desertorum* Fisch. ex Link.

EREMOPYRUM (Ledeb.) Jaub. & Spach   **239**
.
5 species. SE Europe to C Asia, Pakistan, N Africa. Stony slopes, steppes and semi-desert. Almost an annual version of *Agropyron*.

bonaepartis (Spreng.) Nevski
• A casual of wool and docks. N Africa, SW Asia. BRISTM, LTN. D17*, D18, D20*, D22*, D31, D48*, D49, J1(5:136; 11:522), R36, R48, R49, R61, R62, R118. *Agropyron bonaepartis* (Spreng.) T.Durand & Schinz; *A.patulum* Trin.; *A.squarrosum* (Roth) Link; *Triticum bonaepartis* Spreng. **Fig.10.**

orientale (L.) Jaub. & Spach
Pre-1930 only. A grain or wool casual. Eurasia, N Africa. BM, LCN, OXF, SLBI. D1, D18, D20*, D22*, D31, D75*, R36, R49. *Agropyron orientale* (L.) Roem. & Schult.; *Secale orientale* L.; *Triticum orientale* (L.) M.Bieb.

triticeum (Gaertn.) Nevski
Pre-1930 only. Grimsby docks (N Lincs) in c.1900; Leith docks (Midlothian) in 1908. Eurasia, (N America). SLBI. D1, D6, D18, D23*, D75*, D81*, D153*, J36(1905:103), R36, R49. *Agropyron prostratum* (Pall.) P.Beauv.; *A.triticeum* Gaertn.; *Secale prostratum* Pall.; *Triticum prostratum* (Pall.) L.f.

SECALE L.   **240**

4 species. E Europe to C Asia, Spain and N Africa. Sandy soils and dry hill sides. *S.cereale* (Rye) is a cereal.

cereale L.   Rye
••• A casual of wool, grass seed, grain and bird-seed; an escape from or relic of cultivation as a cereal; once found as a weed in a fenugreek crop. W Asia, (widespread). BM, BRISTM, CGE, DBN, E, LCN, NMW, OXF, RNG, SLBI, TCD, WCR. D1, D2, D3*, D6*, D12*, D19*, D20*, D26*, D55*, D75, D115*, J1(9:469; 10:363), R1, R2, R8, R21, R24, R36, R39, R40, R49, R55, R62, R65, R113. *Triticum cereale* (L.) Salisb. **Fig.11.**

montanum Guss.
Pre-1930 only. A casual on waste ground. Med., Caucasus, SW Asia to N India. BM. D1, D6, D17*, D18, D20*, D22*, J1(5:261), R55. *S.dalmaticum* Vis.

× **TRITICOSECALE** Wittm. ex A.Camus   **240×242**

1 nothospecies. An artificially produced hybrid *Triticum aestivum* × *Secale cereale* (Triticale), which is being widely grown as a cereal crop in East Anglia, and has occurred as a casual. (Europe, N America, New Zealand). There is no valid specific level name; only cultivar names exist. RNG, HbTBR. D2, D37*, J26(70:160), J52(35:144-149; 36:445-452), R6.

DASYPYRUM (Coss. & Durieu) T.Durand   **241**

2 species. Med., SE Europe, Turkey, N Africa. Stony slopes.

villosum (L.) Coss. & Durieu ex Borbás
*   Probably a wool alien on wasteland near Rothwell (SW Yorks) in 1985; also
    pre-1930. Med., SW Asia. BM, HbCGH. D1, D18, D75*, D115*,
    J15(112:28), R86. *Agropyron villosum* (L.) Link; *Haynaldia villosa* (L.) Schur;
    Secale villosum L.; *Triticum villosum* (L.) M.Bieb. **Fig.11.**

TRITICUM L.   **242**

10-20 species. A most important genus, probably originating in the Middle
East or SW Asia, of which some forms have been domesticated for at least
6000 years. *T.monococcum* (Einkorn), *T.dicoccon* (Emmer) and *T.spelta*
(Spelt) are the most primitive species. Of more recent origin, wheats in which
the ripe grain is readily separated, are *T.turgidum* (Rivet Wheat, Cone Wheat,
Poulard Wheat), *T.durum* (Pasta Wheat, Macaroni Wheat, Durum Wheat) and
T.aestivum (Bread Wheat, Common Wheat). As with other cereal grasses,
there is a profusion of weakly defined minor segregates. This genus is
dubiously distinct from *Aegilops*, and several intergeneric nothospecies
(× *Aegilotriticum* P.Fourn.) are known (see ref.D20*).

aestivum L.   **Bread Wheat**
    ●●●● A wool, dock and bird-seed casual; an escape from or relic of cultivation
    on arable land. Origin obscure, probably SW Asia, (widespread). D1, D2,
    D3*, D4, D6*, D12*, D19*, D26*, J1(10:363), J10(28:386), R3, R21, R36,
    R39, R40, R55, R65, R86, R113. *T.sativum* Lam.; *T.vulgare* Vill. Includes
    T.compactum Host. Probably of ancient hybrid origin involving species of
    Triticum and *Aegilops*.

dicoccon Schrank   **Emmer**
    Pre-1930 only. Origin obscure, probably SW Asia, (widespread). D1, D20*,
    D55*, D115*, R36. *T.dicoccum* (Schrank) Schübl.; *T.spelta* L. var. *dicoccum*
    (Schrank) Schübl. The most important cereal in Ancient Egypt.

durum Desf.   -   **Pasta Wheat**
    ●● A casual of wool and found on tips; cultivated from bird-seed. Origin
    obscure, (widespread). BM, K, NMW, RNG. D1, D2, D18, D20*, D55*,
    D115*, J8(15:19), J10(38:45), J15(108:34), R4, R9, R23, R36, R39, R44,
    R45, R65, R86, R88.

monococcum L.   **Einkorn**
*   A casual on tips, possibly from bird-seed. Origin obscure, probably
    SW Asia, (widespread). BRISTM. D1, D18, D20*, J1(12:305; 13:112), R45.

spelta L.   **Spelt**
*   Mostly pre-1930; a casual at Dublin Port in 1990. A hybrid of obscure
    ancient origin, (widespread). DBN, NMW. D1, D19*, D20*, D75, D115*,
    J9(24:339-342), R23, R36, R40, R113. Grown in Guernsey in Neolithic times,
    according to ref.R11.

turgidum L.   **Rivet Wheat**
●●● (but most records are in error). A casual of waste-land, bird-seed and animal feed; also cultivated from wool; possibly a relic of cultivation, becoming very scarce. A hybrid of obscure origin, probably SW Asia, (widespread). BRISTM, LIV, OXF, SLBI, ZCM. D1, D2, D18, D19*, D20*, D55*, D75, D115*, J1(13:222), J10(32:21), J27(10:1966-1967), R23, R36, R38, R55, R65, R82.

AEGILOPS L.   **243**
22 species. Med., Middle East to Pakistan and C Asia. Annuals growing on stony slopes, dry grassland and weedy places. The generic account of M.W.van Slageren in ref. D133* has been followed, which mostly agrees with the earlier work of K.Hammer in ref.J53(91:225-258), J96*(28:33-180).

bicornis (Forssk.) Jaub. & Spach
Pre-1930; also a casual by a paper factory. Med., NE Africa and SW Asia. K. D17*, D20*, D133*, D177*, J1(8:37; 10:363), R36. *Triticum bicorne* Forssk.
biuncialis Vis.
● A wool casual. Med., SW Asia, N Africa. K, RNG. D1, D17*, D18, D49, D75*, D131*(t.1, fig.2), D133*, R1, R5, R118. *A.lorentii* Hochst.
comosa Sm.
Pre-1930 only. Leith docks (Midlothian) in 1906. S Greece, W Turkey. DBN, SLBI. D1, D22*, D75*, D133*, J96*(28:81), R36. *T. comosum* (Sm.) K.Richt.
crassa Boiss.
Pre-1930 only; Slateford near Edinburgh in 1906; also formerly cultivated in R.B.G., Kew (Surrey). Middle East to C Asia. LIV, SLBI. D17*, D18, D22*, D49, D133*, J96*(28:77-78), R36. *Triticum crassum* (Boiss.) Aitch. & Hemsl.
cylindrica Host
●● A casual of wool, grain, docks and wasteland; a weed in sainfoin at Cambridge in 1964. E Europe, SW Asia, (N America). BM, BRISTM, K, NMW, OXF, RNG, SLBI. D1, D6*, D18, D23*, D41*, D42*, D75*, D89*, D115*, D118*, D133*, J1(8:425; 10:363; 11:291,522), J6(1:70), J8(25:14), J23(2:357), R5, R8, ?R36, R38, R40, R55, R61. *A.tauschii* auct., non Coss.; *Triticum cylindricum* (Host) Ces., Pass. & Gibelli. **Fig.21.**
geniculata Roth
● A casual of wool, esparto and docks. Med., (N America). BM, K, NMW, RNG. D1, D17*, D18, D43, D75*, D89*, D115*, D117*, D133*, J1(7:1027; 8:143; 9:693; 10:363), J18(379:25), J23(10:38), R2, R23, R36, ?R38. *A.ovata* L. pro parte; *Triticum ovatum* (L.) Gren. & Godr.; *T.vagans* (Jord. & Fourr.) Greuter.

neglecta Req. ex Bertol.
- A casual of docks, tips, grain and possibly bird-seed; cultivated at R.B.G., Kew (Surrey). Med., SW Asia. BM, BRISTM, NMW, RNG, ?SLBI. D1, D18, D20*, D30, D75*, D115*, D117*, D133*, J1(8:182; 10:363), R36, R45, R55. *A.ovata* L. pro parte; *A.triaristata* Willd., nom. illeg.; *Triticum triaristatum* Gren. & Godr., nom. illeg.

peregrina (Hack.) Maire & Weiller
Pre-1930 only. A grain casual from Slateford and Leith docks (Midlothian) in 1906; rarely cultivated in several botanical gardens. N Africa, E Med., SW Asia. E, K(holotype), RNG, SLBI. D17*, D18, D20*, D133*, D177*, J36(1907:101-103; 1908*:105-106, t.3), J96*(28:84, 93), R36. *A.variabilis* Eig; *Triticum peregrinum* Hack. This species was described as new to science by E.Hackel from the Scottish material. *A.uniaristata* Vis. is incorrectly given as a synonym in ref.D1.

speltoides Tausch subsp. **ligustica** (Savign.) Zhuk.
- A casual of wool, grain, papermills and docks, established at Bristol for several years; cultivated in botanic gardens. E Med. BM, BRISTM, DBN, K, NMW, RNG. D49, D75*, D133*, J1(12:67,305), J10(28:386), J18(376:25), J96*(28:68), R2, R49. *A.ligustica* (Savign.) Coss.; *Agropyron ligusticum* Savign. A hybrid with *A.speltoides* subsp. *speltoides* was recorded from Blackmoor (N Hants) in 1970 in ref.R2.

speltoides Tausch subsp. **speltoides**
- A casual of wool and waste land; also a weed in R.B.G., Kew (Surrey). SE Europe, SW Asia. K, LTN, RNG. D1, D17*, D18, D22*, D49, D115*, D133*, J96*(28:68), R48, R88, R118. *A.bicornis* auct., non (Forssk.) Jaub. & Spach; *Triticum speltoides* (Tausch) Godr.

tauschii Coss.
- A casual of wool and docks; cultivated in botanic gardens. SW Asia. D18, D22*, D48*, D49, D133*, J10(38:45), J18(379:25), J96*(28:75-76), R65. *A.squarrosa* auct., non L.

triuncialis L.
- • A casual of wool, docks and wasteland; cultivated in botanic gardens. Med., SW Asia, (N America). BRISTM, K, LCN, OXF, RNG, SLBI. D1, D6*, D17*, D18, D20*, D22*, D31*, D75*, D89*, D115*, D117*, D118*, D133*, J1(7:1027; 8:592; 9:533; 12:305), R3, R23, R36, R49, R55. *A.squarrosa* L., non auct.; *Triticum triunciale* (L.) Raspail.

umbellulata Zhuk.
Pre-1930 only. Leith docks (Midlothian) in 1906, 1912. Crete, SW Asia. D1, D18, D22*, D48*, D133*, J96*(28:83).

vavilovii (Zhuk.) Chennav.
Pre-1930 only. A casual in Leith docks (Midlothian) in 1906-7. W Asia. K, RNG. D133*, J57*(23:85-178). *A.crassa* Boiss. subsp. *vavilovii* Zhuk.

ventricosa Tausch
- •• A casual of wool, ballast, docks and waste ground; cultivated in R.B.G.,
  Kew (Surrey). Med. BM, BRISTM, E, K(type), LIV, NMW, OXF, RNG,
  SLBI. D1, D20*, D31*, D75*, D115*, D117*, D133*, J1(8:143,284,592;
  9:533; 10:363), J96*(28:79), R23, R36, R100. *Triticum ventricosum* (Tausch)
  Ces., Pass. & Gibelli. Includes var. *comosa* (Coss. & Durieu) Eig. **Fig.4.**

CENTOTHECEAE

CHASMANTHIUM Link   251

6 species. Eastern USA, Mexico. Woodland and semi-arid scrub. Formerly
included in the genus *Uniola* L.

latifolium (Michx.) Link
- • On a tip near Ware (Herts) in 1977; rarely cultivated in gardens. Eastern
  USA, Mexico. HbCGH. D6*, D41*, D78*, R65. *Uniola latifolia* Michx.
  Fig.20.

ARUNDINEAE

TRIBOLIUM Desv.   255

c.10 species. S Africa. Dry bushland. The genus includes *Lasiochloa* Kunth.
See ref.J7(40:795-799).

echinatum (Thunb.) Renvoize
- • A wool casual. S Africa. BM, E, K, RNG. D5, D87, R2, R5, R51.
  Alopecurus echinatus Thunb.; *Lasiochloa ciliaris* Kunth; *L.echinata* (Thunb.)
  Henrard. The BM specimen, one of the earliest recorded wool aliens found
  near Chester and dating from 1872, ref.J1(1:142), was incorrectly determined
  as *Echinaria capitata*.

[**hispidum** (Thunb.) Renvoize
  A wool casual. S Africa. K. D5*, D87, R2. *Dactylis hispida* Thunb.;
  Lasiochloa longifolia (Schrad.) Kunth. This specimen has been re-determined
  as *T.echinatum*. **Fig.10.**]

DANTHONIA DC.   265

20 species. Europe, N and S America. Grassland and open woods. Includes
the genus *Sieglingia* Bernh. Most of the former species are placed in the genus
Rytidosperma.

montevidensis Hack. & Arechav.
- A wool casual. S America. K, HbCGH, HbTBR. D12*, D151*, R3.
Fig.21.

PENTASCHISTIS (Nees) Spach   **268**

c.65 species. Mainly S Africa; 6 species from Cameroun to Yemen and Tanzania; 3 species in Madagascar. Mountain heath. See ref.J83(12:1-123).

airoides (Nees) Stapf
- A wool casual. S Africa, (Australia). E, K, RNG. D5*, D8, D27*, D38, D87*, D93*, R1, R2, R5, R51, R86. *Pentameris airoides* Nees. **Fig.17.**

aristifolia Schweick.
- A wool casual. S Africa. HbTBR. D5, D87, R2. A non-flowering grass identified by C.E.Hubbard from the unique hair-like points to the fine leaves.

RYTIDOSPERMA Steud.   **272**

c.90 species. Mainly Australia, New Zealand and southern Africa; also Indonesia, Himalayas, Arabia, Ethiopia, Madagascar and Argentina. Mountain grassland, a few species descending to the lowlands. Previously included in the genus *Danthonia*, differing in the ciliate (not glabrous) lodicules and by having the hairs on the lemma in rows or tufts (not evenly distributed), see ref.J7(39:835-836).

caespitosum (Gaudich.) Connor & Edgar
- A wool casual. Australia. K, RNG. D8*, D10*, D24, D29, D38, D44*, D58*, D59*, D60*, D93*, R1, R3, R47. *Danthonia caespitosa* Gaudich.; *D.semiannularis* auct., non (Labill.) R.Br.; *Notodanthonia caespitosa* (Gaudich.) Zotov.

nudum (Hook.f.) Connor & Edgar
Pre-1930 only. A wool casual. New Zealand. E. D58*, J1(5:56), R4, R36. *Danthonia nuda* Hook.f.

penicillatum (Labill.) Connor & Edgar
- A wool casual. Australia. E, RNG. D10*, D24*, D38, D44*, D93*, R1, R3, R5, R38, R47, R118. *Arundo penicillata* Labill.; *Danthonia penicillata* (Labill.) P.Beauv.; *Notodanthonia penicillata* (Labill.) Zotov.

pilosum (R.Br.) Connor & Edgar
- A wool casual. Australia, (California, Hawaii). E, K, OXF. D7, D8*, D10*, D24, D27*, D29, D38, D44*, D58*, D59, D93*, D116*, D118*, J1(5:56), R3, R4, R36. *Danthonia pilosa* R.Br.; *Notodanthonia pilosa* (R.Br.) Zotov.

racemosum (R.Br.) Connor & Edgar var. **obtusatum** (F.Muell. ex Benth.) Connor & Edgar
- A wool casual. Australia. K. D7, D10*, D93*, R1, R3, R5. *Danthonia racemosa* var. *obtusata* F.Muell. ex Benth.; *Notodanthonia racemosa* var. *obtusata* (F.Muell. ex Benth.) Veldkamp.

racemosum (R.Br.) Connor & Edgar var. **racemosum**
•• A wool casual. Australia, (New Zealand). BM, CGE, E, K, LIV, LTN, OXF, RNG. D2*, D7, D8*, D10*, D26*, D29, D38, D58*, D93*, J18(376:25), R2, R5, R36, R48, R51. *Danthonia racemosa* R.Br.; *Notodanthonia racemosa* (R.Br.) Zotov.

semiannulare (Labill.) Connor & Edgar
Pre-1930 only. A wool casual. Australia. E, OXF. D7, D8*, D27*, D29, D38, D44*, D93*, D129*, R4, R36. *Arundo semiannularis* Labill.; *Danthonia semiannularis* (Labill.) R.Br.; *Notodanthonia semiannularis* (Labill.) Zotov. According to ref.J63(17:311-337), all New Zealand plants under this name refer to the endemic *R.unarede* (Raoul) Connor & Edgar (e.g. ref.D58*, D79*, D168*).

setaceum (R.Br.) Connor & Edgar
• A wool casual; also cultivated from wool. Australia. K, RNG, HbCGH. D7, D8*, D10*, D29, D38, D60*, D93*, R1, R2, R5, R65, R118. *Danthonia setacea* R.Br.; *Notodanthonia setacea* (R.Br.) Veldkamp.

thomsonii (Buchanan) Connor & Edgar
• A wool casual; also cultivated from wool. New Zealand. E, K, ?RNG, HbCGH. D58*, R3, R5, R65. *Danthonia thomsonii* Buchanan.

KARROOCHLOA Conert & Türpe   **272a**

5 species. Southern Africa. Grassy places. Closely related to the genus *Rytidosperma*.

[curva (Nees) Conert & Türpe
Cultivated from wool shoddy in 1954. Cape district of S Africa. BM. D5*, D87. *Danthonia curva* Nees.]

SCHISMUS P.Beauv.   **276**

5 species. S Africa; Med. and Middle East. Dry open places.

arabicus Nees
• A wool casual. E Med., SW Asia, (Australia, N America). K, LTN, ?RNG, HbCGH. D1, D2, D6*, D8, D17*, D18*, D20*, D43, D81*, D118*, R2, R48, R65. Easily confused with *S.barbatus*.

barbatus (L.) Thell.   Kelch-grass
•• A wool and esparto casual. Atlantic Is, Med., SW Asia, (widespread). BM, CGE, E, K, LTN, NMW, RNG. D1, D2*, D5*, D6*, D12*, D17*, D20*, D30*, D31*, D75*, D93*, D118*, J6(4:406), J15(108:34), R1, R2, R5, R47, R51, R86. *S.calycinus* (Loefl.) K.Koch; *S.marginatus* P.Beauv.; *Festuca barbata* L. **Fig.7.**

CORTADERIA Stapf   **288**

24 species. Mainly in S America, with 4 species in New Zealand and 1 in New Guinea. Hillsides, scrubland and ruderal sites. *C.selloana* (Pampas-grass) is a common garden ornamental grass. Ref.J52(23:595-605).

[jubata (Lem.) Stapf
A potential alien as it is much more aggressive than *C.selloana* and is reported to be self-fertile. Bolivia, Argentina, Ecuador, Peru, (N America, S Africa, New Zealand). D58*, D172*, J52(23:595-605), J67*(t.7607), J110*(15:179). *Gynerium jubatum* Lem. Fertile hybrids with other species have been reported.]

richardii (Endl.) Zotov
• Established on cliffs at Lyme Regis (Dorset), regenerating vigorously in 1993; self-sown tussock on steep slope above tip, SW of Pendinas, Aberystwyth (Cards) in 1993; Wokingham (Berks); wasteland at Llanelli (Carms) in 1994; perhaps increasing; cultivated in gardens. New Zealand, (Australia). NMW, RNG. D14, D47, D58*, D61, D188*, D189*, J16(58:26, 59:18), R7, R9, R33. *Arundo richardii* Endl. This species flowers from late June to August, about three months earlier than *C.selloana* and has a dingier white inflorescence, and often self-seeds. According to J84(110:138) much grown in Scotland. In the past it was usually misnamed as the New Zealand *C.conspicua* (G.Forst.) Stapf (*Chionochloa conspicua* (G.Forst.) Zotov), a handsome grass not yet recorded as an escape.

selloana (Schult. & Schult.f.) Asch. & Graebn.   **Pampas-grass**
•• Introduced or a garden escape on roadsides, railway banks and dunes in the south; well-established for over 60 years at St. Catherine, Jersey; naturalised on waste ground at Luton (Beds) in 1990; extensively naturalised and seeding on cliffs at Blackpool Sands near Dartmouth and on dunes at Instow (both S Devon) in 1994; increasing, and reliably reported to have produced seedlings (e.g. at Kew Bridge (Surrey) in 1978 (ref.R120) and at Englefield Green (Surrey) in 1981 (ref.R121), although as the species is virtually dioecious this must be of rare occurrence. S America, (widespread). BM, OXF, RNG. D1, D2, D6*, D12*, D15*, D19*, D21*, D26*, D58*, D93*, D118*, J1(12:64), J27(13:1972-1973), J29(11:73), R10, R23, R24, R36, R38, R40, R41, R42, R43, R45, R52, R68, R104, R118. *C.argentea* (Nees) Stapf; *Arundo selloana* Schult. & Schult.f.; *Gynerium argenteum* Nees. **Fig.14.**

ARUNDO L.   **290**

3 species. Med. to China, widely introduced. River banks and damp places. *A.donax* is grown for its canes.

donax L.
• A casual. Asia, (widespread). D1, D6*, D12*, D17*, J37(2:1938-1952), R23. **Fig.14.**

ARISTIDEAE

ARISTIDA L.   299

c.250 species. Tropics and warm temperate regions. Dry or weedy places.
Spikelets 1-flowered, usually with a trifid awn which is often raised on a
twisted column.

adscensionis L.
> •• A wool casual. Tropics, warm temperate regions. BM, K, OXF, RNG,
> SLBI. D1, D6*, D17*, D18*, D20*, D30*, D31, D41*, D81*, D89*, D115*,
> D118*, R1, R2, R5. *A.bromoides* Kunth. Includes *A.coerulescens* Desf.
> **Fig.11.**

benthamii Henrard
> • A wool casual. Australia. RNG. D7, D16*, D29, D93*, R3, R47.

congesta Roem. & Schult.
> • A wool casual. Arabia, E Africa from Med. to the Cape. K, RNG. D5*,
> D13, D37*, D98*, D134*, J58*(109-171), R2, R3, R5, R47, R65. One
> specimen was originally determined at Kew as *A.elytrophoides* Chiov. in error.

contorta F.Muell.
> • A wool casual. Australia. E, RNG. D7, D8, D10*, D16*, D27*, D38,
> D44*, D93*, R3, R5. *A.arenaria* Gaudich.

oligantha Michx.
> • A wool casual. N America. K, LIV, RNG. D6*, D23*, D40*, D41*,
> D42*, D53*, D89*, D118*, R2, R65.

ramosa R.Br.
> • A wool casual. Australia. E, K. D7, D26*, D44*, D93*, R3.

PAPPOPHOREAE

ENNEAPOGON Desv. ex P.Beauv.   301

28 species. Tropics and sub-tropics, especially Australia and Africa. Dry open
places in bush and semi-desert.

avenaceus (Lindl.) C.E.Hubb.
> • A wool casual. Australia. RNG. D7, D8, D10*, D16*, D27*, D38, D62*,
> D93*, J38(153:65), R3. *Pappophorum avenaceum* Lindl.

desvauxii P.Beauv.
> • A wool casual. Throughout Africa, extending eastwards through Arabia to
> India, China, N and S America. BM, E, K, LIV, RNG. D5*, D6*, D13,
> D17*, D20*, D37*, D41*, D43, D81*, D118*, D135*, D177*, R2, R3, R65.
> Includes *E.brachystachyus* (Jaub. & Spach) Stapf. **Fig.7.**

nigricans (R.Br.) P.Beauv.
> • A wool casual. Australia. RNG, HbTBR. D7, D8*, D16, D24*, D26*,
> D38, D44*, D93*, R2. *Pappophorum nigricans* R.Br.

SCHMIDTIA Steud.   302

2 species. Africa and Pakistan. Woodland or bushland on dry sandy soils. Differs from *Enneapogon* in the lemma having 5 awns alternating between 6 hyaline lobes (not 9 awns, unlobed).

kalihariensis Stent
- A wool casual. Northwestern S Africa to Chad and Sudan. BM, E, K, LIV, LTN, RNG.   D5*, D75*, D87, D144*, D145*, D146, J68(2:421-423), J85*(39:322), R1, R3, R5, R38, R47, R65. Usually written as *S.kalahariensis*, reflecting the correct spelling of the Kalahari Desert. A sour-smelling grass clothed with sticky glandular hairs. **Fig.7.**

ERAGROSTIDEAE

TRIRAPHIS R.Br.   324

8 species. Africa and Arabia; 1 species in Australia. Savanna, often in stony or sandy places. The curious disjunct distribution may indicate that the Australian species was an early alien introduced with sheep from Africa.

mollis R.Br.
- A wool casual. Australia, (New Guinea). BM, CGE, E, K, RNG. D7, D8*, D16*, D26*, D38, D93*, R1, R2, R5. Very similar to the Ethiopian endemic grass *T.compacta* Cope, see ref.J7(35:566). Now well-established in New Guinea, originally introduced by livestock according to ref.D169. **Fig.24.**

TRIDENS Roem. & Schult.   327

18 species. Eastern USA to Argentina; 1 species in Angola. Meadows and open woods.

brasiliensis Nees ex Steud.
- A wool casual. S America. E, K. D12*, D174*, R3. **Fig.24.**

MUNROA Torr.   335

5 species. USA and Mexico; Peru to Argentina. Dry plains.

squarrosa (Nutt.) Torr.   **False Buffalo-grass**
- A wool casual. USA, Mexico. E, K. D6*, D118*, D176, R3. *Crypsis squarrosa* Nutt. **Fig.18.**

LEPTOCHLOA P.Beauv.   337

c.40 species. Tropics; warm temperate America and Australia. Woodland and savanna, on dry or swampy soils; often a weed in disturbed places. Now includes the genus *Diplachne* P.Beauv.

ciliolata (Jedwabn.) S.T.Blake
- A wool casual. Australia. CGE, E, K, LIV, RNG. D7, D16*, D93*, D190*, R2, R5, R65. *L.debilis* Stapf ex C.E.Hubb. *Eragrostis ciliolata* Jedwabn.

decipiens (R.Br.) Stapf ex Maiden
- A wool casual. Australia. BM, CGE, E, K, RNG. D16, D26*, D29, D93*, D190*, R2, R5, R65. *Poa decipiens* R.Br.

divaricatissima S.T.Blake
- A wool casual. Australia. BM, E, K, RNG, SLBI. D7, D16, D93*, R2, R5, R65. The wool alien record of *L.squarrosa* Pilg. (from Tanzania, Madagascar) in BM, RNG (see ref.R1, R3) is an error for this species.

cf. **fascicularis** (Lam.) A.Gray
- A wool casual from Blackmoor (N Hants) in 1973-4. N and S America, Mexico. HbCGH, HbEJC. D6*, D12, D41*, D63*, D89*, D118*. *Diplachne fascicularis* (Lam.) P.Beauv.; *Festuca fascicularis* Lam.

fusca (L.) Kunth   Brown Beetle-grass
- •• A wool casual. Tropics, subtropics. BM, E, K, LTN, RNG, SLBI. D2*, D5*, D8*, D12, D13*, D17*, D20*, D26*, D27*, D37*, D75*, D81*, D89*, D93*, D135, J1(5:312; 12:303), R1, R2, R5, R20, R36, R38, R54, R65. *Diplachne fusca* (L.) P.Beauv. ex Roem. & Schult.; *D.malabarica* (L.) Merr.; *D.reptatrix* (L.) Druce; *Festuca fusca* L.; *F.reptatrix* L. This species bears a striking similarity to *Eragrostis plana*, with which it has often been confused, but has a long membranous ligule, not a short ciliate one. Some of the early records may be in error for *L.muelleri*. **Fig.14.**

muelleri (Benth.) Stace
- A wool casual. Australia. K, LIV, LTN, RNG, SLBI. D2, D8, D27*, D59, D93*, J23(18:413), R1, R2, R48, R65, R105. *Diplachne muelleri* Benth. Equated with *L.fusca* in ref.D7.

peacockii (Maiden & Betche) Domin
- A wool casual. Australia. E, K. D7, D16, D93*, R1, R3, R5. *Diplachne peacockii* Maiden & Betche.

uninervia (J.Presl) Hitchc. & Chase
- A casual of wool and bird-seed. N and S America. BM, K, SLBI, HbTBR. D2, D6*, D12*, D15*, D41*, D75*, D89*, D93*, D116*, D118, J23(14:230), R2, R5, R21, R38, R65, R88. *Diplachne uninervia* (J.Presl) Parodi; *Megastachya uninervia* J.Presl. The plant recorded as *D.fusca* from Brislington tip, Bristol in 1978 in ref.J10(38:45) has been re-determined as this species.

ERAGROSTIS Wolf   356

c.350 species. Tropics and subtropics. In most habitats, especially dry weedy places. *E.tef* (Teff) is grown as a cereal in Ethiopia, and *E.curvula* (African Love-grass) is cultivated for pasture. **Key on p.119.**

[articulata (Schrank) Nees
   A wool casual. Tropical S America. RNG. D63, D151*, R34. *Poa articulata* Schrank. Probably an error for *E.schweinfurthii*.]
aspera (Jacq.) Nees
   • A wool casual. Tropical and S Africa, India. BM, RNG. D5*, D13*, D37*, D89*, D135*, R34. *Poa aspera* Jacq.
atrovirens (Desf.) Trin. ex Steud.
   • A wool casual. Africa, S Asia, (becoming widespread). K, RNG. D5*, D13, D36*, D37*, D89*, D121*, R2, R34. *E.biformis* (Kunth) Benth.; *Poa atrovirens* Desf. This species, alien in USA, was incorrectly named in ref.D6* as *E.chariis* (Schult.) Hitchc., which is a synonym for *E.nutans* (Retz.) Steud., a different SE Asian species.
bahiensis Schrad. ex Schult.
   • A wool casual. S America, (Australia, N America). K, SLBI, HbTBR. D6*, D12, D15*, D63*, R2, R34. *E.atrovirens* auct., non (Desf.) Trin. ex Steud.; including var. *contracta* Döll (also in HbTBR). Very similar to *E.atrovirens*, but with 2 (not 3) anthers per floret.
barbinodis Hack.
   • A wool casual. S Africa, (E Africa). K. D5*, D13, R2, R34.
barrelieri Daveau
   •• A casual of docks and wool. Med., W Asia, (widespread). BM, BRISTM, E, K, LTN, NMW, RNG. D2, D5*, D6*, D8*, D15*, D17*, D20*, D22*, D30*, D31*, D41*, D89*, D93*, D115*, D117*, D118*, J1(8:37; 10:361), J15(108:34), R1, R3, R34, R36, R65, R86.
benthamii Mattei
   • A wool casual. Australia. E. K, RNG. D7, D10*, D29, D181*, D190, R2, R5, R34. *E.brownii* var. *patens* Benth.; *E.philippica* Jedwabn.
bicolor Nees
   • A wool casual. S Africa. E, RNG. D5*, R3, R34.
brownii (Kunth) Nees ex Hook. & Arn.
   • A wool casual. Australia, (New Zealand, Hawaii). E, K, LTN, RNG, SLBI. D2, D7, D8*, D10*, D16, D27*, D29, D38, D44*, D93*, D116, R1, R2, R5, R34, R65. *Poa brownii* Kunth (corrected from *P.brownei*). The name *E.brownii* auct. has also been used to describe several different species from India, SE Asia and USA.
caesia Stapf
   • A wool casual. S Africa. E. D5*, R3, R5, R34.
capillaris (L.) Nees
   • A wool casual at Blackmoor (N Hants) in 1971; also on the canal bank at Aintree (S Lancs) in 1914. N America. HbTBR. D6*, D40*, D41*, D42*, D53*, D75*, J1(5:56), R34, R36, R66. *Poa capillaris* L. More recently the wool alien *E.trachycarpa* has been misnamed as this species.
chloromelas Steud.
   •• A wool casual. S Africa, (Australia). BM, CGE, E, K, LIV, NMW, OXF, RNG, SLBI. D5*, D6, D14, D24, D29, J1(4:218), J18(376:25), R1,

R2, R4, R5, R23, R34, R36, R65. Considered by some authors, including
ref.D2, D13, to be a form of *E.curvula*.

cilianensis (All.) Vignolo ex Janch.   Stink-grass

●●● A casual of wool, grain, docks, bird-seed and oil-seed. Med., Asia,
(widespread). BEL, BM, BRISTM, CGE, DBN, E, K, LIV, LTN, NMW,
OXF, RNG, SLBI. D1, D2*, D5*, D6*, D12*, D13*, D15*, D17*, D19*,
D20*, D22*, D37*, D75*, D81*, D89*, D93*, D115*, D117*, D118*,
J1(10:361; 12:65,83), J8(35:14), J10(28:313; 38:45), J23(1:261; 14:229),
J26(57:30), R1, R2, R5, R21, R24, R34, R36, R38, R44, R54, R68, R86,
R88, R113. *E.major* Host; *E.megastachya* (Koeler) Link; *Briza eragrostis* L.;
Poa cilianensis All.; *P.megastachya* Koeler. **Fig.24.**

curvula (Schrad.) Nees   African Love-grass

●● A wool and dock casual; well established on ballast of an old railway track
beside a road at Southampton (S Hants) in 1989; several clumps established and
setting good seed in disused railway yard at Feltham (Middlesex) in 1995.
S Africa, (widespread). BM, CGE, E, K, LIV, LTN, NMW, OXF, RNG,
SLBI. D2*, D5*, D6*, D12, D15, D21*, D27*, D42*, D89*, D93*, D117*,
D118*, J1(5:314,847), J8*(63:1,28-30), J23(19:153), R1, R2, R3, R34, R38,
R48, R51, R65, R105. *Poa curvula* Schrad.; includes *E.curvula* subsp.
conferta Nees; *E.subulata* Nees.

dielsii Pilg. ex Diels & E.Pritz.

● A wool casual. Australia. BM, CGE, E, K, LIV, LTN, NMW, RNG. D7,
D8*, D10*, D27*, D38, D93*, R1, R2, R5, R34, R54, R65. *E.falcata*
Benth., non (Gaudich.) Gaudich. ex Steud. **Fig.18.**

echinochloidea Stapf

● A wool casual. S Africa, (Palestine). K, RNG. D5*, D17*, D106*, R2,
R34.

elongata (Willd.) J.Jacq.

● A wool casual. Tropical Asia, Australia. RNG. D7, D8*, D10*, D16,
D27*, D29, D38, D93*, R3, R34. *E.diandra* (R.Br.) Steud.; *Poa diandra*
R.Br.; *P.elongata* Willd.

[**falcata** (Gaudich.) Gaudich. ex Steud.
A wool casual. Australia. BM. D7, D8, D10*, D27*, D62*, D93*, R34.
Poa falcata Gaudich. A dubious record, probably immature *E.dielsii* or
E.lacunaria. Not to be confused with *E.falcata* Benth., a synonym of
E.dielsii.]

glandulosipedata De Winter

● A wool casual. Southern Africa. K, HbTBR. D106*, J39(11:169-286), R2,
R34.

heteromera Stapf

● A wool casual. Tropical and S Africa. HbTBR. D5*, D13*, D36*, D62*,
D87, D106*, R3, R34. Includes *E.wilmsii* Stapf.

kennedyae F.Turner

● A wool casual. Australia. E, K. D7, D8*, D10*, D93*, R3, R34.

kiwuensis Jedwabn.
- A wool casual. E tropical Africa, Ethiopia, Yemen. E, K, RNG. D13*, D36*, D37*, D178, J86*(40/1:t.67), R2, R34.

lacunaria F.Muell. ex Benth.
- A wool casual. Australia. BM, CGE, E, K, LIV, RNG. D7, D8, D10*, D38, D62*, D64*, D93*, R2, R5, R34, R65.

lehmanniana Nees
- A wool casual. S Africa, (E Africa, N America). BM, CGE, E, K, NMW, RNG, SLBI. D2, D5*, D6, D13, D41, D87*, D106*, D118*, R2, R5, R34, R65, R105.

leptocarpa Benth.
- A wool casual. Australia. K. D7, D8*, D10*, D62*, D93*, R3, R34.

leptostachya (R.Br.) Steud.
- A wool casual. Australia. BM, E, K, LIV, RNG. D7, D16, D26*, D29, D93*, D190*, R1, R2, R5, R34, R65, R86. *Poa leptostachya* R.Br.

lugens Nees
- A wool casual. N and S America. E, K, LIV, RNG. D2, D6*, D12*, D15*, D41, D63*, D174*, R2, R5, R34, R65. *E.flaccida* Lindm.

macilenta (A.Rich.) Steud.
- A wool casual. Tropical Africa. BM(cultivated), E, K, RNG. D13*, D36*, D37*, R2, R5, R34. *Poa macilenta* A.Rich.

[**mexicana** (Hornem.) Link
A wool casual, but needs confirmation. N and S America, (Australia). K(origin unknown). D6*, D10*, D14, D29, D38, D41, D53, D75*, D89*, D93*, D118, J62(58:377-381), R34, R47, R118. *Poa mexicana* Hornem. Very close to *E.neomexicana*.]

microcarpa Vickery
- A wool casual. Australia. E, RNG. D7, D10*, D93*, R3, R34.

minor Host   Small Love-grass
- ●●● A casual of wool, waste ground, docks, bird-seed and grain. Med., Asia, (widespread). BM, BRISTM, CGE, E, K, LIV, LTN, OXF, RNG, SLBI. D1, D2*, D6*, D13, D17*, D19*, D39*, D40*, D42*, D75*, D81*, D89*, D115*, D117*, D118*, J1(9:378; 10:361), J23(1:242), R1, R2, R5, R8, R34, R36, R40, R47, R65, R86, R92, R107. *E.eragrostis* (L.) P.Beauv., nom. inval.; *E.poiformis* Link; *E.pooides* P.Beauv. (corrected from *E.poaeoides*); *Poa eragrostis* L. The record in ref.J1(12:65) was an error for *E.pilosa*.

molybdea Vickery
- A wool casual. Australia. LTN, HbTBR. D7, D10*, D16, D29, D93*, R2, R34, R48, R105.

neesii Trin.
- A wool casual. S America. E, K, LIV, RNG. D12*, D15*, D63, D174*, R2, R5, R34, R65.

neomexicana Vasey ex L.H.Dewey
- ●● A casual of wool, tips, docks and bird-seed. N America, (S America, Australia). BM, K, LTN, NMW, RNG. D2, D6*, D10*, D12*, D15*, D42*,

J8(28:18; 33*:1),   J10(38:45),   J18(385:35),   J23(14:229),   J26(58:63),
J62(58:377-381), R2, R21, R34, R38, R44, R65, R88, R105. Some authors
(e.g. ref.D93*, D118, D143) consider this species to be conspecific with
E.mexicana.

obtusa Munro ex Stapf
* A wool casual. S Africa. BM, K, LIV, RNG. D5*, R1, R2, R5, R34,
R65. *Briza geniculata* Thunb.

[**paniciformis** (A.Braun) Steud.
Pre-1930 only. A garden weed in Oxford in 1861. Tropical Africa. BM.
D13*, D36*, D37*, J86*(40/1:t.64).   *Poa paniciformis* A.Braun.   An
extremely dubious record.]

parviflora (R.Br.) Trin.   Weeping Love-grass
•• A wool casual. Australia. BM, CGE, E, K, LIV, LTN, NMW, OXF,
RNG. D2*, D7, D8, D10*, D16, D29, D38, D44*, D45*(as *E.pilosa*), D75*,
D93*, R1, R2, R5, R34, R51, R54, ?R55, R65, R86.   *E.pelucida* (R.Br.)
Steud.; *E.pilosa* Benth., non (L.) P.Beauv.; *Poa parviflora* R.Br.   Not
conspecific with *E.virescens*, as suggested in ref.D2.

patentissima Hack.
* A wool casual. S Africa. K, RNG, HbTBR. D5*, R2, R34, R65.

pectinacea (Michx.) Nees
* A casual of wool and docks. N and C America, (France, S America). BM,
BRISTM, E, K, NMW, OXF, RNG. D2, D6*, D12, D23*, D40*, D42*,
D53*, D77*, D89*, D115*, D116, D118*, J1(12:65), J10(28:313; 30:20), R5,
R34.   *E.caroliniana* (Spreng.) Scribn.; *E.diffusa* Buckley (see ref.D77);
E.nigricans (Kunth) Steud.; *Poa caroliniana* Spreng.; *P.pectinacea* Michx.
Confused with *E.pilosa*, with which it may be conspecific.

pergracilis S.T.Blake
* A wool casual. Australia. K. D7, D10*, D93*, R3.

pilosa (L.) P.Beauv.   Jersey Love-grass
•• A casual of wool, bird-seed, oil-seed, grain and wasteland; established since
at least 1921 near Millbrook, and in a garden and greenhouse at St Ouen, both
in Jersey. Eurasia, N Africa, (widespread). BM, BRISTM, CGE, E, K, OXF,
RNG. D1, D2, D6*, D12*, D15*, D17*, D19*, D20*, D23*, D42*, D81*,
D89*, D93*, D115*, D118*, J1(10:361; 11:518), J6(1:66), J10(1943),
J23(1:242), R2, R5, R12, R20, R21, R34, R40, R42, R65, R68.
E.damiensiana (Bonnet) Thell.; *E.multispicula* Kitag.; *E.peregrina* Wiegand;
Poa pilosa L. Includes *E.multicaulis* Steud. (see ref.D77*): although many
authors have maintained this as a distinct species, none of the supposed
taxonomic differences seem to work in practice.   Recorded in error for
E.virescens, see ref.J18(376:26).

plana Nees
* A wool casual. Tropical and S Africa. BM, E, NMW, RNG. D2, D5*,
D65, D75, D82*, D139*, R2, R34, R65. *Diplachne hackeliana* Thell., a wool
alien from Galashiels (Selkirks) supposedly new to science in E (see
ref.J53(14:213), R4, R13, R36), has now been re-determined as this species

(ref.R116). Very closely resembles *Leptochloa fusca*, which has a membranous (not a ciliate) ligule.

planiculmis Nees
- • A wool casual from Blackmoor (N Hants) in 1971 and Flitwick (Beds) in 1985; also probably cultivated from wool. S Africa. BM, K, HbTBR. D5, D65, J18(409:39), R2, R34, R65, R118.

procumbens Nees
- • A wool casual. S Africa. LTN, RNG. D5*, D65, R2, R5, R34, R48, R65, R118.

[**racemosa** (Thunb.) Steud.
A wool casual. Tropical and southern Africa. E, RNG. D5*, D13*, D36*, D37*, R2, R34. *Poa racemosa* Thunb. Probably in error for *E.schweinfurthii*.]

rotifer Rendle
- • A wool casual. Southern Africa. K. D5*, D13*, D65, D106*, R3, R34. *E.margaritacea* Stapf.

schweinfurthii Chiov.
- • A wool casual. E tropical Africa, Arabia, Sri Lanka. E, K, RNG. D13, D37*, D100*, D178, R2, R3, R34, R48, R65. Previously confused with *E.articulata* and *E.racemosa*. The small difference from *E.kiwuensis* is keyed out in ref.D178.

[cf. **setifolia** Nees
A wool casual. Australia. D7, D8, D10*, D27*, D59*, D62*, D93*, R34. Unconfirmed; possibly re-determined as immature *E.dielsii* or *E.lacunaria*.]

tef (Zucc.) Trotter   Teff
- •• A casual of wool, also cultivated from bird-seed; a garden escape. NE Africa, SW Asia, (S Africa, India, Australia). BM, CGE, E, K, LIV, NMW, RNG. D2*, D5*, D13*, D36*, D37*, D75*, R1, R2, R21, R34, R51. *E.abyssinica* (Jacq.) Link; *Poa abyssinica* Jacq.; *P.tef* Zucc.

tenuifolia (A.Rich.) Hochst. ex Steud.
- • A wool casual. NE Africa, W Asia, (widespread). K, RNG. D10*, D13*, D16*, D36, D37*, D89*, D93*, R2, R34, ?R65. *Poa tenuifolia* A.Rich.

trachycarpa (Benth.) Domin
- • A wool casual. Australia. BM, CGE, E, K, LIV, LTN, NMW, RNG. D2, D7, D10*, D16, D24, D29, D38, D64*, D93*, R2, R34, R47, R65. *E. nigra* Nees ex Steud. var. *trachycarpa* Benth.

trichophora Coss. & Durieu
- • A wool casual. N and S Africa. RNG, HbTBR. D5*, D20*, D31, R2, R3, R34, R51. *E.atherstonei* Stapf.

[**verticillata** (Cav.) P.Beauv.
A casual, recorded by J.E.Lousley. Spain. RNG. D137*, R34. *Poa verticillata* Cav. Apparently a form of *E.pilosa* according to ref.D138, S12.]

virescens J.Presl
- •• A casual of wool and tips; also cultivated from bird-seed; an occasional weed in the grass order beds at R.B.G., Kew (Surrey). S America,

(widespread). BM, K, LIV, LTN, RNG. D5, D6, D12*, D15*, D89*, D117*,
J18(334:22; 376:26), J62(58:377-381), R2, R21, R34, R48. According to
ref.D143 synonymous with the very variable *E.mexicana*, but not so considered
here. Wrongly equated in ref.D2 to *E.pectinacea*.
wilmaniae C.E.Hubb. & Schweick.
• A wool casual. S Africa. HbTBR. D5*, R2, R34. *E.macrochlamys* Pilg.
var. *wilmaniae* (C.E.Hubb. & Schweick.) De Winter.

HARPACHNE Hochst. ex A.Rich.   **366**

2 species. E and NE Africa. Open grassland.

schimperi Hochst. ex A.Rich.
• A wool casual. Arabia, E and NE Africa. BM, K, RNG. D13*, D37*,
D86*, J87(74:236), R1, R2. **Fig.18.**

ELEUSINE Gaertn.   **370**

9 species. Mostly from E and NE tropical Africa, 1 species from S America
and 1 species a cosmopolitan weed of warm climates. Savanna and upland
grass. *E.coracana* (Finger Millet or Ragi) is widely grown as a cereal in
Africa, India and China. Ref.J7(27:251-270).

coracana (L.) Gaertn.   **Finger Millet**
1930 only. A dock casual; also cultivated from bird-seed. Origin obscure,
cultivated in Africa, Asia, N America and Australia. BRISTM. D5*, D6,
D20*, D36*, D37*, D55*, D67*, D75, D81*, D89*, D115, D129*, J1(9:286;
10:359, re-determined), J10(29:352). *E. indica* var. *coracana* (L.) Ridley;
Cynosurus coracanus L. Derived from *E.indica*, with which hybrids readily
occur in crops, and possibly conspecific with subsp. *africana* (see
ref.J62(76:410-411).
floccifolia (Forssk.) Spreng.
• A wool casual. NE Africa, Yemen, (Kenya). K. D13, D37*, R1.
Cynosurus floccifolius Forssk.
indica (L.) Gaertn. subsp. **africana** (Kenn.-O'Byrne) S.Phillips
•• A casual of wool, tips and bird-seed. Tropical Africa. BM, BRISTM,
CGE, K, LTN, NMW, RNG. D2*, D36*, J1(10:359,re-determined), J6(3:50),
J10(29:352), R1, R2, R5, R21, R38, R47, R51, R55, R86, R93. *E.africana*
Kenn.-O'Byrne. Until quite recently included in subsp. *indica*. **Fig.18.**
indica (L.) Gaertn. subsp. **indica**
•• A casual of ballast, docks, grain, bird-seed, cotton and oil-seed; a
greenhouse weed at Câtel in Guernsey. Tropics and subtropics. BM,
BRISTM, CGE, E, NMW, RNG, SLBI. D2, D36*, D63*, D75*. D81*,
D89*, D93*, D115*, D116*, D118*, J1(5:54,257), J5(1858), J8(18:10; 34:33),
J10(30:19; 47:31), J18(397:34), J26(56:85), J41(6:86), R5, R8, R11, R12,
R20, R21, R36, R38, R42, R45, R57, R65, R66, R107. *Cynosurus indicus* L.

multiflora Hochst. ex A.Rich.   **Fat-spiked Yard-grass**
•• A wool casual; also cultivated from bird-seed. Arabia, Ethiopia, E tropical Africa, (Mexico). ABD, BM, CGE, E, K, LTN, NMW, RNG. D2, D5, D37*, D78*, D143, R1, R2, R5, R54, R65, R86.

tristachya (Lam.) Lam.   **American Yard-grass**
• A wool and bird-seed casual. S America, (widespread). BM, CGE, E, K, LIV, LTN, RNG. D1, D2, D5, D6, D8*, D12*, D15*, D24*, D26*, D75, D93*, D115*, D118, J18(394:36), R2, R5, R21, R48, R65, R105. *E.italica* Terr.; *Cynosurus tristachyus* Lam.

DACTYLOCTENIUM Willd.   373

13 species. E Africa and India, 1 species a pantropical weed and 1 species confined to Australia. Dry sandy or saline soils.

aegyptium (L.) Willd.
• A greenhouse weed at Pulborough (W Sussex) in 1961. Pre-1930, possibly a wool or dock alien, but the Bristol record, ref.J1(4:287), was an error for *D.radulans* (see ref.J10(1948:207), and the other record from Stalybridge (S Lancs) in 1914 needs confirmation; also cultivated from bird-seed. Tropics and subtropics of Africa and Asia, (widespread). RNG, HbCGH. D1, D5*, D6*, D13, D17*, D18*, D20*, D75*, D81*, D89*, D93*, D115*, D116*, R21, R36, R66. *Cynosurus aegyptius* L.; published as *D.aegyptiacum* (L.) Willd.; *Eleusine aegyptia* (L.) Desf. published as *E.aegyptica*.

radulans (R.Br.) P.Beauv.   **Button-grass**
•• A wool casual. Australia. BM, BRISTM, CGE, E, K, LTN, NMW, RNG. D2*, D8*, D16*, D29, D38, D93*, J10(?1948:207), R1, R2, R5, R20, R38, R54, R65, R88, R102. *D.aegyptium* var. *radulans* (R.Br.) Hack.; *Eleusine radulans* R.Br. **Fig.7.**

SPOROBOLUS R.Br.   377

c.160 species. Tropics and subtropics. Mostly growing in dry open places subject to grazing, but also on heavy clay or saline soils. **Key on p.125.**

africanus (Poir.) Robyns & Tournay   **African Dropseed**
•• A wool casual. Tropical and S Africa, Arabia, ?Sri Lanka, (Australasia, Hawaii). BM, CGE, E, K, LTN, NMW, RNG. D2*, D5*, D8*, D16, D26*, D27*, D37*, D38, D44*, D116, D129*, R1, R2, R5, R47, R65. *S.capensis* (Willd.) Kunth; *S.indicus* var. *africanus* (Poir.) Jovet & Guédès; *S.indicus* var. *capensis* (P.Beauv.) Peter; *Agrostis africana* Poir.; *Vilfa capensis* (Willd.) P.Beauv. **Fig.22.**

asper (Michx.) Kunth
• A wool casual. N America. K, HbTBR. D6*, D41*, J21*(34:1-24), R3. *Agrostis aspera* Michx.

caroli Mez
- A wool casual; also cultivated from wool. Australia. E, RNG, HbTBR. D8*, D16*, D27*, D38, D62*, D93*, R2, R5, R65. *S.lindleyi* (Steud.) Benth. pro parte.

creber De Nardi
- A wool casual. Australia. K. D10*, D93*, D190, R3. *S.indicus* var. *creber* (De Nardi) Veldkamp. Confused with *S.elongatus*.

cryptandrus (Torr.) A.Gray
- A wool casual. N and S America, Mexico (Europe). BM(cultivated), K, LIV, RNG, SLBI. D6*, D12, D23*, D40*, D41*, D42*, D53*, D75*, D118*, D153*, J21*(34:1-24), J32(52:125-126), J111*(59:117-134), R2, R3, R65. *Agrostis cryptandra* Torr. Now considered synonymous with the S American *S.subinclusus* Phil. (see ref.D12, D52, D72).

elongatus R.Br.
- •• A wool casual. Australia. BM, E, K, LIV, RNG. D2, D8*, D10*, D16*, D24*, D29*, D93*, D111*, D149*, R1, R2, R5, R65, R86.

cf. **engleri** Pilg.
- A wool casual. S Africa. RNG. D5, D106*, R3.

fimbriatus (Trin.) Nees
- A wool casual. Tropical and S Africa. K, ?LTN, NMW, RNG, SLBI. D5*, D13, D86*, D106*, R2, R48, R65. *Vilfa fimbriata* Trin.

indicus (L.) R.Br.
- A casual of wool, oil-seed and soya waste, also cultivated from soya waste. Tropics and subtropics of N and S America, (widespread). BM, K, OXF, RNG. D1, D2, D6*, D12*, D15*, D17*, D41*, D75*, D89*, D115*, D116*, D118, J1(5:312; 6:320), R3, R36, R65. *S.berteroanus* (Trin.) Hitchc. & Chase; *S.poiretii* (Roem. & Schult.) Hitchc.; *S.tenacissimus* auct., non (L.) R.Br.; *Agrostis indica* L.; *Axonopus poiretii* Roem. & Schult.; *Vilfa tenacissima* Kunth. Confused with *S.africanus*.

cf. **ioclados** (Nees ex Trin.) Nees
- A wool casual. Africa, Arabia, Pakistan, India. BM, RNG. D5, D13, D37*, D82*, D106*, R1. *S.marginatus* Hochst. ex A.Rich.; *Vilfa ioclados* Nees ex Trin.

mitchellii (Trin.) C.E.Hubb. ex S.T.Blake
- A wool casual. Malasia, Australia. K, LIV, RNG. D8*, D10, D16, D27*, D38, D59*, D62*, D93*, R2, R65. *S.benthamii* F.Muell.; *Vilfa mitchellii* Trin.

[**panicoides** A.Rich.
Possibly a casual; also cultivated from bird-seed in BM, and in a garden in LIV. Africa. D5*, D13*, D37*, D82*, D98*, D106*, R21.]

pyramidatus (Lam.) Hitchc.
Pre-1930 only. Tropical and subtropical America. D6*, D12, D15*, D40*, D41*, D53, D63*, J1(7:457,1025), R23, R36. *S.argutus* (Nees) Kunth; *Agrostis pyramidata* Lam.; *Vilfa arguta* Nees. In ref.D5 this grass is wrongly given as native in S Africa, in error for *S.coromandelinus* (Retz.) Kunth from

the Old World tropics, see ref.D13, D82. Not to be confused with the common tropical African *S.pyramidalis* P.Beauv.

CRYPSIS Ait.   378

8 species. Med. and the Middle East, extending to China and central Africa; naturalized in S Africa and America. Wet, often saline, soils.

aculeata (L.) Ait.
Pre-1930 only. A grain casual. Eurasia, N Africa, (N America). BM. D1, D17*, D18, D19*, D20*, D22*, D25*, D31*, D81*, D115*, D117*, J1(7:1025), ?J40(3:336), R8, R23, R36.   *Pallasia aculeata* (L.) Druce; *Schoenus aculeatus* L.

schoenoides (L.) Lam.
Pre-1930 only. A ballast, grain and dock casual. Eurasia, N and E tropical Africa, (N America). K.   D1, D6*, D13*, D17*, D18, D20*, D22*, D31, D32*, D40*, D42*, D75*, D115*, D117*, D118*, J1(7:1026), J39(45:88), R8, R36, R62.   *Heleochloa schoenoides* (L.) Host ex Roem.; *Phleum schoenoides* L. Also listed for Surrey by C.E.Salmon (ref.R96), but according to A.C.Leslie (ref.R44) this record may be the ?*C.aculeata* previously listed by J.A.Brewer (ref.R106) which was based on ref.J40(3:336). **Fig.23.**

MUHLENBERGIA Schreb.   381

c.160 species. New World, especially southern USA and Mexico; c.8 species in southern Asia. Habitat variable, but commonly in dry open grassland in warm climates. The genus is sometimes misspelt as *Muehlenbergia*.

cf. **distichophylla** (J.Presl) Kunth
Pre-1930 only. A fodder grass. Mexico. BM. D85, D91, D97, D104*, D143, D176, D185, R23.   *Podosemum distichophyllum* J.Presl.   Close to *M.emersleyi* Vasey.

[**frondosa** (Poir.) Fernald
A weedy species that has occurred in NW Europe and may have been overlooked. N America, (N Italy). D6*, D41*, D75, D115*.   *M.mexicana* auct., non (L.) Trin.; *Agrostis frondosa* Poir.]

racemosa (Michx.) Britton, Sterns & Pogg.
• A casual; Glasgow in 1921; Isle of Barra in 1939; also cultivated for many years in R.B.G., Kew (Surrey). N America. K, OXF. D6*, D23*, D40*, D41*, D42*, D75*, J1(6:321), R36.   *M.glomerata* Trin.; *Agrostis racemosa* Michx. **Fig.23.**

schreberi J.F.Gmel.
• A wool casual from Blackmoor (N Hants) in 1970.   N and S America, Mexico, (N Italy). K. D6*, D12*, D15*, D40*, D41*, D42*, D89*, D115*, D118, D151*, D174*, J88(144:117), R2.   *M.diffusa* Willd.

CYNODONTEAE

ASTREBLA F.Muell.   **386**

4 species. Australia. Dry grassland.

lappacea (Lindl.) Domin
- A wool casual. Australia. RNG. D7, D8*, D16*, D62*, D93*, D94.
A.triticoides (Lindl.) F.Muell. ex Benth.; *Danthonia lappacea* Lindl.;
D.triticoides Lindl. **Fig.23.**

CHLORIS Sw.   **391**

c.50 species. Tropical and warm temperate regions. Mainly in short grassland
and disturbed places. *C.gayana* Kunth (Rhodes-grass) is an important tropical
forage grass. Ref.J104(29:1-133).

divaricata R.Br.   **Australian Rhodes-grass**
- • A wool casual. Australia. BM, CGE, E, K, LTN, RNG. D2, D7, D10*,
D16*, D27*, D29, D93*, J59*(1:41-46), R1, R2, R5, R36, R47, R65, R93.
pectinata Benth.
- A wool casual. Australia. BM, K, NMW, RNG. D7, D8*, D10*, D62*,
D93*, R2. *C.divaricata* var. *minor* J.M.Black.
pumilio R.Br.
- A wool casual. Australia. K, HbTBR. D7, D57*, D69*, R2.
pycnothrix Trin.
- A wool casual. Tropical Africa, (S America). BM(cultivated), K, RNG.
D5*, D13, D36*, D37*, D63*, D89*, D129*, J59*(1:41-46), R1, R3, R5.
C.beyrichiana Kunth. The critical differences from the similar species
C.radiata have been given by S.A.Renvoize in ref.D63.
radiata (L.) Sw.
- A cotton and possible wool casual; cotton dump at Oldham (S Lancs) in
1961. Tropical America. K, RNG. D6, D11*, D63, D75, D78*, D87,
D172*, R36. *Agrostis radiata* L. The early wool-alien record from Cheshire
in ref.J4(1:142), R8 at BM has been re-determined as *C.truncata*. Misspelt as
C.radicata in ref.R8.
truncata R.Br.   **Windmill-grass**
- • A wool casual. Australia. BM, CGE, E, K, LIV, LTN, NMW, RNG.
D2*, D7, D8*, D10*, D16*, D24*, D26*, D27*, D29, D38, D44*, D75*,
D93*, J59*(1:41-46), R1, R2, R4, R5, R36, R38, R54, R65, R86. Grown as
an ornamental grass in Europe and USA. **Fig.23.**
ventricosa R.Br.
- A wool casual. Australia. BM, BRISTM, E, K, RNG. D6, D7, D10*,
D16*, D29, D38, D64*, D93*, J10(?1948:207), R1, R2, R5, R36, R65, R88.
The putative hybrid with *C.truncata* in K resembles pure *C.truncata*. Grown
as an ornamental grass in USA.

virgata Sw.   Feathery Rhodes-grass
•• A casual of wool, docks and tips. Tropics and subtropics. BM, BRISTM,
E, K, LIV, LTN, NMW, RNG. D2, D5*, D6*, D7, D8*, D10*, D12*,
D16*, D17*, D20*, D27*, D41*, D63*, D75*, D81*, D89*, D93*, D116*,
D118, J1(1858; 5:312), J10(30:19), J15(108:34), J23(2:59), J59*(1:41-46), R1,
R2, R36, R38, R54, R65, R86, R107. *C.barbata* (L.) Sw. var. *decora* (Nees
ex Steud.) Benth.; *C.compressa* DC.; *C.elegans* Kunth.

ENTEROPOGON Nees   396

c.22 species. Tropics and temperate Australia. Short grass savanna. Often
confused with *Chloris*, but differing in the dorsally compressed (not subterete)
grain and dorsally (not laterally) compressed lemma.

acicularis (Lindl.) Lazarides
• A wool casual. Australia. BM, K, NMW, RNG. D7, D8*, D10*, D16*,
D27*, D29, D38, D62*, D93*, J14(97:113), R1, R2. *Chloris acicularis* Lindl.
Includes *E.ramosus* B.K.Simon. **Fig.13.**

SCHEDONNARDUS Steud.   402

1 species. N America, introduced to Argentina. Prairies. A tumbleweed
grass.

paniculatus (Nutt.) Trel.   Tumble-grass
• A wool casual. N America, (Argentina). BM, RNG, HbTBR. D6*, D12*,
D23*, D40*, D41*, D42*, D53*, R2, R65. *Lepturus paniculatus* Nutt. **Fig.17.**

CYNODON Rich.   409

c.8 species. Old World tropics; 1 species pantropical and extending into warm
temperate regions. Inhabited, grazed or weedy places. *C.dactylon* (Bermuda-
grass, Star-grass, Dhub) is the commonest tropical lawn grass. Other species
are used for lawns or forage.

aethiopicus Clayton & J.R.Harlan
• A wool casual. Africa, (Australia). K, HbTBR. D7, D13*, D37*, D82,
D190*, R3.
dactylon (L.) Pers.   Bermuda-grass
••• A casual of tips, docks and wool; introduced long ago and now very well
established, or possibly native, in a few sandy maritime localities in
SW England, S Wales and the Channel Islands; also established in several
inland places, e.g. Reigate Heath and R.B.G., Kew (both Surrey); also
cultivated from bird-seed. Tropics and warm temperate regions worldwide.
BEL, BM, BRISTM, CGE, E, K, LTN, NMW, OXF, RNG, TOR. D1, D2*,
D3*, D4, D19*, D37*, D75*, D89*, D93*, D115*, R8, R21, R86. *Capriola
dactylon* (L.) Kuntze; *Panicum dactylon* L. One of the commonest grasses in
the world.

incompletus Nees var. **hirsutus** (Stent) de Wet & J.R.Harlan
- •• A wool casual. S Africa, (Australia, Argentina, Uruguay). BM, K, RNG. D5*, D7, D12*, D82, R1, R3, R5, R38, R54, R65. *C.hirsutus* Stent.

incompletus Nees var. **incompletus**
- •• A wool casual; a large patch survived in an orchard at Wingham (E Kent) from 1983 to at least 1985. Africa, (Australia). BM, CGE, E, K, LIV, LTN, NMW, RNG. D2, D5*, D7, D29, D82, D93*, J6(3:50), J7(1921:281-282), J8(42:18), R1, R2, R5, R38, R47, R51, R86. **Fig.15.**

transvaalensis Burtt Davy
- • A wool casual. S Africa, (widespread as a lawn grass in hot countries). HbTBR. D5*, D6, D7, D37*, D43, D82, D93*, D118, R3.

SPARTINA Schreb.   **415**

c.15 species. Both coasts of the Americas, Atlantic coast of Europe and Africa; especially temperate and subtropical regions. Mainly intertidal mud flats, but some species extend to coastal dunes and inland freshwater swamps. Ref.J89(32:158-167).

alterniflora Loisel. var. **alterniflora**
- • Introduced c.1816 and long naturalised in Southampton Water (S Hants), where it has now become very scarce; more recently introduced in Poole Harbour (Dorset), the Blackwater Estuary (N Essex) and Udale Bay (E Ross). Coasts of N and S America, (France). BM, BRISTM, K, RNG, WCR. D1, D2, D3*, D4, D6*, D11*, D12*, D19*, D23*, D40*, D52*, D63*, D151*, R16, R36, R107, R113. *S.brasiliensis* Raddi. A hybrid with *S.maritima* (Curtis) Fernald (*S.* × *townsendii* H. & J.Groves) in Southampton Water gave rise to the native species *S.anglica* C.E.Hubb., now the commonest *Spartina* in the British Isles, including Ireland (where it may have been sometimes introduced according to ref.R113). Putative backcrosses from *S.anglica* to *S.alterniflora* have been recorded.

alterniflora Loisel. var. **glabra** (Muhl. ex Bigelow) Fernald
- • Planted and persisting on a few mud-flats at Eling on Southampton Water (S Hants) since 1924, at Keysworth in Poole Harbour (Dorset) since 1963, and at Udale Bay (E Ross) since 1947; earlier introductions in Poole Harbour (Dorset) and at Blakeney Point (E Norfolk) died soon after planting; the record from Essex mentioned in ref.D76 has not been traced. Eastern coasts of USA and S America, (N France). BM, K, RNG. D41*, D76, J60*(5:19-95). *S.glabra* Muhl. ex Bigelow. C.A.Stace in ref.D2 and most modern authors have sunk this variety into *S.alterniflora*.

pectinata Bosc ex Link   **Prairie Cord-grass**
- • Introduced and long established at Costelloe Lodge (W Galway); at Seaton Burn (S Northumb); a variegated variety by the Basingstoke Canal near Farnborough (N Hants); beside the River Blackwater, Farnborough Green (Herts) in 1986; by the car park at Wisley Gardens (Surrey). N America. BM, DBN, K, NCE, RNG, TCD. D2*, D6*, D23*, D40*, D41*, D42*,

J6(7:505,594), J8(32:20), J9(16:74-75), J18(419:15), R32, R108, R122, R124.
The Irish plant was originally misnamed as *S.cynosuroides* (L.) Roth.

CHONDROSUM Desv.   416

14 species. Canada to Argentina, but centred on southwestern USA, Mexico.
Hill slopes and open plains. Several species provide valuable grazing on the
prairies. The genus is often included in *Bouteloua* but differs in the pectinately
arranged spikelets, with the florets falling from the persistent glumes (not falling
entire).

trifidum (Thurb.) Clayton   Red Grama
• A wool casual. N America. HbTBR. D6*, D41*, D43, D118*, R2.
C.trinii E.Fourn.; *Bouteloua trifida* Thurb. **Fig.13.**

BOUTELOUA Lag.   418

24 species. Canada to Argentina, but centred in Mexico. Hill slopes and open
plains. Many species are important forage grasses.

cf. **curtipendula** (Michx.) Torr.   Side-oats Grama
• A wool casual. N and S America. HbTBR. D6*, D15, D23*, D40*, D41*,
D53*, D118*, R2. *Chloris curtipendula* Michx.

TRAGUS Haller   434

7 species. Tropics and warm temperate regions. Sandy and weedy places.
Ref.J7(36:55-61).

australianus S.T.Blake   Australian Bur-grass
•• A wool casual. Australia. BM, CGE, E, K, LTN, NMW, RNG. D2*,
D7, D8*, D16*, D26*, D38, D75*, D93*, R1, R2, R5, R38, R54.
T.racemosus Benth., non (L.) All.; misspelt as *T.australiensis*.

berteronianus Schult.   African Bur-grass
•• A wool casual. Africa, S Asia, (N and S America). BM, CGE, E, K,
RNG. D2, D5*, D6*, D13*, D37*, D39*, D41*, D65, D75*, D81*, D89*,
D116*, J8(47:34), J15(114:106), R1, R2, R5, R54.

koelerioides Asch.
• A wool casual. S Africa. BM, E, K, RNG. D5*, D106*, D140*, R1, R2,
R5, R54, R118.

racemosus (L.) All.   European Bur-grass
•• A wool casual. Old World tropics and warm temperate regions, excluding
Australasia, (N America). BEL, BM, CGE, E, K, LTN, NMW, RNG. D1,
D2, D5*, D6*, D12*, D18, D20*, D31*, D39*, D75*, D115*, J1(5:133),
J6(3:441), R1, R2, R5, R8, R36, R38, R51, R54, R102. *T.heptaneuron*
Clayton; *Cenchrus racemosus* L. Most of the records may refer to
T.australianus, which is hardly distinct. **Fig.15.**

PANICEAE

THYRIDOLEPIS S.T.Blake   **447**

3 species. Australia. Dry grassland and scrub.

xerophila (Domin) S.T.Blake
- A wool casual. Australia. BM, K, RNG. D7, D8, D16, D26*, D93*, D93*, R2, R65, R110. *Neurachne xerophila* Domin. **Fig.6.**

OPLISMENUS P.Beauv.   **451**

5 species. Tropical and subtropical regions; 1 species in Europe and SW Asia. Forest shade.

[hirtellus (L.) P.Beauv.
Cultivated from bird-seed. Tropics. BM. D6*, D13, D36*, D37*, D41*, D63*, D88*, D116*, J8(28:18), R21. *Panicum hirtellum* L. An error for *Arthraxon hispidus*.]

PANICUM L.   **455**

c.470 species. Pantropical and warm temperáte regions, extending to temperate N America. Desert, savanna, swamp and forest. *P.miliaceum* (Common Millet, Proso Millet) is grown as a cereal. *P.maximum* and *P.coloratum* are widely grown for fodder. **Key on p.127.**

antidotale Retz.
Pre-1930 only. A casual. Middle East, Pakistan, India, (widespread). D16*, D17*, D41*, D55*, D67, D75*, D88*, D93*, D116, D118, R109. *P.miliare* Lam.

buncei F.Muell. ex Benth.
- A wool casual. Australia. E, K, RNG. D10*, D16, D93*, D190*, R1, R2, R5, R65.

capillare L.   Witch-grass
- ••• A casual of bird-seed, agricultural seed, wool, oil-seed, docks and wasteland. N America, (widespread). BM, BRISTM, CGE, DBN, E, K, LTN, NMW, RNG, SLBI. D1, D2*, D4, D6*, D12*, D15*, D17*, D20*, D41*, D75*, D88*, D93*, D115*, J1(10:358; 11:46), ?J3(1867), J6(1:183), J10(38:45), J18(407:41), J23(8:187), R1, R5, R8, R21, R25, R36, R39, R40, R47, R50, R54, R55, R57, R58, R62, R81, R84, R113. Includes *P.barbipulvinatum* Nash; *P.capillare* var. *occidentale* Rydb., non *P.occidentale* Scribn. **Fig.25.**

coloratum L.
- A wool casual. Arabia, Egypt to S Africa, (widespread). BM, E, K, LIV, NMW, RNG. D5*, D7, D10*, D13, D16, D37*, D39*, D93*, D116, R3, R65.

decompositum R.Br.
- A wool casual. Australia. BM, K, NMW, RNG. D7, D8*, D10*, D16, D27*, D29, D38, D93*, R1, R2, R47, R65. A tumbleweed.

dichotomiflorum Michx. Autumn Millet
•• A casual of wool, railway land, docks, bird-seed and oil-seed; a regular component of soya-bean waste. N and S America, (S Europe, Asia, New Zealand). BM, E, K, LIV, NMW, RNG. D1, D2*, D6*, D12*, D15*, D23*, D40*, D41*, D75*, D88*, D115*, D116, J1(13:278), J8*(27:16-17), J10(47:31), J18(407:41; 409:39), J23(14:230), J26(60:87), J41(6:90), R3, R5, R21, R38, R55, R65, R88. *P.chloroticum* Nees ex Trin.

effusum R.Br.
- A wool casual; its reported occurence in bird-seed seems unlikely. Australia. BM, BRISTM, E, K, LIV, NMW, RNG. D7, D8*, D10*, D16*, D24*, D26*, D27*, D38, D44*, D93*, D129*, J10(28:248), J23(16:170), R2, R5, R21, R57, R88.

gilvum Launert
- A wool casual; also an introduced garden weed. S Africa, (Australia). BM, E, K, LIV, NMW, RNG, SLBI. D5, D7, D68, D93*, D106*, J8*(27:16-17), J90*(8:161), R3, R65. *P.laevifolium* Hack. var. *contractum* Pilg.; *P.schinzii* auct., non Hack.

laevinode Lindl.
- A wool casual. Australia. RNG, HbTBR. D7, D8*, D93*, D181*, R2, R65. *P.whitei* J.M.Black.

maximum Jacq.
Pre-1930 only. A grain casual at Splott (Glam) in 1925. Tropical and subtropical Africa, (widespread). D1, D5*, D6*, D13, D17*, D37*, D68, D75*, D88*, D93*, D116, J1(7:1025), R36. The Isle of Wight specimens in CGE found about 1925 (ref.J1(9:760), R30) were re-determined by Thellung as *P.schinzii* cf. var. *amboense* Hack. (see ref.J1(7:1069). The recent record from Romsey (Cambs) in ref.J8(34:33) has also been re-determined as *P.schinzii* (ref.R83). A widespread tropical forage grass that soon escapes.

miliaceum L. Common Millet
•••• A casual of bird-seed, grain and oil-seed, now very common on tips, and under-recorded; grown as pheasant food in Norfolk according to ref.R19. Origin obscure, probably India, (widespread). D1, D2*, D4, D6*, D12*, D15*, D17*, D19*, D20*, D75*, D88*, D93*, D115*, D117*, R8, R21.

mitchellii Benth.
- A wool casual. Australia. K, HbTBR. D7, D105, R2.

cf. **novemnerve** Stapf
- A wool casual. Southern tropical Africa. HbTBR. D5, D65, D68, D82*, D98*, D106*, R2.

obseptum Trin. ex Nees
- A wool casual. Australia. K, HbTBR. D7, D10*, D16, D29, D38, D93*, D190*, R2.

queenslandicum Domin
- A wool casual. Australia. K, SLBI, HbTBR. D10*, D16*, D29, D93*, R2.

repens L.
Pre-1930 only.   Tropics and subtropics, and warm temperate regions, (Australia).   D1, D5, D6*, D13*, D15*, D17*, D18, D20*, D31*, D37*, D41*, D75*, D81*, D88*, D93*, D115*, D116, D117*, R36.

schinzii Hack. ex Schinz   Transvaal Millet
- • • A casual of wool, bird-seed, docks and grain. Tropical and S Africa, (India, Australia). BM, CGE, E, K, LIV, LTN, NMW, RNG, SLBI. D2*, D5*, D7, D10*, D65, D68, D75*, D88*, D135, J1(5:255,311; 7:1069 re-determined; 8:422), J8(34:33 re-determined), J23(9:189), J29(21:43), R1, R5, R20, R21, R36, R38, R39, R44, R45, R49, R54, R55, R57, R66. *P.laevifolium* Hack.

stapfianum Fourc.
- A wool casual. S Africa. RNG. D5*, D68, D106*, D140*, R110. *P.minus* Stapf.

subalbidum Kunth
- A casual of wool, tips and possibly oil-seed. Tropical and S Africa. K, RNG, SLBI, HbTBR. D2, D5, D37*, D65, D68, D82*, D139*, R1, R2, R38, R47, R65. *P.glabrescens* Steud.; *P.longijubatum* Stapf. Over-recorded in error for *P.dichotomiflorum*.

subxerophilum Domin
- A wool casual. Australia. BM, K, LIV, RNG, SLBI. D7, D10*, D16, D93*, R2, R65.

virgatum L.
- A casual near Salisbury (S Wilts) in 1934. N and C America, (widespread). K. D6*, D40*, D41*, D42*, D53, D88*, D116, D129*, J1(11:46), J43(1937), R84. Sometimes used as a dried ornamental grass, and also in floral wreaths.

STEINCHISMA Raf.   459

4 species.   Southern USA to Argentina.   Damp grassland.   Difficult to distinguish from *Panicum* until the fruit ripens and the palea develops its characteristic thickening.

hians (Elliot) Nash
- A wool casual, found only once at Blackmoor (N Hants) in 1973. Southern USA to Argentina. K. D6*, D12*, D63*, R3. *Panicum hians* Elliot; *P.milioides* Nees. **Fig.26.**

ECHINOCHLOA P.Beauv.   **476**

c.35 species. Tropical and warm temperate regions of the world. In water or
damp places, also as a weed. Several species are grown as minor grain crops.
E.crus-galli (Cockspur, Barnyard-grass) and the closely related *E.oryzoides* are
widespread serious weeds. Ref.J91*(Sept.1965:1-).

colona (L.) Link   Shama Millet
•• A casual of wool, grain, tips, bird-seed, oil-seed and cotton. Widespread
in the tropics and subtropics. BM, BRISTM, K, LTN, NMW, OXF, RNG.
D1, D2*, D6*, D15*, D16*, D17*, D20*, D75*, D88*, D93*, D115*,
D117*, J1(9:144; 10:358; 12:82), J8*(27:16-19), J10(38:45), J23(9:189),
J26(58:63), J41*(6:89), R1, R2, R5, R21, R36, R38, R39, R41, R45*, R47,
R49, R55, R59, R69, R86, R88, R111. *Panicum colonum* L. According to
many botanists, e.g. ref.D53, R125, the correct spelling is *E.colonum*.
crus-galli (L.) P.Beauv.   Cockspur
•••• A casual of wool, cotton and agricultural seed on agricultural land, and
of bird-seed and oil-seed on tips; sometimes persistent in southern England;
abundant on site of former woodyard near Lampeter College (Cards) in 1993;
frequent but under-recorded. A widespread weed in warm countries. D1,
D2*, D3*, D4, D5*, D6*, D88*, D93*, D115*, D117*, J16(58:26), R8, R21,
R86, R122. *Panicum crus-galli* L. A very variable grass often split into
closely related species. The original spelling of *crusgalli*, without the hyphen,
is best regarded as a typographical error according to E.J.Clement, since in
ref.S11 the hyphenated spelling appears in an appendix where all the epithets
are listed. However most modern authors use the original unhyphenated form.
Fig.25.
crus-pavonis (Kunth) Schult.
• A casual in Bristol docks (W Gloucs) in 1924, 1940; also in carrot fields at
Fareham (S Hants) in 1938 and Great Bircham (W Norfolk) and Chippenham
(Cambs) in 1949; possibly a wool alien. Tropical Africa, S America,
(Australia). BRISTM, K, RNG. D6*, D12*, D15*, D37*, D63*, D88*,
D93*, D115*, D118, D174*, J1(10:37,358), J23(2:58), ?R2, R58. *Oplismenus
crus-pavonis* Kunth.
esculenta (A.Braun) H.Scholz   Japanese Millet
••• A bird-seed casual frequent on tips.   Asia, (widespread cereal). BM,
CGE, E, K, LIV, NMW, OXF, RNG. D2, D44*, D55*, D93*, J8*(27:16-
19), J10(37:31; 38:45), J23(14:434), J41*(6:89), R5, R21, R23, R38, R41*,
R45*, R55, R59, R86, R88, R91, R105. *E.frumentacea* auct., non Link;
E.utilis Ohwi & Yabuno; *Panicum esculentum* A.Braun. A cereal of Japanese
origin derived from *E.crus-galli*.
frumentacea (Roxb.) Link   White Millet
•• A bird-seed casual fairly frequent on tips.   Asia, (widespread cereal).
BM, BRISTM, K, LSR, OXF, NMW, RNG. D2*, D6*, D55*, D93*, D115,
J1(5:311; 10:358), J8(25:17; 27:16-18), J10(38:45), J18(403:38), J23(14:434),
R21, R24, R36, R52, R57, R59, R86, R88. *Panicum frumentaceum* Roxb.

Much confused with *E. esculenta*. The taxonomy of the two species is critically discussed in ref.J44(27:296-305), J45(19:177-325), D2 and D66. A cereal of Indian origin derived from *E. colona*.

muricata (Michx.) Fernald
- A casual of bird-seed and carrot seed, found at Crouch End (S Essex) in 1898, and St. Peters, Guernsey in 1977. N America. K. D41*, D42*, D118, J8(17:16-18), J78*(446:1-5), R11. Includes *E.microstachya* (Wiegand) Rydb. *Panicum muricatum* Michx. Scarcely distinct from *E.crus-galli* and *E.pungens*.

oryzoides (Ard.) Fritsch
  Pre-1930 only. Origin obscure, (widespread). D13, D18, D32*, D93*, D115*, D118, D174*, J78*(446:1-5), R36. *E.hostii* (M.Bieb.) Link; *Panicum crus-galli* L. var. *hostii* (M.Bieb.) Druce; *P.oryzoides* Ard.; *P.stagninum* auct., non Retz. Close to *E.crus-galli*, and not to be confused with *E.oryzicola* (Vasinger) Vasinger (*P.crus-galli* var. *oryzicola* Vasinger) of e.g. ref.D117*, D126, J80*(t.2698); both species are serious weeds of rice fields.

pungens (Poir.) Rydb.
- A wool casual. N America. E, LTN. D42*, D53, R1, R5, R58, R118. *Panicum pungens* Poir. Probably confused with *E.crus-galli*, of which it is given as a variety in ref.D6.

pyramidalis (Lam.) Hitchc. & Chase
- A wool casual. Africa, Arabia, (Mexico, C America). K, RNG. D5*, D11, D13, D37*, D65, D68, D78*, D139*, R2. *E.holubii* (Stapf) Stapf; *Panicum holubii* Stapf; *P.pyramidale* Lam.

turneriana (Domin) J.M.Black
- A wool casual. Australia. RNG, HbEJC, HbTBR. D7, D8, D93*, R2, R48. *Panicum turnerianum* Domin.

BRACHIARIA (Trin.) Griseb.   **485**

c.100 species. Tropics, mainly Old World. A wide range of habitats, from semi-desert to swamp. Several species are widely grown for pasture. Many species merge into *Urochloa*.

deflexa (Schumach.) C.E.Hubb. ex Robyns
- A casual on a tip at Cherry Hinton (Cambs), perhaps from bird-seed. Arabia, tropical Africa, India, sometimes cultivated as a minor cereal in W Africa. D13, D36*, D37*, D88*, D135, J8*(51:1,31). *Panicum deflexum* Schumach.; *Pseudobrachiaria deflexa* (Schumach.) Launert.

eruciformis (Sm.) Griseb.
- A casual of wool and perhaps bird-seed; also on a roadside at Walton-in-Gordano (N Somerset) in 1935. Warm regions of the Old World, (widespread). RNG, HbTBR. D1, D2, D5*, D6*, D13, D17*, D18, D22*, D37*, D39*, D51*, D88*, D93*, D115*, D117*, D139*, J1(11:46), R2, R21. *B.isachne* (Roth ex Roem. & Schult.) Stapf; *Panicum eruciforme* Sm.; *P.isachne* Roth ex Roem. & Schult. The specimens from bird-seed in BM and NMW have

been re-determined as *Echinochloa colona*, which is superficially similar but has no ligule.

gilesii (Benth.) Chase
- A wool casual found only once in flower at Blackmoor (N Hants) in 1973. Australia. E, K. D7, D8*, D16, D62*, D93*, R3. *Panicum gilesii* Benth.; *Urochloa gilesii* (Benth.) Hughes.

marlothii (Hack.) Stent
- A casual of wool and cotton; found in a carrot field at Little Shelford (Cambs) in 1955; also occured spontaneously in a pot of cacti in an office in central London in 1965. S Africa. CGE, K, RNG. D5, D68, D87*, D106*, J8(18:11; 27*:19; 29:10), J90*(8:161), R2, R55, R110. *Panicum marlothii* Hack.

platyphylla Nash   **Broad-leaved Signal-grass**
- • A casual of tips, bird-seed and oil-seed. N and S America, (Africa). BM, E, K, NMW, RNG. D2*, D6*, D12*, D15*, D41*, D88*, J8(34:33; 47:36; 51*:1), J18(391:35), J26(61:101), R5, R21, R24, R44. *B.extensa* Chase; *Paspalum platyphyllum* Griseb., nom. illeg. The specimen from Guildford tip (Surrey) in 1970 was originally misnamed as the similar *B.brizantha* (Hochst. ex A.Rich.) Stapf from tropical Africa. **Fig.25.**

UROCHLOA P.Beauv.   487

12 species. Old World tropics, mainly Africa. Savanna. The upper lemma is usually obtuse with a long mucro enclosed within the spikelet.

panicoides P.Beauv.   **Sharp-flowered Signal-grass**
- • A casual of bird-seed, tips and wool; also an impurity of imported seed from Natal at R.B.G., Kew (Surrey). Arabia, Africa, India, (Australia, Mexico). BM, E, K, NMW, RNG. D2*, D5*, D13, D16, D37*, D88*, D93*, D135, D143, J8*(51:1), J23(9:189), J26(49:17; 54:64; 56:85,88), R5, R21, R44, R45, R49. *U.helopus* (Trin.) Stapf; *Panicum urochloa* Desv. **Fig.25.**

ERIOCHLOA Kunth   488

30 species. Tropics and subtropics. Damp soil and weedy places. The genus is distinguished by the small globose bead at the base of each spikelet. Ref.J56(12:165-207).

contracta Hitchc.
- A casual at Avonmouth docks (W Gloucs) in 1952. N America. K. D6*, D41*, D42*, D53*, D118*, J6(1:494), J10(28:312).

crebra S.T.Blake
- A wool casual. Australia. BM, E, K, LIV, LTN. D2, D7, D16, D93*, D190, R1, R2, R5, R48, R65, R105.

fatmensis (Hochst. & Steud.) Clayton
- A wool casual. Tropical and southern Africa, Arabia, India. K, RNG. D2, D13*, D37*, R3. *E.acrotricha* (Steud.) Hack. ex Thell., nom. illeg., non

(Hook.f.) Hack. ex Schinz; *E.nubica* (Steud.) Hack. & Stapf ex Thell.; *Helopus acrotrichus* Steud.; *Monachne acrotricha* (Steud.) Druce; *Panicum fatmense* Hochst. & Steud.   According to ref.R3 the RNG specimen was wrongly determined as *E.pseudoacrotricha*. This species is very close to *E.procera*.

lemmonii Vasey & Scribn.
- A wool casual. Southern USA, Mexico.   D6*, D41, D42*, D43, D176, R1, R3, R118.   Includes *E.gracilis* (E.Fourn.) Hitchc.   The location of specimens is unknown.

procera (Retz.) C.E.Hubb.
- A wool casual. Tropical Asia, (widespread). K, RNG. D6*, D7, D13, D16, D29, D37*, D93*, D100*, D135, R2, R110. *E.ramosa* (Retz.) Kuntze; *Agrostis procera* Retz.; *Milium ramosum* Retz.

pseudoacrotricha (Stapf ex Thell.) J.M.Black   **Perennial Cup-grass**
- •• A wool casual. Australia. BM, CGE, E, K, LTN, NMW, OXF, RNG. D2*, D7, D8*, D10*, D16*, D26*, D38, D93*, R1, R2, R5, R47, R65, R110. *E.ramosa* var. *pseudoacrotricha* Stapf ex Thell.   The wool alien in OXF collected from Galashiels (Selkirks) in 1915, mentioned in ref.R4, R13, R36, was originally named as *E.acrotricha*; it has been re-determined by C.E.Hubbard as this species. **Fig.22.**

villosa (Thunb.) Kunth
A dock alien at Avonmouth (W Gloucs) in 1930. E Asia, (N America). BM, BRISTM, K, OXF, RNG. D1, D6, D42*, D47, D56, D111*, D136*, D149*, D184*, J1(9:285; 10:359). *Panicum tuberculiflorum* Steud.; *Paspalum villosum* Thunb.

PASPALUM L.   495

c.330 species. Tropics, mainly New World. Savanna, forest margins and damp places; two species in salt marshes. A race of the wild species *P.scrobiculatum* L. has been grown as a cereal (Kodo) in India for about 3000 years. *P.dilatatum* (Dallis-grass) and *P.notatum* (Bahia-grass) are grown for fodder.

dilatatum Poir.   **Dallis-grass**
- •• A wool and dock casual; also possibly a bird-seed casual, as at Castletown car park (Man) in 1990, at Brookwood Hospital (Surrey) and in an urban street in N London in 1994. S America, (widespread). BM, BRISTM, E, K, LIV, LTN, NMW, OXF, RNG, SLBI. D1, D5*, D6*, D12*, D15*, D16*, D20*, D25*, D26*, D88*, D93*, D115*, D116, J1(7:456,1024; 10:359), J24(1993:5), R1, R2, R5, R19, R36, R38, R47, R65, R86. *P.platense* Spreng.; *Digitaria dilatata* (Poir.) Coste. A tropical fodder grass which soon becomes a weed. **Fig.19.**

distichum L.
- •• An esparto, wool and probably bird-seed alien; established for several years on sandy ground below the walls of Mousehole harbour (W Cornwall); recently found at the entrance to the Kingsland Basin, by the Grand Union Canal at

Hackney (Middlesex); cultivated from soya and cotton seed. Tropics and warm temperate regions. BM, K, LANC, OXF, RNG, SLBI. D1, D2*, D5*, D6*, D7, D8*, D17*, D22*, D31*, D48, D70, J8*(39:10-11), J18(376:24-26), J26(64:120-121), J46(7:5), R3, R52, R65, ?R66.   *P.distichon* sphalm.; *P.distichum* subsp. *paspalodes* (Michx.) Thell.; *P.paspalodes* (Michx.) Scribn.; *P.paspaloides* sphalm.; *Digitaria paspalodes* Michx.   Previously the name *P.distichum* L. was applied by many authors (e.g. ref.D1, D48, D51, D70, D71, D142) to the closely similar *P. vaginatum* (q.v.), which is a more tropical grass of saline habitats, *P.distichum* auct., non L. being reserved for *P.paspalodes*. A useful discussion of the apparently insuperable nomenclatural problem (due to the type sheet of Linnaeus bearing a mixture of both species) has been given by T.A.Cope in ref.D51; this problem has now been resolved in ref.J52(32:281).

[notatum Flügge   Bahia-grass
Cultivated from wool shoddy.   Mexico, W Indies, S America, (widespread). BM, HbCGH.   D6*, D7, D11, D37*, D41*, D63*, D82*, D88*, D93*, D129*.   *P.uruguayense* Arechav.   Widely planted as a tropical pasture grass, and often escaping.]

racemosum Lam.
Pre-1930 only.   Bristol docks c.1929; early records from Jersey and Swansea refer to escaped or cultivated plants in parks or gardens.   S America. BRISTM, K, OXF.   D172, J1(6:633; 10:359), R36.   *P.elegans* auct., non Roem. & Schult.; *P.stoloniferum* Willd.   Formerly grown as a forage crop in Egypt (see ref.D177).

[urvillei Steud.
Cultivated from soya-bean waste. S America, (widespread). BM, NMW. D1, D6*, D12*, D41*, D63*, D88*, D116, J61*(126:95-102).   A tropical fodder grass which soon becomes a weed.]

[vaginatum Sw.
Doubtfully recorded as an alien.   Tropics and warm temperate regions. D1, D6*, D7, D12*, D13, D37*, D48, D70, ?R66.   *P.distichum* auct., non L.; *P.distichum* var. *vaginatum* (Sw.) Griseb.   Due to the nomenclatural confusion discussed under *P.distichum* (q.v.), the records need confirmation. *P. vaginatum* differs from *P.distichum* in the upper glume which is glabrous (not appressed-pubescent), the lower glume which is absent (not often present as a small scale), and the spikelets which are ovate-elliptic and flattened (not ovate and relatively plump, being plano-convex).]

AXONOPUS P.Beauv.   **500**

c.110 species.   Tropical and subtropical America; 1 species in Africa. Savanna, forest clearings and weedy places.   *A.compressus* (Carpet-grass) is widely naturalised as a lawn grass in the humid tropics.

affinis Chase
- A wool casual. N and S America, (Africa, Australia). BM(cultivated), K, RNG. D5*, D6*, D12*, D15*, D16, D26*, D41*, D87*, D93*, R2, R65, R110. According to ref.D87 the plant naturalised in S Africa is this species and not *A.compressus* (as in ref.D5).

cf. **compressus** (Sw.) P.Beauv.   Carpet-grass
- A wool casual. Southern USA to Brazil, (widespread). LIV. D5*, D6*, D13, D15*, D16*, D93*. *Panicum compressum* Sw. Fig.8.

SETARIA P.Beauv.   503

c.100 species. Tropics and subtropics. Habitat variable, including grassland, woodland and weedy places. *S.italica* (Foxtail Bristle-grass, Foxtail Millet, Italian Millet), a major cereal in China, was domesticated about 7000 years ago. *S.sphacelata* is grown for pasture. *S.palmifolia* (J.König) Stapf is a vegetable in New Guinea, and also a hothouse ornamental. The full synonymy of the genus has been given in 1994 by R.D.Webster in ref.J56(15:447-489).

dielsii Herrm.
- A wool casual found once at Blackmoor (N Hants) in 1965 and named by C.E.Hubbard. Australia. K. D7, D8*, D27*, D62*, R94.

faberi Herrm.   Nodding Bristle-grass
•• A casual of docks, grain, bird-seed and oil-seed; a regular component of soya-bean waste; Sharpness and Avonmouth docks (W Gloucs) in 1984-7; found by a corn silo at Newmarket (Cambs) in 1979. E Asia, (W Asia, N America). BM, NMW, HbEJC, HbTBR. D6*, D42*, D53, D56, D88*, D118, D124*, D136*, J8(17:14; 42:16), J10(47:31), J17(24:35; 33:51), J18(376:25; 388:36; 400:35; 407:41; 409:39), J26(56:85,89; 64:120), J41(6:90), R19, R21, R38, R61, R65, R68.

italica (L.) P.Beauv.   Foxtail Bristle-grass
•••• A casual of bird-seed and grain, common on tips. Origin obscure, probably derived from *S.viridis*, (widespread crop). D1, D2, D6*, D19*, D20*, D42*, D55*, D75*, D81*, D88*, D93*, R8, R21. *Panicum germanicum* Miller; *P.italicum* L.

parviflora (Poir.) Kerguélen   Knotroot Bristle-grass
•• A casual of wool and bird-seed. N and S America, (widespread). BM, BRISTM, E, K, LTN, NMW, OXF, RNG, SLBI. D1, D2, D6*, D15*, D16*, D27*, D41*, D75*, D88*, D93*, D115*, J1(8:764; 10:359; 12:82), J8(26*:16-17; 34:33), J10(38:45; 47:31), J18(403:38), J23(9:189; 13:343), R1, R2, R4, R12, R21, R36, R38, R44, R45, R47, R88. *S.geniculata* auct., non (Willd.) P.Beauv.; *S.gracilis* Kunth; *S.imberbis* (Poir.) Roem. & Schult.; *Cenchrus parviflorus* Poir.

pumila (Poir.) Roem. & Schult.   Yellow Bristle-grass
••• A casual of wool, grain, bird-seed, agricultural seed and oil-seed, rarely persistent; common on tips but under-recorded. Tropical and warm temperate regions of Eurasia and Africa, (widespread). BM, BRISTM, CGE, DBN, E,

K, LTN, NMW, OXF, RNG, SLBI. D1, D2*, D3*, D4, D5*, D6*, D19*, D29, D36*, D75*, D88*, D93*, D115*, R1, R2, R5, R8, R21, R86, R113. *S.glauca* auct., non (L.) P.Beauv.; *S.lutescens* auct., non (Weigel) F.T.Hubb.; *S.rubiginosa* (Steud.) Miq.; *Panicum pumilum* Poir. Includes *S.pallidefusca* (Schumach.) Stapf & C.E.Hubb.; The name *S.lutescens* (Weigel) F.T.Hubb., previously commonly applied to this species, is in fact a synonym of *Pennisetum glaucum* (see ref.D13, D51, D68, J52(25:297-304)). **Fig.8.**

[sphacelata (Schumach.) Stapf & C.E.Hubb. ex M.B.Moss
    Cultivated from bird-seed. Arabia, Africa, (widespread). BM. D5, D6, D13, D36*, D37*, D88*, D93*, D118, R21.   *S.anceps* Stapf; *S.aurea* Chev.; *Panicum sphacelatum* Schumach.]

verticillata (L.) P.Beauv.   **Rough Bristle-grass**
    ••• A casual of bird-seed, oil-seed, wool, cotton and esparto, sometimes persistent. Tropics and warm temperate regions. BEL, BM, BRISTM, CGE, E, K, LTN, NMW, OXF, RNG, SLBI. D1, D2*, D3*, D4, D5*, D6*, D75*, D93*, D115*, J1(5:406; 10:359), J8(18:11), J18(391:35), J35(65:197), R1, R2, R3, R5, R8, R21, R24, R27, R36, R39, R40, R43, R49, R54, R55, R56, R57, R59, R60, R62, R66, R86. Includes *S.adhaerens* (Forssk.) Chiov.; *S.aparine* (Steud.) Chiov.; *S.panicea* (L.) Schinz & Thell.; *Panicum aparine* Steud.; *P.verticillatum* L. Contrary to ref.D2, D117* and many other works, the separation of *S.adhaerens* as a distinct species is not justified because there is a continuous gradation in the taxonomic characters.

viridis (L.) P.Beauv.   **Green Bristle-grass**
    •••• A casual of bird-seed, agricultural seed, oil-seed, wool, esparto and grain; common on tips. Eurasia, N Africa, (widespread). D1, D2, D3*, D4, D6*, D17*, R8, R21.   *Panicum viride* L. Includes *S.weinmannii* Roem. & Schult. *S.* × *verticilliformis* Dumort. (*S.* × *ambigua* (Guss.) Guss.), the putative hybrid with *S.verticillata* (e.g. see ref.D177, D178, D180*), was recorded in error for *S.parviflora* pre-1930 in ref.J1(5:311; 10:359) from Avonmouth docks (W Gloucs), in OXF; there is also a specimen in K from an old greenhouse at Chatteris (Cambs) in 1901 of uncertain status. However, many botanists now consider that *S.* × *verticilliformis* is only a variety of the previous species, *S.verticillata* var. *ambigua* (Guss.) Parl. (*S.viridis* var. *ambigua* (Guss.) Coss. & Durieu).

vulpiseta (Lam.) Roem. & Schult.
    A casual at Avonmouth docks (W Gloucs) in 1930. SW USA, Mexico, West Indies to Argentina. BRISTM. D6*, D11, D41, D151*, D172, D176, J1(10:359), J47(84:94-105), R62. *S.macrostachya* Kunth; *Panicum vulpisetum* Lam. We have followed ref.D63* in equating *S.vulpiseta* and *S.macrostachya*, but others, e.g. ref.D72, D85, D170, disagree. The specimen cultivated from bird-seed which was recorded in ref.R21 has been re-determined as *S.italica*.

PASPALIDIUM Stapf   **504**

c.40 species. Tropics and subtropics. In swamps, forest and on dry slopes.
The short racemes of the inflorescence each end in an inconspicuous point.

gracile (R.Br.) Hughes
• A wool casual. Australia. HbTBR. D7, D105, D190*, R2. *Panicum
gracile* R.Br.
jubiflorum (Trin.) Hughes
• A wool casual. Australia. BM, E, K, LTN, RNG. D7, D10*, D190, R1,
R2, R5, R47, R65. *Panicum jubiflorum* Trin. **Fig.8.**

TRICHOLAENA Schrad. ex Schult. & Schult.f.   **514**

4 species. Med. and Africa to India. Sandy and stony places.

monachne (Trin.) Stapf & C.E.Hubb.
• A wool casual. Tropical and S Africa. RNG. D5*, D13*, D82*, D106*,
R3, R110. *Panicum monachne* Trin. **Fig.22.**

MELINIS P.Beauv.   **517**

c.25 species. Africa. Savanna woodland, open grassland and disturbed places.
Following ref.D109 this genus now includes *Rhynchelytrum* Nees.

repens (Willd.) Zizka
• A wool casual. Africa, (widespread). K, LIV, RNG. D13*, D36*, D37*,
D88*, D93*, D116*, R1, R54. *M.rosea* (Nees) Hack.; *Rhynchelytrum repens*
(Willd.) C.E.Hubb.; *R.roseum* (Nees) Stapf & C.E.Hubb.; *R.villosum* (Parl.)
Chiov.; *Saccharum repens* Willd.; *Tricholaena rosea* Nees. **Fig.26.**

HOMOPHOLIS C.E.Hubb.   **520**

2 species. Australia. Woodland shade. Similar to *Panicum*, but the acuminate
lower glume is from 2/3 to as long as the spikelet with prominently thickened
ridged nerves, and the upper lemma is c.1/2 as long as the spikelet with a short
beak.

proluta (F.Muell.) R.D.Webster
• A wool casual. Australia. BM, K, RNG. D7, D8, D16, D38, D45*, D93*,
J48(2:1891), R3, R47. *Panicum prolutum* F.Muell. **Fig.12.**

DIGITARIA Haller   **524**

c.230 species. Tropical and warm temperate regions. In various habitats. The
genus includes minor cereals, lawn and pasture grasses, and sand-dune
colonisers, in addition to widespread serious weeds, such as *D.ischaemum*
(Smooth Finger-grass, Red Millet) and *D.sanguinalis* (Hairy Finger-grass,

Crab-grass).   The monograph by J.T.Henrard (ref.D90) describes the entire
genus in great detail. **Key on p.130.**

aequiglumis (Hack. & Arechav.) Parodi
* A wool casual. S America, (Australia). K, RNG, HbCGH.   D7, D8, D10*,
D12*, D15*, D93*, R2, R65, R110.   *Panicum aequiglumis* Hack. & Arechav.

ammophila Hughes
* A wool casual.   Australia.   BM, K, RNG, SLBI.   D7, D8*, D10*, D16*,
D38, D44*, D93*, R2, R5, R65, R110.   *Panicum ammophilum* F.Muell., non
Trin. nec Steud.   A tumbleweed.

breviglumis (Domin) Henrard
* A wool casual.   Australia.   BM, K, RNG.   D7, D10*, D16*, D29, D93*,
R2, R110.   *Panicum breviglume* Domin.   Includes *D.diminuta* Hughes,
separated by some authors on small differences in the nerves of the lemmas.

brownii (Roem. & Schult.) Hughes
* A wool casual.   Australia.   BM, E, K, LIV, RNG.   D7, D8, D10*, D16*,
D27*, D38, D44*, D62*, D93*, R2, R5, R65, R110.   *Panicum brownii* Roem.
& Schult.

ciliaris (Retz.) Koeler   **Tropical Finger-grass**
** A casual of wool, bird-seed, oil-seed and cotton; now frequent on tips.
Tropics and subtropics.   ABD, BM, CGE, E, K, OXF, RNG.   D1, D2, D9*,
D10*, D15*, D16*, D29, D40*, D75*, D81*, D88*, D93*, D115*, J8(18:10),
J10(38:45; 41:90), J18(391:135), J23(13:343; 14:229), J26(56:89), J41(6:90),
R1, R2, R5, R21, R38, R45, R47, R50, R55, R59, R66, R88.   *D.adscendens*
(Kunth) Henrard; *D.marginata* Link; *Panicum adscendens* Kunth; *P.ciliare*
Retz.

cognata (Schult.) Pilg.   **Fall Witch-grass**
* A wool casual.   Eastern N America.   K, OXF, RNG, SLBI.   D6*, D40*,
D41*, D42*, J94*(19:613-627), R2, R110.   *Leptoloma cognata* (Schult.)
Chase; *Panicum cognatum* Schult.   A prairie tumbleweed.

ctenantha (F.Muell.) Hughes
* A wool casual.   Australia.   K, RNG.   D7, D62*, D105, D181*, R48, R105,
R110.   *D.robusta* Hughes; *Panicum ctenanthum* F.Muell.

didactyla Willd.   **Blue Couch**
* A wool casual; also grown at R.B.G., Kew as a weed from turf of *Cynodon
dactylon* originating from the Seychelles in 1971.   Mascarene Islands,
(Australia, Malaya).   K, RNG.   D9*, D10*, D16*, D29, D93*, D139*, R1,
R20, R38.   Grown as a lawn grass in E Asia and Australia.

diffusa Vickery
* A wool casual.   Australia.   K, RNG.   D7, D10*, D16*, D29, D38, D93*,
R2, R5.

divaricatissima (R.Br.) Hughes
* A wool casual.   Australia.   BM, E, K, RNG.   D7, D8, D16*, D29, D38,
D93*, D190, R2, R5, R110.   *Panicum divaricatissimum* R.Br.   A tumbleweed.

eriantha Steud.   Pangola-grass
* A wool casual. S Africa, (Australia). K, HbTBR. D5*, D90*, D106*, D140*, R2.

hubbardii Henrard
* A wool casual. Australia. BM, E, K, LIV, RNG. D7, D10*, D93*, R3.

ischaemum (Schreb. ex Schweigg.) Schreb. ex Muhl.   Smooth Finger-grass
•• Long established and very locally abundant in sandy fields in southern England, especially at Pyrford (Surrey); a weed in crops of maize (as in Belgium); a casual of wool, bird-seed and agricultural seed; recently (1989) appeared at disused railway sidings, Alphington Street, Exeter (S Devon). Eurasia, (widespread). BM, CGE, E, K, NMW, OXF, RNG. D1, D2*, D3*, D4, D10*, D19*, D25*, D41*, D75, D81*, D88*, D93*, D115*, J1(11:287), J6(4:489), J14(122:221; 123:249), R1(cultivated), R2, R5, R8, R21, R27, R36, R39, R58, R59, R64*, R78. *D.filiformis* auct., non (L.) Koeler; *D.humifusa* Pers.; *D.linearis* Crép., non (L.) Pers.; *Panicum glabrum* (Schrad.) Gaudin; *P.humifusum* (Pers.) Kunth; *P.ischaemum* Schreb. ex Schweigg.; *P.lineare* auct., non L.; *Syntherisma glabrum* Schrad.

milanjiana (Rendle) Stapf
* A wool casual. Tropical and S Africa, (widespread). K. D13, D37*, D82*, D86*, D90*, D106*, R1, R5. *D.exasperata* Henrard; *Panicum milanjianum* Rendle.

parviflora (R.Br.) Hughes
* A wool casual. Australia. BM, K, NMW, RNG, SLBI. D10*, D93*, D190, R3. *Panicum parviflorum* R.Br. Possibly an error for *D.ramularis*.

ramularis (Trin.) Henrard
* A wool casual. Australia. K. D10*, D93*, D190, R2. *D.tenuissima* (Benth.) Hughes; *Panicum ramulare* Trin.; *P.tenuissimum* Benth.

sanguinalis (L.) Scop.   Hairy Finger-grass
••• Established in the Isles of Scilly and the Channel Islands; persistent in pavement cracks in several towns in southern England, including Gosport and Southampton (both S Hants) in 1990 and Padstow (W Cornwall) in 1994; also a casual of wool, bird-seed, agricultural seed, oil-seed, docks and grain. Med., Asia, (widespread). BM, BRISTM, CGE, DBN, E, K, LTN, NMW, OXF, RNG, SLBI, WCR. D1, D2*, D3*, D4, D10*, D17*, D19*, D75*, D81*, D88*, D93*, D115*, D117*, J1(10:359), J26(63:141), J41(6:90), J43(1950), R1, R2, R5, R8, R21, R36, R39, R40, R43, R49, R54, R55, R56, R57, R58, R60, R62, R71, R84, R86, R123. *Panicum sanguinale* L.

ternata (A.Rich.) Stapf
* A wool casual; also cultivated from bird-seed. Yemen, tropical and S Africa, India, Burma, China, (widespread). BM, K, OXF, RNG. D5*, D10*, D13, D37*, D82*, D88*, D90*, D93*, D135, J1(6:633), J73*(21:65), R2, R21, R36. *D.argyrostachya* (Steud.) Fernald; *Cynodon ternatus* A.Rich.; *Panicum ternatum* (A.Rich.) Hochst. ex Steud. **Fig.26.**

velutina (Forssk.) P.Beauv.
- A wool casual; also appeared in a York garden in 1989, probably originating from bird-seed. Arabia, tropical and S Africa. BM, CGE, E, RNG. D5*, D13, J15(115:153), R3, R5. *D.horizontalis* auct., non Willd.; *D.zeyheri* (Nees) Henrard; *Phalaris velutina* Forssk. The determination of the wool-alien specimen from Blackmoor (N Hants) 1966 in BM was an error for *D.ammophila*.

violascens Link
- A wool casual; also cultivated from soya-bean waste. Tropics and subtropics, (widespread). BM, NMW, RNG, SLBI. D6*, D7, D9*, D10*, D13, D16*, D63*, D81*, D88*, D93*, D116, D141, J23(14:453), R2, R65, R110. *D.chinensis* (Nees) A.Camus; *D.ischaemum* var. *violascens* (Link) Radford; *Panicum violascens* (Link) Kunth.

PENNISETUM Rich.　　　　　　　　　　　　　　　　　　　　533

c.80 species. Tropics. Woodland, savanna and weedy places. *P.glaucum* (Pearl Millet) has been grown as a cereal in W Africa for 2000-3000 years. *P.purpureum* Schumach. (Elephant-grass) and *P.clandestinum* (Kikuyu-grass) are widely grown for pasture.

alopecuroides (L.) Spreng.
- A wool casual. Himalayas, S China, Japan, SE Asia, Australia, (Caucasus, USA). K, HbTBR. D6, D10*, D26*, D81*, D88*, D93*, D124*, D136*, D149*, R3. *Panicum alopecuroides* L. An ornamental grass that escapes.

clandestinum Hochst. ex Chiov.　　　　　　　　　　　　　　Kikuyu-grass
- A wool casual. Tropical Africa, (widespread). BM, K, LIV, NMW, RNG. D5*, D6*, D13, D15*, D16*, D20*, D37*, D44*, D88*, D93*, D116*, D118*, J15(108:34), R2, R3, R38, R48, R54, R65, R86, R110. Although usually a stoloniferous procumbent non-flowering grass in temperate regions, it flowered in the field in the hot summer of 1973 at Blackmoor (N Hants). **Fig.15.**

glaucum (L.) R.Br.　　　　　　　　　　　　　　　　　　　Pearl Millet
- Found as a garden weed at Leicester in 1915; also occured in a mixture of maize and millet planted for pheasant cover at Cavenham (W Suffolk) in 1992. Tropical Africa, (widely cultivated in the tropics). ?RNG. D13, D37*, D88*, D93*, D135, J1(4:593). *P.americanum* (L.) Leeke; *P.fallax* (Fig. & De Not.) Stapf & C.E.Hubb.; *P.typhoides* (Burm.) Stapf & C.E.Hubb.; *P.violaceum* (Lam.) Rich.; *Panicum americanum* L.; *P.glaucum* L.; *P.lutescens* Weigel, nom. superfl.; *Setaria glauca* (L.) P.Beauv.; *S.lutescens* (Weigel) F.T.Hubb. A very variable species which is much confused nomenclaturally with *Setaria pumila* (q.v.).

[**nubicum** (Hochst.) K.Schum. ex Engl.
Cultivated from bird-seed. NE Africa, Arabia. BM, K, NMW, HbCGH. J8(28:18), J80*(t.3643), J112*(14:366,392), R21. *Beckeropsis nubica* (Hochst.) Fig. & De Not.; *Gymnothrix nubica* Hochst.]

[petiolaris (Hochst.) Chiov.
  Cultivated from bird-seed.   NE Africa.   NMW, HbCGH.   J8(28:18),
  J59(3*:55-57; 4:165), J80*(t.3643), R21. *Beckeropsis petiolaris* (Hochst.) Fig.
  & De Not.; *Gymnothrix petiolaris* Hochst.]
sphacelatum (Nees) T.Durand & Schinz
  • A wool casual.   E tropical and NE Africa, S Africa.   E, K, RNG, SLBI.
  D5*, D13, R3.   *Gymnothrix sphacelata* Nees. **Fig.26.**
thunbergii Kunth
  • A wool casual from Yeovil tip (S Somerset) in 1958; also cultivated from
  bird-seed, but needs confirmation.   Tropical and southern Africa, Yemen,
  Sri Lanka, (Australia). K. D13, D37*, D190, R21, R65. *P.glabrum* Hochst.
  ex Steud. The wool-alien record from Blackmoor (N Hants) in 1973 (ref.R2,
  R3) was an error for *P.sphacelatum*.

CENCHRUS L.   534

  22 species. Tropics and sub-tropics. Bush land, open grassland and weedy
  places. *C.ciliaris* (Buffel-grass) is a forage species resistant to drought and
  hard grazing. Ref.J92(37:259-351).

ciliaris L.   Buffel-grass
  • A wool casual.   Africa, SW Asia, India, (widespread).   BM, CGE, E, K,
  LTN. D1, D5*, D16*, D17*, D20*, D27*, D37*, D41*, D63*, D88*, D93*,
  D115*, D118, D135*, R1, R2, R5, R47, R65.   *Pennisetum cenchroides*
  A.Rich.; *P.ciliare* (L.) Link. An apomictic and variable grass used for pasture.
echinatus L.   Spiny Sandbur
  • A casual of wool and soya-bean.   N and S America, (widespread).   K, MNE,
  RNG. D2*, D6*, D15*, D16*, D17*, D26*, D63*, D88*, D93*, D118,
  J41(6:86), R38, R48, R65, R105.
incertus M.A.Curtis
  • A wool casual; also cultivated from bird-seed.   N and S America,
  (widespread).   BM, E, K, NMW, RNG.   D2, D5*, D7, D15*, D16, D17,
  D41*, D44*, D75*, D88*(pp.30,32), D93*, D115*, D118, J15(108:34), R1,
  R2, R5, R21, R48, R65, R86, R110. *C.pauciflorus* Benth.; *C.tribuloides* auct.
  pro parte, non L.
longispinus (Hack.) Fernald
  • A wool alien; cultivated from bird-seed and also from pheasant food near
  Cambridge in 1994. N America, (Europe, Australia). K. D1, D2, D7, D10*,
  D42*, D53*, D59*, D88, D93*, D118*, R83. *C.echinatus* forma *longispinus*
  Hack.; *C.pauciflorus* var. *longispinus* (Hack.) Jansen & Wacht.; *C.tribuloides*
  auct. pro parte, non L. This species is much confused with *C.incertus*. **Fig.8.**
pennisetiformis Hochst. & Steud. ex Steud.
  • A wool casual.   Tropical E Africa to India, (Australia).   BM, CGE, E, K,
  LIV, RNG, SLBI. D13*, D37*, D93*, D135, R2, R5, R65, R110. Appears
  to be the hybrid *C.ciliaris* × *C.setigerus*.

setigerus Vahl
- A wool casual. Tropical E Africa, SW Asia to India, (Australia). E, K, RNG. D13, D16, D37*, D39a*, D93*, D95*, J93*(15:283), R1, R2, R5, R118.

[tribuloides L.
- A wool casual. Eastern USA, West Indies. BM, RNG. D6*, D40*, D53, D88*, R1. *C.vaginatus* Steud. These records are almost certainly an error for *C.incertus* or *C.longispinus*.]

SNOWDENIA C.E.Hubb.   537

4 species. NE tropical Africa, Arabia. Forest margins.

polystachya (Fresen.) Pilg.
- A wool casual. NE tropical Africa, Arabia. CGE, E, K, RNG. D13, D36*, D37*, J58*(109:165-171), R1, R5. *Beckera polystachya* Fresen. **Fig.19.**

ANDROPOGONEAE

MISCANTHUS Andersson   570

c.20 species. Mainly SE Asia, but extending to Africa. Open places, as hillsides and marshes. Several of the larger species are grown in gardens.

sacchariflorus (Maxim.) Hack.
- A garden escape, established by a gravel pit near Twyford (Berks) in 1973. E Asia. RNG. D6, D14, D56, D81*, D111*, D136*, D149*, D184*, J55(26:33), R9. *M.saccharifer* Benth.; *Imperata sacchariflora* Maxim.

sinensis Andersson
- One large clump established in a gravel pit at Ripley (Surrey) in 1983; a common ornamental grass; recently grown experimentally in western Europe including Britain as a bio-mass crop. SE Asia, (widespread). D6*, D14, D18, D26*, D56, D81*, D93*, D115, D118, R114. *Eulalia japonica* Trin. Hybrid strains with *M.sacchariflorus* have also been grown. **Fig.14.**

MICROSTEGIUM Nees   578

c.15 species. Tropical Asia; probably introduced in Africa. Shady places.

[vimineum (Trin.) A.Camus
Cultivated from bird-seed. Tropical Asia, (USA). BM, HbCGH. D6*, D81*, D88*, R21. *Andropogon vimineus* Trin.; *Eulalia viminea* (Trin.) Kuntze. **Fig.12.**]

SORGHUM Moench   **584**

c.20 species. Tropics and subtropics of the Old World; 1 species endemic in
Mexico. Forest margins and savanna, with a preference for ruderal habitats.
S.bicolor (Great Millet, Sorghum) is an important tropical cereal, probably first
domesticated in the Sudan over 3000 years ago. *S.halepense* (Johnson-grass)
is grown for forage. Ref.J105(65:477-484).

arundinaceum (Desv.) Stapf
  • A cotton casual at Oldham (S Lancs) in 1976. Africa to India and Australia,
  (tropical America). K, HbEJC. D13*, D37*, D63*, D93, D142*, J8(18:11),
  J20*(55:227-229). *S.bicolor* subsp. *arundinaceum* (Desv.) de Wet &
  J.R.Harlan; *Andropogon arundinaceus* Willd., non Bergius nec Scop.; *Rhaphis
  arundinacea* Desv. Includes *S.lanceolatum* Stapf; *S.verticilliflorum* (Steud.)
  Stapf. A very variable plant, split into 13 species in ref.J20(55:191-260).
bicolor (L.) Moench   **Great Millet**
  ••• A casual of wool and bird-seed, found on tips and around docks. Origin
  obscure, probably Sudan, (widespread crop). BM, BRISTM, K, LSR, LTN,
  NMW, OXF, RNG, SLBI. D1, D2, D15*, D16, D20*, D25*, D55*, D67*,
  D75*, D115*, J1(10:458; 11:47,288; 12:82), J10(28:313; 29:107),
  J14(123:249), J18(340:27), J23(1:242; 9:188; 16:170), R1, R5, R11, R20,
  R21, R36, R38, R39, R40, R55, R59, R61, R62, R64, R73, R105.
  S.caffrorum (Retz.) P.Beauv.; *S.cernuum* (Ard.) Host; *S.dochna* (Forssk.)
  Snowden; *S.saccharatum* (L.) Pers.; *S.sorghum* (L.) Druce; *S.vulgare* Pers.;
  Andropogon sorghum (L.) Brot.; *Holcus bicolor* L.; *H.sorghum* L. A very
  variable species, largely due to cultivation of various strains, and divisible into
  several subspecies that are poorly delimited.
halepense (L.) Pers.   **Johnson-grass**
  ••• A casual of wool, bird-seed, oil-seed and wasteland, sometimes persistent
  for a few years, as at Erith Oil Works (W Kent) and Southampton (S Hants).
  Med., SW Asia, (widespread). BM, BRISTM, E, K, NMW, RNG. D1, D2*,
  D5*, D6*, D15*, D16*, D17*, D19*, D20*, D25*, D75*, D88*, D115*,
  D116*, D117*, J1(10:359; 11:517; 12:82), J10(38:45), J18(407:41), J23(9:188;
  11:273), R1, R2, R5, R20, R21, R36, R39, R41, R54, R55, R57, R59, R82,
  R86. *Andropogon halepensis* (L.) Brot.; *Holcus halepensis* L. **Fig.20.**

DICHANTHIUM Willemet   **591**

c.20 species. Old World tropics. Open places from subdesert to marsh land,
particularly when subject to disturbance. The lower glumes are sometimes
pitted. Separated from *Bothriochloa* by having racemes with solid pedicels and
internodes, without a translucent median line.

[**annulatum** (Forssk.) Stapf
  Cultivated from wool carpet waste in 1986. Tropical Africa and Asia,
  (widespread). HbCGH. D5*, D13, D37*, D41*, D81*, D87*, D88*, D135,
  R65. *Andropogon annulatus* Forssk.; including var. *papillosum* (A.Rich.)

de Wet & J.R.Harlan; *D.papillosum* (A.Rich.) Stapf; *Andropogon papillosus*
A.Rich.]

sericeum (R.Br.) A.Camus subsp. **humilius** (J.M.Black) B.K.Simon
• A wool casual. Australia. K, LIV, RNG. D7, D8*, D10*(as *D.affine*),
D16*, D27*, R2, R65, R110. *D.humilius* J.M.Black.

sericeum (R.Br.) A.Camus subsp. **sericeum**
• A wool casual. Australia, SE Asia. BM, E, K, LTN, RNG. D7, D8*,
D16*, D26*, D27*, D41*, D44*, D93*, R1, R3, R5, R47, R110. *D.affine*
(R.Br.) A.Camus; *Andropogon sericeus* R.Br. **Fig.19.**

BOTHRIOCHLOA Kuntze   595

c.35 species. Tropics and warm temperate regions. Open grassy places. The
lower glumes are often pitted.

decipiens (Hack.) C.E.Hubb.
• A wool casual. Australia. E, K, LIV, RNG. D7, D10*, D16*, D29, D93*,
R2, R5, R65, R110. *Andropogon pertusus* (L.) Willd. var. *decipiens* Hack.

insculpta (Hochst. ex A.Rich.) A.Camus
• A wool casual. Sicily, Africa to Yemen, (Australia). BM, RNG. D1, D5*,
D13, D37*, D82*, R1, R3, R65. *Andropogon insculptus* Hochst. ex A.Rich.;
Dichanthium insculptum (Hochst. ex A.Rich.) Clayton. Possibly an erroneous
identification for another species.

ischaemum (L.) Keng
• A wool casual. Europe, N Africa, SW Asia, (USA, Mexico). LIV, RNG.
D1, D18, D20*, D22*, D25*, D31*, D41*, D81*, D88*, D115*, R65.
Andropogon ischaemum L.; *Dichanthium ischaemum* (L.) Roberty. Includes
var. *songarica* (Rupr. ex Fisch. & C.A.Mey.) Celarier & J.R.Harlan. **Fig.19.**

macra (Steud.) S.T.Blake
• A wool casual. Australia. E, K, RNG. D7, D10*, D16*, D26*, D38,
D44*, D93*, R2, R5, R65, R110. *B.ambigua* S.T.Blake; *Andropogon macer*
Steud.

ANDROPOGON L.   606

c.100 species. Tropics and warm temperate regions. Savanna and uplands.

distachyos L.
Pre-1930 only. A casual on ballast. Atlantic Is, Med., Arabia, Africa,
Thailand, (Australia). BM. D1, D25*, D37*, D115*.

ARTHRAXON P.Beauv.   610

c.10 species. Old World tropics, mainly India. Rocky slopes, shady slopes
and old farmland.

hispidus (Thunb.) Makino
- A casual, probably from bird-seed, near Palace Gate, Kensington Gardens (Middlesex) in 1989; also cultivated from bird-seed. S Asia, Australia, (USA). BM. D6*, D18, D81*, D93*, J26(69:143; 73:57), J73*(27:273), R21. *Phalaris hispida* Thunb. Includes *A.cryptatherus* (Hack.) Koidz. (*A.hispidus* var. *cryptatherus* (Hack.) Honda). **Fig.13.**

HYPARRHENIA Andersson ex E.Fourn.   **612**

55 species. Mainly Africa, a few species extending to other tropical regions; 1 variable species in the Med. Often dominant in savanna. Widely used for thatching in Africa. *H.rufa* (Nees) Stapf is widely introduced for forage.

[anthistirioides (Hochst. ex A.Rich.) Stapf
Cultivated from bird-seed. Tanzania, NE Africa. BM, HbCGH. D13, D37*, R21. *Andropogon anthistirioides* Hochst. ex A.Rich. The name is frequently misspelt, as in ref.D37, R21.]
hirta (L.) Stapf
- A wool casual; also on ballast in 1873. Atlantic Is, Med., Africa, SW Asia, (Australia, N and C America). BM, K, LIV, RNG. D1, D5*, D17*, D20*, D25*, D26*, D30*, D31*, D37*, D115*, D117*, D118*, J8(28:18), R21. *Andropogon hirtus* L.; *Cymbopogon hirtus* (L.) Stapf. **Fig.11.**

ZEA L.   **646**

4 species. Central America. Field margins and mountain forest. *Z.mays* (Maize, Corn, Mealies) is a staple cereal in warm regions, also grown for forage, oil, syrup and alcohol. It is not known in the wild, but was apparently domesticated about 7000 years ago.

mays L.   Maize
- • A relic or escape from cultivation; a casual of bird-seed, pet food and food refuse on tips. Origin obscure, probably C America, (widespread crop). BM, BRISTM, LIV, NMW, OXF, RNG, TOR. D1, D2, D6*, D15*, D18, D19*, D20*, D44*, D55*, D67*, D75, D115*, J1(10:359), J10(38:45), R5, R8, R21, R24, R36, R39, R40, R54, R55, R59, R71, R77. **Fig.20.**

COIX L.   **651**

c.5 species. Tropical Asia. Forest margins and swamps. The fruits of *C.lacryma-jobi* (Job's Tears) are used throughout the tropics to make ornamental beads.

lacryma-jobi L.   Job's Tears
- A casual on wasteland at Oxford and Jersey over 50 years ago. Tropical Asia, (widespread). BM, BRISTM, K, OXF. D1, D6*, D13*, D18, D20*, D22*, D67*, D81*, D88*, D115*, D116*, J1(12:302), R36, R40. **Fig.20.**

KEYS

BAMBUSEAE (by D.T.Holyoak)

1	Main stems almost square in section	**Chimonobambusa quadrangularis**
1	Main stems cylindrical or flattened or grooved on one side	2

2   Main stems cylindrical throughout (except sometimes just above each node)
      3

2   Main stems flattened or grooved on one side, at least at upper internodes
      16

3   Nodes of mid-region of main stems mostly with 1(-2) lateral branches   4

3   Nodes of mid-region of main stems mostly with 3 or more lateral branches
      11

4   Leaf blades pubescent or downy, with or without coloured stripes; stems less than 2m high   5

4   Leaf blades glabrous (or at most, minutely downy beneath), although the margins are sometimes hairy or ciliate, without coloured stripes   6

5   Leaf blades pubescent on the lower side, not striped   **Sasaella ramosa**

5   Leaf blades persistently soft-downy on both sides, yellow to light green with darker green stripes of various breadths   **Pleioblastus auricomus**

6   Most leaves less than 5× as long as wide, with 5-14 veins on each side of the midrib   7

6   Most leaves greater than 5× as long as wide, with 2-9 veins on each side of the midrib   8

7   Stems up to 3m high, 10mm diameter; leaves up to 7.0(-9.5)cm wide, with (7-)8-14(-16) veins on each side of the midrib; leaves acuminate, with margins not extensively withered; false-petioles usually green; stem sheaths minutely downy   **Sasa palmata**

7   Stems up to 1.5m high, 7mm diameter; leaves up to 6cm wide, with (5-)6-9 veins on each side of the midrib; leaves more abruptly tapered, with margins often whitish and withered all round the leaf; false-petioles often purplish; stem sheaths often pubescent with white hairs when young   **Sasa veitchii**

8   Stems up to 5m high; leaves 15-30×2-4cm, with 5-9 veins on each side of the midrib; 3/4 of the underside of the leaf glaucous   **Pseudosasa japonica**

8   Stems up to 2m high; leaves 2.5-20.0×0.3-2.5cm, with 2-7 veins on each side of the midrib   9

9   Leaves the same colour on both surfaces; stems to up 15mm diameter
      Pleioblastus chino

9   Underside of leaves paler than upperside on one or both sides of the midrib; stems up to 10mm diameter   10

10 Stems up to 2m high and 10mm diameter; leaves 8-20×1.0-2.5cm
                                            Pleioblastus humilis
10 Stems up to 0.75(-1.20)m high and 3mm diameter; leaves 2.5-7.0×0.3-
    1.5cm   **Pleioblastus pygmaeus**

11 Tallest mature stems typically 2-3m high; nodes of mid-region of main stem
    usually with 3 branches; leaves 8-16×0.6-1.2cm, minutely downy beneath
                                            Chimonobambusa marmorea
11 Tallest mature stems typically greater than 3m; nodes of mid-region of main
    stem often with more than 3 branches; leaves glabrous beneath   12

12 Leaves 1.5-2.5cm wide, mostly with 4-7 veins on each side of the midrib; 1/2
    of underside of the leaf glaucous   **Pleioblastus simonii**
12 Leaves less than 1.2(-1.5)cm wide, mostly with 2-4 veins on each side of the
    midrib   13

13 Leaf-bristles smooth (use ×10 magnification); stem sheaths densely setose;
    stems often purplish; leaf sheath oral setae transparent and smooth, resembling
    glass cylinders   **Fargesia spathacea**
13 Leaf-bristles rough (use ×10 magnification) or rarely absent; stem sheaths
    glabrous (except at the margins)   14

14 Rhizomes long, so stems well-spaced; inflorescence exserted; leaves 6-12cm
    long; leaf sheath oral setae opaque and ± scabrous, especially in the basal
    half   **Yushania anceps**
14 Rhizomes short, so stems tufted; inflorescence partly enveloped by long
    spathaceous bracts   15

15 Stem sheaths with long ciliate ligules; leaf sheaths with long dark ligules;
    leaves 9-13cm long   **Thamnocalamus spathiflorus**
15 Stem sheaths with very short glabrous ligules; leaf sheaths with short light-
    coloured ligules; leaves 6-10cm long   **Fargesia murielae**

16 Nodes of the mid-region of the main stems mostly with 3-5 branches; stems
    often flattened or grooved only at the upper internodes
                                            Semiarundinaria fastuosa
16 Nodes of the mid-region of the main stems mostly with 2 unequal branches
    and often a very small 3rd; stems flattened or grooved on one side throughout
    (*Phyllostachys sp.*)   17

17 Lowest nodes asymmetrical; basal internodes conspicuously shorter than those
    above   **Phyllostachys aurea**
17 Lowest nodes symmetrical; basal internodes not conspicuously shorter than
    those above   18

18 Stems somewhat zig-zag; leaf sheaths usually without auricles or bristles
                                            Phyllostachys flexuosa
18 Stems straight; leaf sheaths usually with auricles and bristles, at least when
    young   19

19 Stem sheaths usually without spots; leaves often less than 5cm long; stem
    internodes often black, blotched or spotted black   **Phyllostachys nigra**
19 Stem sheaths spotted or streaked; leaves mostly longer than 7cm   20

20 White waxy bloom present below the nodes; leaves up to 3.8cm wide; leaf
    sheaths usually with auricles, with bristles which are small and deciduous or
    absent   **Phyllostachys viridiglaucescens**
20 Without white waxy bloom below the nodes; leaves up to 4.5cm wide; leaf
    sheaths usually without auricles, with conspicuous bristles up to 12mm long
                                        Phyllostachys bambusoides

Notes:

The key relies mainly on vegetative characters because most naturalised
bamboos only flower at long intervals. For reliable identification it is
important to select mature stems; young stems are often unidentifiable.
Measurements of leaves should be based on a representative sample from well
above mid-height on the stem. Specimens should consist of (a) a piece of the
middle part of the stem with at least one typical node, (b) a piece of the upper
part of the stem with a representative complement of branches, (c)
representative leaves, (d) accurate notes of stem height, habit, etc., (e)
inflorescences when present.

STIPA   94

1   Glumes over 40mm and awn over 20cm long, with plumose setae. (For
    critical differences see Ref.D1)   **pennata, joannis**
1   Glumes and awn shorter, without plumose setae   2

2   Glumes 25-35mm   3
2   Glumes less than 20mm long (except sometimes *S.filiculmis*)   5

3   Ht. -150(-200)cm; panicles 25-35 cm long, narrow, dense; lemmas c.10mm
    long, membranous, deeply bifid; awns 4-6 cm long, with a hairy column; non-
    flowering shoots with 2 lanate projections 2.5-3.0cm long, ending in a
    plumose subulate apex, protruding from the mouth of the sheath.
                                                          tenacissima
3   Panicles lax; awns scabrid throughout their length; different combination of
    the other characters   4

4   Ht. -250cm; lemma 14-18mm long, membranous, deeply bifid, pale brown;
    awn 7-12cm long   **gigantea**
4   Ht. -100cm; lemma 10-14mm long, coriaceous, pale green; awn 12-20cm
    long   **capillata**

5   Annual; ht. less than 40cm; panicle erect, very dense, eventually twisted into
    a characteristic tail   **capensis**
5   Perennial; ht. usually greater than 40cm; panicle usually less dense,
    untwisted   6

6   Lemma surmounted by a corona (a cylindrical whitish terminal membrane)
    0.2-7.5mm long   7
6   Lemma without a corona (or less than 0.1mm long)   17

7   Corona 5.5-7.5mm long, acutely bilobed; glumes 15-18mm long
                                                           charruana
7   Corona 0.2-1.3mm long; glumes usually shorter   8

8   Lower glume usually longer than 13mm; lemma usually longer than 6mm 9
8   Lower glume up to 11mm long; lemma usually less than 5mm long (except for
    S.formicarum)   11

9   Corona 0.2-0.3mm long; awn 9-11cm long   **tenuis**
9   Corona over 0.4mm long; awn 5-9cm long   10

10 Lemma 7-10(-13)mm long, 1.0-1.5mm dia.; corona 0.4-0.7mm long, slightly
    contracted at the base   **neesiana**
10 Lemma 6-9mm long, c.0.8mm dia.; corona 0.5mm long, cylindric and not
    contracted at the base, so that it is continuous with the sides of the lemma
                                                          poeppigiana

11 Lower glume 10-11mm long; corona 1.0-1.3mm long; lemma 4.5-6.5mm
    long   **formicarum**
11 Lower glume less than 10mm and corona less than 1.0mm long   12

12 Corona 0.5-0.7mm long; awn 2.5-3.5cm long; lemma 3-5mm long,
    glabrous   **hyalina**
12 Corona 0.2-0.4mm long; lemma usually less than 4mm long (except
    S.brachyphylla)   13

13 Lemma uniformly sparsely pilose   14
13 Lemma glabrous   16

14 Mature lemma pale; corona cylindrical (0.6mm dia.); awns 1.2-1.4cm long,
    shortly hairy   **brachychaetoides**
14 Mature lemma brown; corona cup-shaped or obconical (0.4mm dia.)   15

15 Lemma 3.5-4.0mm with callus 0.5mm long; awn 2.3-3.5cm long, glabrous;
    panicle branches bearing c.10 spikelets   **philippii**
15 Lemma 4-6mm with callus 1mm long; awn c.2cm long, with the first segment
    twisted, pubescent; panicle branches bearing 1-3 spikelets **brachyphylla**

16 Lemma obovoid, with a basal tuft of long (5mm) hairs rising above it; corona
    long-ciliate (hairs 1-2mm); awn less than 4cm long   **pampeana**
16 Lemma narrowly cylindrical without a basal tuft of hairs; corona very short-
    ciliate (hairs 0.1mm); awn 5-9cm long   **tenuissima**

17 Lower glume 16-25mm long; lemma 7-8mm long, 0.5-0.6mm dia.; awn 7.0-
    9.0cm long   **filiculmis**
17 Lower glume, awn and usually the lemma shorter   18

18 Lemma with a ring or tuft of apical hairs (coma)   19
18 Lemma without distinct apical hairs   24

19 Coma tufted, 2.5-7.0mm long   20
19 Coma in a ring, 0.5-1.7mm long   22

20 Coma 4.0-7.0mm long, pure white; lemma glabrous, narrow (6-9mm
    long×0.4mm dia.)   **papposa**
20 Coma 2.5-5.0mm long, dirty white; lemma hairy, rather plump (c.1mm
    dia.)   21

21 Coma 2.5-3.0mm long; lower glume 6-10mm long; lemma 4-5mm long; awn
    2.5-3.0cm long   **ambigua**
21 Coma 3.0-5.0mm long; lower glume 12-16mm long; lemma 6-8mm long; awn
    4.0-5.5cm long   **blackii**

22 Not densely caespitose; panicle green or yellow, spreading or loosely
contracted; ligules 0.5-3.0mm long, membranous; awn (1.5-)2.0-3.0cm long;
glumes 9-12mm long, aristate; lemma swollen, 5-7mm long, ± hairy,
especially on the margins, yellow or brown; palea enclosed in the lemma
                                                                    aristiglumis
22 Densely caespitose; panicle pale to brown; ligules very short, ciliate; awn less
than 2cm long; glumes 7-10mm long, acute or shortly aristate; lemma 4.5-
7.0mm long; palea tip soon visible, sticking out sideways from the lemma
                                                                                    23

23 Lemma all hairy; caryopsis oblong (c.3×1mm)   **brachychaeta**
23 Lemma hairy on the principal nerve and margins; caryopsis obovoid
(c.3.0×1.4mm)   **caudata**

24 Awn bristle falcate, 5-8cm long; mature lemmas greenish to pale brown 25
24 Awn bristle not falcate, though sometimes straight; awn up to 3cm long;
mature lemmas brown   27

25 Panicle dense, contracted, shining; leaves coarse   **nitida**
25 Panicle loose and wavy; leaves fine   26

26 Ht. 20-50cm; awn hairs less than 0.2mm long; lemma 4-6mm long   27
26 Ht. 30-80cm; awn hairs 0.25-1.5mm long; lemma 5-7mm long   **variabilis**

27 Inflorescence narrow; ligules 0.6-1.0mm long   **scabra** subsp. **scabra**
27 Inflorescence spreading; ligules 0.3-0.6mm long   **scabra** subsp. **falcata**

28 Lemma glabrous (at least in the upper 4/5 of its length), papillose; awn 2.5-
3.0cm long   **juergensii**
28 Lemma hairy   29

29 Awn straight, 1.0-1.5cm long   **dregiana**
29 Awn geniculate, 2.5-3.0cm long   30

30 Glumes 8-9mm long; lemmas 5mm long   **richardsonii**
30 Glumes 5-6mm long; lemmas 4mm long; stem branched, straight and wiry
('bamboo' like) with short filiform pungent leaves well-spaced up the stem and
short loose sheaths which soon wither; panicle subverticillate
                                                                   verticillata

Note:
    The key by B.K.Simon (ref.D7) has been used for many of the Australian
species.

POA   **124**

1   Small annual (occasionally short-lived perennial), ht.3-30cm; leaves short,
    ± flat, panicle branches single or paired   2
1   Perennial, usually taller   3

2   Florets ± crowded; lower panicle branches spreading or deflexed after
    anthesis; spikelets 3-10mm long; lemmas 2.5-4.0mm long; anthers 0.7-1.3mm
    long   **annua**
2   Florets rather distant; lower panicle branches erect to spreading after anthesis;
    spikelets 2-4mm long; lemmas 2.0-2.5mm long; anthers 0.2-0.5mm long
                                                                   infirma

3   Plants hermaphrodite   4
3   Plants dioecious; caespitose; leaves narrow, with long ligules; panicle linear-
    oblong, interrupted, dense   **ligularis**

4   Large tussock-grass with short-awned lemmas   **flabellata**
4   Lemmas unawned   5

5   Culms slender with bulbous bases   **bulbosa**
5   Culm bases not markedly bulbous   6

6   Some leaves 5-12mm wide   7
6   Leaves up to 4mm wide   8

7   Panicle branches short, erecto-patent; glumes unequal; lemmas sparsely
    webbed at the base   **chaixii**
7   Panicle branches long, arcuate-patent; glumes subequal; lemmas distinctly
    webbed at the base   **remota**

8   Creeping rhizomes present, spreading out beyond the basal tuft; lemmas
    webbed at the base   9
8   Rhizomes short, not spreading beyond the basal tuft, or absent   12

9   Panicle very loose, with branches in distant pairs (or the lowest sometimes in
    3's); ligules 3-5mm long; mature spikelets (6-)8-11mm long   **fordeana**
9   Panicle loose or contracted, with branches paired or in clusters of 3-5; ligule
    very short to 3mm long (usually shorter); mature spikelets usually shorter
                                                                        10

10 Culms flattened, wiry, 4-6 noded, often grey-green; branches paired or
    clustered; spikelets 3-10 flowered, 3-8mm long   **compressa**
10 Culms circular in section, 1-4 noded, green; branches in clusters of 3-5;
    spikelets 2-5 flowered, 2.5-6.0mm long   11

11 Basal leaves often long (-30cm) and bristle-like, 1-2mm wide; upper ligule up
    to 1mm long; lemmas 2-3mm long   **angustifolia**
11 Basal leaves often shorter, 2-4(-6)mm wide, folded or flat; upper ligule 1-
    3mm long; lemmas 3-5mm long   **pratensis**

12 Grasses forming ± dense, often large tussocks; basal leaves often very long (-40cm or more) and relatively very narrow (0.5-3.5mm); ligules 0.1-2.0mm long   13

12 Grasses ± densely caespitose but rarely forming a tussock; basal leaves narrow, flat or folded, shorter (-20cm); ligules 0.1-10.0mm long   18

13 Panicle contracted or linear, or if with spreading branches, then at least some short and bearing spikelets almost to the base; spikelets (4-)6-8mm long; lemmas 3-6mm long   **poiformis**

13 Panicle open, with branches naked below; spikelets and lemmas usually smaller   14

14 Leaves ± cylindrical, straight and rigid   15

14 Leaves narrow, long and flaccid   16

15 Lemmas 2.5-3.5mm long   **gunnii**

15 Lemmas c.4.5mm long   **costiniana**

16 Culms with aerial shoots or stolons, finally far-spreading; mature leaves distinctly bluish, c.0.5mm wide   **sieberiana** var. **cyanophylla**

16 Culms without aerial shoots or stolons; mature leaves green or grey-green, c.1.0-2.5mm wide   17

17 Leaves abaxially smooth; spikelets (3.5-)6.0-9.0mm long; glumes (2.0-)3.5-5.0(-6.0)mm long; lemmas 3-5(-6)mm long   **cita**

17 Leaves usually abaxially scabrous; spikelets 3-7mm long; glumes 1.5-3.5mm long; lemmas c.2-4mm long   **labillardierei**

18 Loosely tufted, stoloniferous;culm leaves 3-20cm long, 1.5-6.0mm wide; ligules pointed, 4-10mm long; leaf-sheaths rough to the touch; panicle branches in clusters of 3-7   **trivialis**

18 Without stolons; culm leaves 0.4-3.0mm wide; ligules blunt, 0.1-5.0(-6.0)mm long; leaf-sheaths not especially rough in most species   19

19 Sometimes with short rhizomes; ht. 80-120cm; panicle narrow, rather dense, 10-15cm long; spikelets hardly compressed, narrow, 8-10mm long; lemmas 4-6mm long   **ampla**

19 Spikelets compressed, usually less than 6mm long; lemmas usually less than 4mm long   20

20 Delicate fine grasses; upper ligule very short, up to 0.5mm long   21

20 Delicate or coarser grasses; upper ligule (0.8-)1.0-5.0(-6.0)mm long   22

21 Laxly tufted with filiform basal leaves; culm leaves c.0.4mm wide; ht. 10-50cm; panicle lax and very delicate; length of the spikelets 3-4mm, lower glume 0.8-1.5mm, upper glume 1.3-1.8mm, lemmas 1.8-2.2mm, paleas 1.2-2.0mm   **imbecilla**

21 Caespitose with few basal leaves; culm leaves 1-3mm wide; ht. 15-90cm; panicle lax or contracted, moderately delicate; length of the spikelets 3-6mm, lower glume 2-3mm, upper glume 2.5-3.5mm, lemmas and paleas 2.6-3.6mm   **nemoralis**

22 Caespitose; ht.15-50cm; ligules 1-2(-3)mm long; culm leaves 1(-2)mm wide;
    panicle 3-10cm long, loose, narrow or contracted, with ascending branches in
    clusters of 1-3   23
22 Loosely caespitose; ht. up to 150cm; ligules typically 2-5mm long; culm
    leaves 2-4mm wide; panicle 10-30cm long   24

23 Loosely caespitose, slightly glaucous, with green spikelets; culms erect from
    a geniculate base, almost smooth below the narrow panicle; panicle branches
    slightly scabrid; upper ligule c.1mm long (details taken from our alien
    material)   **balfourii**
23 Densely caespitose, green with pale brown spikelets; culms numerous, wiry,
    geniculate, distinctly scabrid below the contracted panicle; panicle branches
    very scabrid; upper ligule c.1.5mm long (details taken from our alien
    material)   **sterilis** group

24 Culms relatively stout, erect; ht.30-150cm; panicle ovate, open and loose,
    with spreading almost smooth branches in clusters of 3-6   **palustris**
24 Culms slender, weakly erect or straggling; ht.20-100cm; panicle very loose
    with spreading or erect slightly scabrid branches in remote clusters of 1-3
                                                                             25

25 Panicle linear and contracted, with densely clustered spikelets on ascending
    branches which are appressed to the rhachis   **leptoclada**
25 Panicle very open, with flexuous branches, spreading, ascending or
    reflexed   **schimperiana**

AGROSTIS   197

1   Palea length less than 1/3 lemma   2
1   Palea length greater than 1/3 lemma   9

2   Annual   3
2   Perennial   5

3   Spikelets 2.0-2.5mm long, usually greenish; awn c.3mm long from the middle
     of the lemma; anthers c.1mm long   **pourretii**
3   Spikelets to 2mm long; 0 awn; anthers to 0.5mm long   4

4   Spikelets c.0.8mm long, purplish; anthers c.0.3mm long; leaves flat, to
     1.5mm wide   **tenerrima**
4   Spikelets 1.5-2.0mm long; anthers 0.3-0.5mm long; leaves filiform, less than
     1mm wide   **parviflora**

5   Plant not tufted, with long slender rhizomes; panicle narrow, open, with some
     branches naked below   **diegoensis**
5   Plant tufted, without rhizomes; panicle narrow or open   6

6   Panicle dense, spike-like, small (3-10cm×5-15mm); leaves very narrow
     (0.2-0.3mm wide)   **curtisii**
6   Panicle narrow (leaves over 2mm wide) or very diffuse (leaves c.1-3mm
     wide), usually over 10cm long   7

7   Panicle narrow, with branches crowded and densely flowered to the base
                                                           exarata
7   Panicle very diffuse, the secondary branches arising from towards the end of
     the capillary primary branches   8

8   Ht. 30-100cm; spikelets 2.0-2.7mm long; lemmas 1.5-1.7mm long, distinctly
     longer than the grain; anthers 0.4-0.5mm long; leaves 1-3mm wide
                                                            scabra
8   Ht. 30-40cm; spikelets 1.5-1.7mm long; lemmas 1.0-1.2mm long, scarcely
     longer than the grain; anthers c.0.2mm long; leaves less than 1mm wide
                                                          hyemalis

9   Annual; panicle very lax; spikelets c.1.5mm long; glumes lanceolate, obtuse;
     lemmas c.0.5mm long   **nebulosa**
9   Mostly perennial, or annual with much larger spikelets and acute glumes 10

10   Lemmas pilose on the back   11
10   Lemmas glabrous or sparsely hairy on the sides   15

11   Panicle narrow, loosely contracted, 5-30×1-3cm, with some branches bearing
     spikelets to the base; spikelets 2.0-2.5mm long, awnless or with an awn
     -0.5mm long; ligules c.4mm long   **lacnantha**
11   Spikelets over 3mm long; lemmas long-awned (5-7mm), ending in 4 obscure
     teeth; ligules often very long (-10mm) and acute   12

12 Panicle small (-10cm long) and rather dense; culm smooth below the panicle; spikelets 3-4mm long   **preissii**
12 Panicle much larger (-30cm long), included in the top sheath, or open, or very diffuse   13

13 Perennials with long creeping rhizomes; culm smooth below the panicle (when visible!); rachilla not produced; panicle diffuse with divaricate rather stiff branches; spikelets typically 4.5mm long; lemma 3.5mm long, covered with coarse bristly hairs   **eriantha**
13 Tufted annuals or short-lived perennials; culms retrorsely scabrid below the panicle; rachilla produced   14

14 Spikelets (3.5-)4-5(-6)mm long; panicle branches finally spreading but not drooping; leaves 3-7mm wide; anthers 0.6-1.2mm long   **aemula**
14 Spikelets (2-)3-3.5(-4)mm long; panicle very diffuse with the spikelets on long capillary branches, often finally deflexed; leaves usually less than 2mm wide; anthers 0.2-0.4mm long   **avenacea**

15 Annual; panicle very lax and open; spikelets 4-5mm long; awns 5-6mm long   **billardieri** var. **filifolia**
15 Perennial; panicle oblong to ovate, initially open, sometimes becoming contracted; spikelets 2.0-2.5mm long, not long-awned (except sometimes for *A.castellana*)   16

16 Rhizome short, with up to 3 scale buds; panicle oblong, loose and spreading, becoming contracted after anthesis, 15-20×4-8cm; terminal spikelets awned (-5mm long) from near the lemma base or unawned; lateral spikelets unawned; lemma callus sometimes bearing tufts of 0.3mm long hairs   **castellana**
16 Rhizome longer, with 3 or more scale buds; panicle oblong to ovate, loose and spreading, not contracted after anthesis; spikelets unawned or sometimes with short awns (-2mm) from near the lemma apex; lemma callus very shortly hairy   17

17 Upper ligules of the vegetative shoots 0.5-2.0mm long, shorter than wide; leaves 1-5mm wide   **capillaris**
17 Upper ligules of the vegetative shoots 1.5-6.0mm long, as long as or longer than wide; leaves 2-8mm wide   **gigantea**

Note:
   The very common native grass *A.stolonifera* L. is similar in general appearance to *A.castellana* (and may be confused if the species hybridise); both have well-developed paleas, truncate ligules on the flowering stems and panicles which contract after anthesis. However it differs in having stolons and sometimes short rhizomes (not short stout rhizomes), awns when occasionally present almost terminal on the lemmas (not almost basal), shorter primary panicle branches bearing spikelets nearly to the base (not bare in the lower 1/3-1/2), and the callus of the lemma minutely hairy (not sometimes bearing

tufts of 0.3mm long hairs). Another common native grass, *A.canina* L., which has a minute palea, is unlikely to be confused with *A.exarata* because of its more open panicle with branches which do not bear spikelets in the lower 1/2.

POLYPOGON   212

1   Glumes c.2mm long with 0 awns; panicle densely cylindrical, lobed, sometimes interrupted below with clustered semi-verticillate branches
                                                                      viridis
1   Glumes awned   2

2   Annual; glumes 4-5mm long, tapering into awns 8-9mm long; lemma 2mm long, with a stout dorsal persistent geniculate awn 12mm in total length; callus and base of the glumes densely bearded   **tenellus**
2   Plant with different characters   3

3   Annual; ht. usually less than 50cm   4
3   Perennial; ht. -120cm   7

4   Glumes (3-)4-6mm long, narrow, covered with short stout spinules, hardly emarginate; callus 0.5mm long, expanded at the top, villous   **linearis**
4   Glumes 2-3mm long, with few spinules; callus c.0.2mm long, slightly swollen, ± pubescent   5

5   Glumes 2.0-2.3mm long, deeply bifid to c.1/4 their length; lemma with 0 awn; ht. 5-15cm   **maritimus**
5   Glumes 2-3mm long, slightly emarginate; lemma with a fugacious awn (visibly excurrent from the glumes in some spikelets); ht. 5-50(-80)cm   6

6   Glume awns 2-4mm long; lemma awn c.1mm long   **fugax**
6   Glume awns 6-8mm long; lemma awn c.3mm long   **monspeliensis**

7   Ligule -10mm long; glumes unequal, 2.5-4.0mm long, gradually narrowed into awns 1.5-3.0mm long   **elongatus**
7   Ligule 2-5mm long; glumes abruptly rounded at the summit   8

8   Glumes 1.5-2.0mm long, with delicate flexuous awns 4-6mm long
                                                                     australis
8   Glumes 2.5-3.0mm long, with stiff straight awns 3-5mm long
                                                                   interruptus

Note:
   S.viridis resembles an *Agrostis* species, but the spikelets fall entire with part of the pedicel, not disarticulating above the persistent glumes.

ERAGROSTIS   356

1   Perennial with dense tuft of glaucous basal leaves; panicle open, small (up to 16cm long, 8cm wide); glumes yellowish; lemmas obtuse, variegated (purplish below with a yellow tip)   **bicolor**
1   Grasses with different combinations of characters   2

2   Small desert grass (ht. 15-50cm) with short erect setaceous leaves and a conspicuously swollen ± bulbous base   **setifolia**
2   Base not ± bulbous   3

3   Spikelets terete or strongly biconvex   4
3   Spikelets ± flat   7

4   Lemma with lateral nerves closer to the margin than the middle; spikelets up to 1mm wide, ± straight, pedicellate, and distant in a small diffuse panicle
                                                                    lacunaria
4   Lemma with lateral nerves not more than mid-way between the margin and the middle; panicle ± condensed   5

5   Perennial with long (-2cm) flexuous sickle-shaped spikelets, pedicellate and rather distant   **falcata**
5   Annual; spikelets curved, sessile, often clustered in a small panicle   6

6   Lemma 1.7-2.5mm long; spikelets 1.0-1.5mm wide   **dielsii**
6   Lemma 1.5-1.6mm long; spikelets 0.7-1.0mm wide   **pergracilis**

7   Leaf margins (nearly always) with a row of tuberculate glands; some pedicels / spikelets glandular   8
7   Leaf margins without a row of tuberculate glands   10

8   Spikes contracted, up to 10cm long, terminal and also from all the lower leaf sheaths; lemma acute, 2.0-2.5mm long; grain oblong, light brown
                                                                  procumbens
8   Spikes more open, usually over 10cm long and not arising from most of the lower leaf sheaths; lemma obtuse   9

9   Grain sub-globular, 0.5mm long; lemma (1.7-)2.0-2.8mm long   **cilianensis**
9   Grain broadly oblong, 0.7-0.8mm long; lemma 1.5-2.0mm long   **minor**

10 Spikelets ovate to oblong (up to 1cm long in *E.wilmaniae*), 2.5-4.0mm wide, in a small open or contracted panicle; pedicels shorter than the spikelets
                                                                           11
10 Spikelets lanceolate, linear or oblong, usually less than 2.5mm wide or with long pedicels   13

11 Spikelets 2.5-3.0mm wide; palea keel with a large tooth-like flap from the lower half   **echinochloidea**
11 Spikelets 3-4mm wide; palea keel without a flap   12

12 Annual; ht. usually less than 20cm; panicle contracted; spikelets up to c.10mm long; lemma pale, acute, with prominent lateral nerves; palea acute with scabrous keels   **wilmaniae**
12 Perennial; ht. usually greater than 20cm; panicle ovate (to 12cm long, 8cm wide), spikelets 3-4mm long; lemma pallid to dark grey, boat-shaped, with obscure lateral nerves; palea keels with short rigid patent hairs   **obtusa**

13 Culm base flattened to flabellate (see also *E.planiculmis*); glumes small and unequal (lower less than 2/3 as long as upper)   14
13 Culm base not especially flattened   15

14 Panicle long and narrow (to 30×5cm); lemma obtuse with prominent gland-pitted lateral nerves; anthers 1.6mm long; ripe grain c.1.4mm long with a bumpy surface   **plana**
14 Panicle elliptic (5-20cm long); lemma oblong-elliptic with obscure lateral nerves; anthers 0.5-0.9mm long; grain 1.0mm long; (spikelets have a characteristic saw-tooth profile)   **tenuifolia**

15 Weedy annual with many small axillary panicles emerging from the leaf sheaths   16
15 Few or no axillary panicles from the leaf sheaths   17

16 Panicles ± densely contracted, with/without glands; glumes subequal; spikelets c.7mm long, 2.0-2.5mm wide   **procumbens**
16 Terminal panicle branches and spikelets spreading rigidly; pedicels with glands; glumes unequal; spikelets 5-15mm long, 1.5mm wide; there is a band of glandular tissue below the culm nodes   **barrelieri**

17 Pedicels with conspicuous yellow glands or rings in the upper half (at least on the wool-alien material of *E.neesii* and also sometimes on *E.tenuifolia*)   18
17 Pedicels without yellow glands in the upper half (but *E.glandulosipedata* sometimes has inconspicuous glands in the lower half)   19

18 Panicle rather dense, linear-oblong, (3-9×1-3cm); spikelets 2-7mm long, 1-2mm wide, with 3-15 florets; lemma c.1.5mm long, ovate, with visible lateral nerves   **neesii**
18 Panicle very open, up to 20×10cm; spikelets c.9mm long, 2mm wide, with c.12 florets; lemma 2mm long, bluntly acute, with obscure lateral nerves   **leptostachya**

19 Panicle narrow, straight, contracted, especially when young (but may open out a little when mature); (see also forms of *E.curvula*, *E.bahiensis* var. *contracta*)   20
19 Panicle not contracted   23

20 Spikelets only 1mm long, with 3-5 florets; panicle at first spike-like, but later
    the lower branches may spread   **kennedyae**
20 Spikelets larger, usually with more florets   21

21 Spikelets with 2-7 florets, 1.5-2.4mm wide; lemma 2-3mm long, acuminate,
    sometimes with elongated blackish spots on or near the nerves (not always
    evident)   **caesia**
21 Spikelets with more than 6 florets, up to 2mm wide; lemma less than 2mm
    long, acute   22

22 Spikelets in dense sessile clusters, the panicle often interrupted towards the
    base; lemma with distinct lateral nerves   **elongata**
22 Spikelets shortly pedicelled in a narrow linear panicle; lemma with indistinct
    lateral nerves   **kiwuensis**

23 Mature spikelets usually with 2-6(-7) florets (see also *E.lugens* with (3-)5-9
    florets)   24
23 Mature spikelets usually with more than (5-)6 florets   27

24 Grain circular to spherical, dark red, strongly reticulate with minute apiculi;
    panicle diffuse; spikelets long-pedicelled; florets/spikelet (3-)4-6(-7); sheaths
    ± glabrous; lemmas 1.8-2.0mm long (see note)   **trachycarpa**
24 Grain different; florets/spikelet 2-5   25

25 Annual; grain oblong, dark red, faintly reticulate, sulcate; panicle very
    diffuse, up to 30cm long and 2/3 ht. of plant; spikelets long-pedicelled;
    florets/spikelet 2-4; sheaths hairy, long-pilose at the throat; lemmas 1.3-
    1.5mm long   **capillaris**
25 Perennial; panicle open; spikelets short-pedicelled; sheaths ± glabrous   26

26 Lower panicle branches in distinct whorls well separated up the panicle axis,
    with long white basal hairs; spikelets c.5mm long, pale or grey-green; lemmas
    and upper glume c.2mm long, acute   **trichophora**
26 Panicle much denser, the branches not in obvious whorls; spikelets c.2mm
    long, dark grey; lemmas and upper glume c.1.5mm long, obtuse
                                                          glandulosipedata

27 Lateral pedicels mostly 0.5-3.0cm long (see also *E.lugens*, *E.macilenta*
    sometimes)   28
27 Lateral pedicels mostly less than 0.5cm long   29

28 Annual; panicle effuse, dense, with divaricate branches; spikelets 1.0-1.5mm
    wide; lemmas 1.5 mm long, obtuse   **aspera**
28 Perennial; panicle effuse, loose and open, with divaricate branches; spikelets
    2-3mm wide; lemmas 3mm long, acuminate   **patentissima**

29 Culm base silky-hairy; perennial   30
29 Culm base not silky-hairy, sometimes a little pubescent   34

30 Spikelets 4-10×1mm; lemmas 1.1-1.5mm long, ovate, yellow or purple tipped; lower branches whorled, with the axis glandular above and below each whorl   **rotifer**
30 Spikelets wider than 1.5mm; lemmas longer than 1.5mm, subobtuse, uniform in colour, often dark grey; lower branches usually not whorled   31

31 Culms branched (often fascicled), wiry; lower sheaths papery and unridged; lemmas c.1.6mm long   32
31 Culms unbranched, not wiry; lower sheaths rather tough with strongly ridged nerves; lemmas 1.5-2.5mm long   33

32 Nodes glabrous; not stoloniferous   **lehmanniana**
32 Nodes usually ± bearded; stoloniferous   **barbinodis**

33 Plant with a dense basal tuft of relatively short filiform curling leaves; spikelets spreading in a loose open panicle   **chloromelas**
33 Plant with flat or filiform longer leaves, less tufted; spikelets dense or spreading in an open or rarely contracted panicle; a very variable species merging into *E.chloromelas*   **curvula**

34 Annual or short-lived perennials, often weedy looking   35
34 Perennial (or perhaps annual in *E.schweinfurthii*)   43

35 Grain oblong with a ventral groove   36
35 Grain without a ventral groove   38

36 Spikelets 1.0-1.4mm wide; lemmas 1.0-1.8mm long   **virescens**
36 Spikelets 1.5-2.5mm wide; lemmas usually 2.0-2.3mm long   37

37 Ht. 15-50cm; leaves 3-6mm wide; panicle branches bearing spikelets to near the base; no glandular tissue present below the lower culm nodes
                                                                     mexicana
37 Ht. 75-120cm; leaves 5-12mm wide; panicle branches bare for the lower 2cm; glandular tissue present below the lower culm nodes   **neomexicana**

38 Upper glume 1.7-3.0mm long; lemmas 2.0-2.7mm long, acute; mature florets persistent, holding the semi-elliptic turgid grain (1.0-1.2mm long)   **tef**
38 Upper glume and lemmas usually shorter; grain falling before the florets, usually less than 1mm long   39

39 Glumes subequal, 0.8-1.5mm long; grain broadly oblong to subglobose, c.0.5mm long; panicle diffuse with slender lateral pedicels 2-12mm long; spikelets with 5-14 florets, usually grey to black   **macilenta**
39 Lower glume much shorter than the upper; grain semi-elliptic or oblong-linear, 0.5-1.2mm long   40

40 Grain oblong-linear (length/width 4 or 5/1), 0.7-1.2mm long   **leptocarpa**
40 Grain plumper (length/width c.2/1), 0.5-1.1mm long   41

41 Robust annual or short-lived perennial; ht. usually over 50cm; mature panicle large, 20-30×10-20cm, often without axillary hairs; usually some spikelets with more than 15 florets; lemmas rarely rose-tipped   **parviflora**
41 Weedy annual; ht. usually less than 50cm; panicle usually smaller, often less than 20×10cm, often with axillary hairs; most spikelets with less than 15 florets; some lemmas rose-tipped   42

42 Length ratio of lower glume to lowest lemma 1/2-3/4; lower glume 0.5-1.1mm long; paleas usually persist after the lemmas fall; spikelets 1.2-2.5mm wide with 6-15(-20) florets   **pectinacea**
42 Length ratio of lower glume to lowest lemma 1/4-1/3(-1/2); lower glume 0.3-0.5(-0.8)mm long; some paleas soon deciduous (except in temperate regions); spikelets 0.7-1.2(-1.8)mm wide, with (3-)4-7(-14) florets   **pilosa**

43 Panicle diffuse; lateral pedicels longer than the spikelets; spikelets with 2-8 florets; mouths of the sheaths distinctly hairy   **lugens**
43 Panicle not diffuse; lateral pedicels mostly shorter than the spikelets; spikelets usually with more than 10 florets   44

44 Panicle ovate-lanceolate, less than 20cm long; pedicels short (1-2mm), stiff and spreading; spikelets oblong, typically 3.0-10.0×1.5-2.0mm, with 5-30 florets; glumes subequal   45
44 Grass with a different combination of characters   46

45 Anthers 3, 0.7-1.3mm long   **racemosa**
45 Anthers 2, 0.2-0.6mm long   **schweinfurthii**

46 Tall (-120cm), erect, densely tufted grass with a somewhat flattened straight culm and sheaths; leaves long and filiform; collar inconspicuous; mouth of the sheath hairless; lemmas acute with inconspicuous lateral nerves, dark grey; (resembles *E.curvula* which has a densely hairy base and subobtuse lemmas)   **planiculmis**
46 Grasses with different combinations of characters   47

47 Spikelets narrow, 1.0-1.5mm wide   48
47 Spikelets wider than 1.5mm, typically c.2mm   49

48 Panicle small, 10-20cm long, with the spikelets densely clustered on the spreading branches; spikelets 3-4mm long, with c.8 florets; grain plump, c.0.3mm long   **microcarpa**
48 Panicle 15-30cm long, with spikelets appressed to the branches; spikelets 4-9mm long, with 5-16 florets; grain narrowly oblong, 1mm long
                                                                   heteromera

49 Spikelets clustered on spreading or obliquely ascending branches; mature spikelets often with over 30 florets   50
49 Spikelets clustered or not on spreading or deflexed branches; spikelets with less than 20 imbricate florets   51

50 Rhizomes present; anthers 3; paleas deciduous soon after lemmas fall
                                                                atrovirens
50 0 rhizomes present; anthers 2; paleas persistent after the lemmas fall
                                                                bahiensis

51 Lateral nerves of the lemmas obscure   **molybdea**
51 Lateral nerves of the lemmas prominent   52

52 Panicle usually less than 20cm long; branches relatively short (under 8cm), straight, reflexed or ascending   **brownii**
52 Panicle larger, usually over 20cm long; branches relatively long (over 8cm), flexuous and reflexed   **benthamii**

Note:

In native Australian material of *E.trachycarpa* a few spikelets occasionally have up to 12 florets. The manner in which the mature spikelets break up is usually given as a primary key-character, but unfortunately in British alien material the spikelets rarely ripen, so that this character is useless.

SPOROBOLUS   377

1   Spikelets 4-6mm long; panicle partly included in the inflated upper sheath
                                                                  asper
1   Spikelets 1-3mm long; panicle various   2

2   Tops of the sheaths with a conspicuous tuft of long white hairs; terminal
    panicle partly included in the top sheath, the exserted part becoming open
                                                            cryptandrus
2   Tops of the sheaths without a conspicuous tuft of hairs; panicle various   3

3   Panicle open, with uncrowded spikelets on spreading branches which are
    naked in the lower part; annual or perennial   4
3   Panicle spike-like, contracted or narrow with primary branches bearing
    crowded spikelets to their bases; perennial   8

4   Panicle elliptic to pyramidal, with at least the lower branches in whorls of
    decreasing length up the axis; lower glume much shorter than the upper
    glume, which $\pm$ equals the spikelet length   5
4   Panicle diffuse, with the primary branches single, except sometimes for the
    lowest set of branches which may be whorled or fascicled   7

5   Annual; ht. 15-100cm; spikelets 2-3mm long; panicle narrowly elliptic, 5-
    30cm long   **panicoides**
5   Grasses with a different combination of characters   6

6   Densely tufted perennial; ht. 15-60cm; spikelets 1.5-2.0mm long; panicle 5-
    15(-20)cm long   **ioclados**
6   Short-lived perennial or annual; ht. 10-20cm; spikelets c.1.4-1.7mm long;
    panicle small, 3-7×1-2cm   **pyramidatus**

7   Panicle very diffuse, broadly ovate, with the lowest branches in a whorl or
    fascicle; spikelets 1.2-1.8mm long; lower glume much shorter than the upper
    glume, which $\pm$ equals the spikelet   **caroli**
7   Panicle open, elliptic ovate, with the lowest branches single; lower glume
    shorter than the upper glume, which is c.1/2-3/4 the spikelet length; spikelets
    c.1.0-1.2mm long   **engleri**

8   Panicle linear to lanceolate, 15-50cm long; primary branches up to 10cm long,
    slightly spreading, the lower in several fascicles up the axis; spikelets (on
    appressed secondary branches) clustered along the entire length of the
    branches, or the lower 1/3 of the branches naked; spikelets 1.4-2.2mm long;
    lower glume c.1/2 spikelet, the upper glume $\pm$ equal to the spikelet
                                                            fimbriatus
8   Spikelets in a dense spike-like panicle, or in spicate clusters on branches
    appressed along the axis   9

9   Panicle spike-like, small (3-12cm long), pallid; spikelets c.1.7mm long; glumes subequal, longer than the lemma   **mitchellii**

9   Panicle longer, dark green or brown; glumes unequal, upper glume longer than 1/2 spikelet   10

10   Panicle densely and continuously spicate, with the lower branches appressed, 1-2cm long   11

10   Panicle with the spikelets in spike-like clusters on branches which are ± appressed to the axis; spikelets c.1.4mm long   12

11   Spikelets 2.1-2.5mm long; lemma and palea twice as long as the grain, gaping widely open; grain c.1.2mm long, elliptic and truncate at the top   **africanus**

11   Spikelets 1.8-2.0mm long; lemma and palea scarcely longer than the grain, not gaping open; grain c.1.2mm long, oblong to oblong-elliptic   **indicus**

12   Panicle with short (1-2cm) stiff appressed branches bearing spikelets, well separated up the axis, which is visible for most of the panicle length   **creber**

12   Panicle branches usually longer, not stiffly appressed and tending to diverge in the lower 1/2 of the panicle, but concealing the axis in the upper 1/2 of the panicle   **elongatus**

PANICUM   455

1   Lower glume obtuse, 1/8-1/3 spikelet length   2
1   Lower glume equal to or greater than 1/3 spikelet length (see note 3)   13

2   Large perennial; lower panicle branches whorled; fertile lemma prominently
    transversely ridged   **maximum**
2   Fertile lemma shining, smooth (rarely slightly ridged)   3

3   Lower floret with well-developed palea, stamens; panicle open; perennials
    except for *P.schinzii*   4
3   Lower floret with well- or poorly-developed palea, 0 stamens; panicle open
    or contracted; annual or perennial   7

4   Creeping with long rhizomes; leaves flat or involute, stiff, distichous; spikelets
    2.2-3.0mm long, elliptic acute, becoming more ovate on maturity   **repens**
4   Tufted without long rhizomes (sometimes with short ones); leaves linear, flat,
    not pungent   5

5   Annual; panicle 10-35cm long; spikelets 2.3-2.8mm long, elliptic oblong,
    obtuse or bluntly acute   **schinzii**
5   Perennial; spikelets 2-3mm long, elliptic ovate   6

6   Very densely caespitose, erect; ht. 20-50(-90)cm; leaves up to 5mm wide;
    panicle 10(-20)cm long   **stapfianum**
6   Tufted, often with bent culms; ht. 50-100cm; leaves frequently much wider
    than 5mm; panicle 10-30(-40)cm long   **coloratum**

7   Decumbent stoloniferous perennial; ht. 15-30cm; panicle narrow, only partly
    exserted from the leaf sheath, less than 7cm long; spikelets 2.8-3.3mm long
                                                                    obseptum
7   Erect annual or perennial; ht. usually over 30cm; panicle longer than 7cm
    (except sometimes *P.gilvum*)   8

8   Upper lemma c.1/2 spikelet length; panicle lanceolate, nodding; spikelets
    3.0-4.5mm long   **buncei**
8   Upper lemma ± equal to the spikelet; panicle ± erect; spikelets 2.0-3.5mm
    long   9

9   Large tussock-forming perennial with large very diffuse panicle; primary
    branches rigid, bare of spikelets below, the lower ones often in pseudo-
    whorls; spikelets 2.5-3.5mm long, lanceolate   **decompositum**
9   Annuals or short-lived perennials; panicle narrow to ovate-oblong with ±
    flexuous branches, the lower ones not whorled; spikelets acuminate   10

10 Panicle soon exserted from the upper leaf sheath; glumes without a distinct rhachilla between them   11
10 Panicle (at least in immature alien material) about 1/2 included in the leaf sheath, rather dense with appressed branches and spikelets; many axillary panicles present; weak annuals with many basal branches; ht. less than 70cm; glumes separated by a minute rhachilla   12

11 Annual; ht. 30-70cm; leaves less than 5mm wide; panicle 10-25cm long, with the secondary and tertiary branches spreading from the primary ones; typically the edges of the leaves and sheaths with a few to many long white tubercle-based hairs   **laevinode**
11 Short-lived perennial; ht. 60-200cm; leaves 7-15mm wide; panicle 20-50cm long, with the tertiary and sometimes the secondary branches appressed at maturity to the primary ones   **subalbidum**

12 Lower glume 1-3 nerved; upper glume 7-9 nerved; lower palea c.2.0×0.5mm; spikelets typically 2-3mm long; terminal panicle c.10-30cm long
                                                                dichotomiflorum
12 Lower glume 0-1 nerved; upper glume 9-11 nerved; lower palea poorly developed or 0; spikelets 2.5-4.0mm long; terminal panicle 4-10cm long (see note 1)   **gilvum**

13 Lower floret with anthers; perennial with creeping rootstock; ht. 90-180cm; spikelets 2.4-3.2(-3.6)mm long; lower glume ovate with broad hyaline margins, 1/2-2/3 spikelet length   **antidotale**
13 Lower floret with 0 anthers (except *P. virgatum* which has larger spikelets and an acuminate lower glume); annual or perennial   14

14 Annual with broad (c.1-2cm) hispid/hairy leaves; ovate to oblong spikelets (4.0-)4.5-5.5mm long   **miliaceum**
14 Annual or perennial with spikelets less than 5mm long, or perennial with longer acuminate spikelets   15

15 Plants with hispid hairy leaves and sheaths   16
15 Glabrous perennials (occasionally with slightly hairy leaves in *P. virgatum* and hairy sheaths in *P. mitchellii*); spikelets 2-5(-7)mm long, acuminate   18

16 Perennial tussock-grass with large open panicle with pseudo-whorled lower branches; base and culm nodes very hairy (in alien material); spikelets 2.0-2.5mm long   **effusum**
16 Annual with an open panicle 10-40cm long with unwhorled lower branches; culm nodes ± hairy   17

17 Plant sparsely hispid; panicle ovate, with very flexible branches; spikelets 2.2-2.5mm long; lower lemma and upper glume 7-9 nerved   **novemnerve**
17 Plant usually densely hairy; panicle finally broadly ovate with numerous ± straight divided branches; spikelets 2.0-3.3mm long; lower lemma and upper glume 5-7 nerved   **capillare**

18 Plant with many scaly rhizomes; ht. 100-200cm; spikelets 3.5-5.0mm long,
    finally ± gaping; lower glume c.3/4 spikelet length, ending in a slightly
    recurved cuspidate point   **virgatum**
18 Plant without scaly creeping rhizomes   19

19 Lower glume at least 3/4 spikelet length; spikelets 3-5(-7) mm long-acuminate,
    set towards the ends of the branches in the large open panicle
                                                      queenslandicum
19 Lower glume acute, c.1/2-3/4 spikelet length; spikelets 2.0-2.8mm long   20

20 Panicle with single spikelets at the ends of the straight, rigid branches; lower
    glume 3/4 spikelet length; culm leaves short, 2mm wide at the base, arising
    from nodular bases evenly spaced up the wiry culm (typically 6 per culm)
                                                      subxerophyllum
20 Panicle large, with the branches much divided, more flexuous, and the florets
    more evenly distributed; lower glume c.1/2 spikelet length; upper lemma
    yellow in contrast to the rest of the green or purple floret; culm leaves long,
    4-10mm wide; culms often robust and cane-like   **mitchellii**

Notes:

1. *P.dichotomiflorum* and *P.gilvum* are sometimes difficult to separate
    taxonomically, but occur in quite different geographical areas.

2. Several species which were formerly placed in *Panicum*, namely *Digitaria
    cognata*, *Homopholis proluta* and *Steinchisma hians*, are easily confused with
    Panicum species.

3. In several species (e.g. *P.capillare*) the ± acute lower glume is occasionally
    slightly less than 1/3 spikelet length, but other characters should make
    identification possible.

DIGITARIA   524

1   Spikelets single on long capillary pedicels forming a large diffuse almost spherical panicle; primary branches with many secondary branches, set on a long (10cm or more) axis; spikelets appressed-hairy, narrow acute, 2.5-3.1mm long   **cognata**
1   Spikelets in groups of 2 or 3 on short pedicels along ± unbranched racemes   2

2   Racemes long (-20cm) and rigid, mostly bare of spikelets towards the base, finally spreading out from the long axis; lower racemes whorled, often in groups of 4 or 5; spikelets woolly hairy   3
2   Racemes not long and rigid, bearing spikelets to the base   4

3   Spikelets 2.0-2.8mm long; leaves densely villous   **ammophila**
3   Spikelets over 3.7mm long; leaves hairy   **divaricatissima**

4   Spikelets in groups of 3 on the rhachis; mature fruit dark brown to black   5
4   Spikelets in groups of 2 on the rhachis   7

5   Spikelets usually over 2.0mm long   6
5   Spikelet 1.2-1.6(-1.8)mm long; upper glume from 4/5 to as long as the spikelet   **violascens**

6   Ht. 20-100cm; racemes up to 20cm long; upper glume 1/2-4/5 spikelet length; pedicels with an apical ring of rigid hairs 0.2-1.0mm long   **ternata**
6   Ht. 10-35cm; racemes up to 7cm long; upper glume nearly as long as the spikelet; pedicels without apical hairs   **ischaemum**

7   Lower lemma with 2 prominent hair tufts on each side of the mid-nerve; upper glume silky hairy   **hubbardii**
7   Lower lemma without hair tufts   8

8   Racemes short (-10cm long), singly spaced on an axis which is usually longer than the racemes (see also *D. velutina*); spikelets less than 2.2mm long; lower glumes very small   9
8   Racemes subdigitate or on an axis which is shorter than the racemes   12

9   Upper glume 1/4-1/3 spikelet length; spikelet 1.4-1.8mm long, appressed hairy   **breviglumis**
9   Upper glume over 1/2 spikelet length   10

10 Upper glume 1/2-4/5 spikelet length; spikelet c.1.6mm long, appressed hairy   **ramularis**
10 Upper glume subequal to the spikelet in length   11

11 Upright tufted perennial (ht. 45-150cm); spikelet c.2mm long, sparsely appressed-hairy   **parviflora**
11 Delicate spreading perennial (ht. -40cm); spikelet c.1.5mm, with white or purple hairs between the nerves of the upper glume and lower lemma, which are at first appressed but finally conspicuously spreading   **diffusa**

12 Spikelets 2-3mm long; upper glume as long as the spikelet, densely covered
    with long silky white or purple hairs which exceed the spikelet; racemes 2-4,
    ± erect   **brownii**
12 Spikelets without long dense silky hairs; racemes usually spreading   13

13 Annual with numerous (-20) delicate racemes on an axis 1-7cm long which is
    shorter than the racemes; spikelets 1.5-2.1mm long; upper glume 2/3-4/5
    spikelet length   **velutina**
13 Racemes subdigitate; spikelets exceeding 2.5mm   14

14 Perennial   15
14 Annual   17

15 Mat-forming lawn grass with narrow (1mm) leaves; racemes 2-4, slender,
    2-5cm long; spikelets 2.6mm long; upper glume 1.6mm long; fruit light
    yellow-brown   **didactyla**
15 Tall erect caespitose grasses with much wider leaves; racemes numerous
    (typically c.10), rather stout, 5-25cm long; spikelets c.2.5-3.5mm long   16

16 Nerves of the lower lemma smooth   **eriantha**
16 Nerves of the lower lemma with minute spines   **milanjiana**

17 Spikelets glabrous, narrowly lanceolate, acuminate, 3.7mm long×0.8mm
    wide; lower glume 0; upper glume equal to the spikelet   **aequiglumis**
17 Spikelets lanceolate; lower glume present; upper glume shorter than the
    spikelet   18

18 Spikelets c.2.3-3.5mm long (average 3.1mm), sometimes beset with pectinate
    bristles (especially *D.ciliaris*); raceme axis 5-30mm   19
18 Spikelets large, 3.6-5.5mm long (average 4.6mm), 0.9-1.3mm wide, always(?)
    with prominent orange or pale pectinate bristles; raceme axis 0 **ctenantha**

19 Nerves of lower lemma with minute spines; upper glume 1/3-1/2 as long as
    the spikelet; lower glume c.0.2mm long   **sanguinalis**
19 Nerves of lower lemma smooth; upper glume (1/2-)2/3-3/4 as long as the
    spikelet; lower glume 0.2-0.4mm long   **ciliaris**

ILLUSTRATIONS

By G.M.S. Easy

Fig. 1

Fig. 1. **Ehrharta longiflora**, A × 1/5, B × 4. **E. stipoides**, C × 1/5, D × 4, E × 4. **Stipa ambigua**, F × 1/5, G × 4, H × 4. **S. neesiana**, I × 1/5, J × 4.

Fig. 2. **Piptochaetium bicolor**, A × 1/3, B × 4, C × 4. **Nassella trichotoma**,
D × 1/3, E × 4. **Lamarckia aurea**, F × 1/2, G × 4, H × 4. **Wangenheimia lima**,
I × 1/2, J × 4, K × 4, L × 4.

Fig. 3

Fig. 3. Psilurus incurvus, A × 1, B × 4. **Eremopoa persica**, C × 1/2, D × 4.
Echinaria capitata, E × 1, F × 4. **Sclerochloa dura**, G × 1, H × 1, I × 4.

Fig. 4

Fig. 4. **Hystrix patula**, A × 1/6, B × 1, C × 1. **Aegilops ventricosa**, D × 1/4,
E × 1, F × 1. **Crithopsis delileana**, G × 1/3, H × 1, I × 1. **Taeniatherum
caput-medusae**, J × 1/4, K × 1, L × 1.

Fig. 5

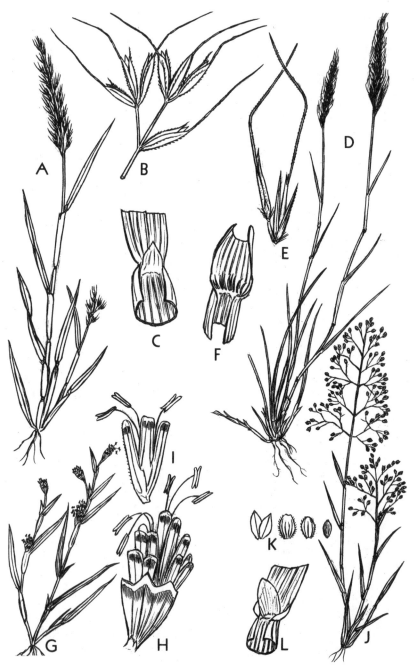

Fig.5. **Chaetopogon fasciculatus**, A × 1/3, B × 3, C × 3., **Dichelachne micrantha**, D × 1/4, E × 4, F × 3. **Cornucopia cucullatum**, E × 1/4, F × 3, G × 3. **Zingeria pisidica**, H × 1/4, I × 3, J × 3.

Fig. 6

Fig. 6. **Triplachne nitens**, A × 1/3, B × 4, C × 4. **Rostraria cristata**, D × 1/3, E × 4, F × 4. **Thyridolepis xerophila**, G × 1/2, H × 4, I × 4. **Ammochloa pungens**, J × 1/2, K × 4.

Fig. 7

Fig. 7. **Enneapogon desvauxii**, A × 1/3, B × 5, C × 5. **Schmidtia kalihariensis**, D × 1/3, E × 5, F × 5. **Schismus barbatus**, G × 1, H × 5, I × 5. **Dactyloctenium radulans**, J × 1/3, K × 5, L × 5.

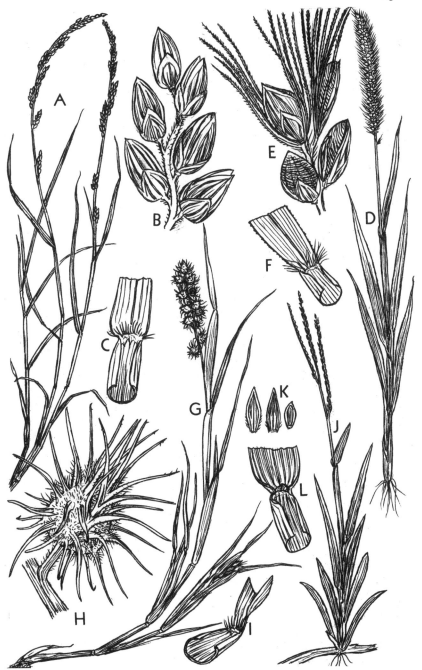

Fig. 8

Fig. 8. **Paspalidium jubiflorum**, A × 1/3, B × 5, C × 3. **Setaria pumila**, D × 1/3, E × 5, F × 3. **Cenchrus longispinus**, G × 1/3, H × 5, I × 3. **Axonopus compressus**, J × 1/3, K × 5, L × 3.

Fig. 9

Fig. 9. **Trisetaria panicea**, A × 1/3, B × 4, C × 4. **Vulpiella tenuis**, D × 1/3, E × 4, F × 4. **Micropyrum tenellum**, G × 1/3, H × 4, I × 4. **Dissanthelium calycinum**, J × 1/3, K × 4, L × 4.

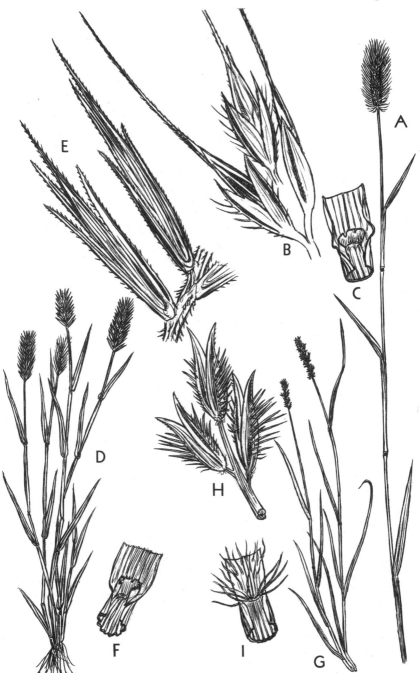

Fig. 10. **Echinopogon ovatus**, A × 1/3, B × 6, C × 6. **Eremopyrum bonaepartis**, D × 1/3, E × 6, F × 6. **Tribolium hispidum**, G × 1/3, H × 6, I × 6.

Fig. 11

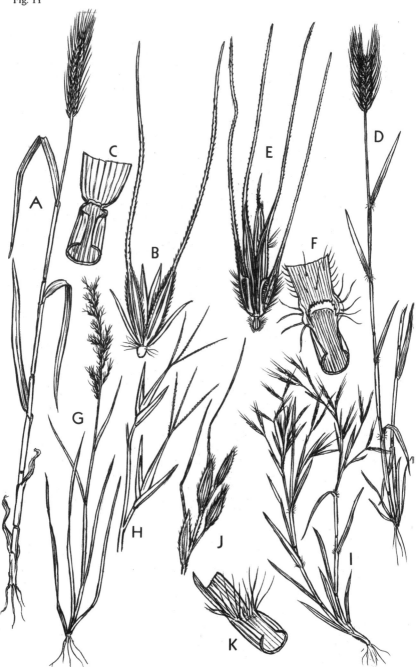

Fig. 11. **Secale cereale**, A × 1/5, B × 3/2, C × 3/2. **Dasypyrum villosum**, D × 1/5, E × 3/2, F × 3/2. **Aristida adscensionis**, G × 1/5, H × 3/2. **Hyparrhenia hirta**, I × 1/5, J × 3/2, K × 3/2.

Fig. 12

Fig. 12. **Anemanthele lessoniana**, A × 1/5, B × 8. **Homopholis proluta**, C × 1/5, D × 8, E × 8. **Microstegium vimineum**, F × 1/5, G × 8, H × 8. **Castellia tuberculata**, I × 1/5, J × 8, K × 8.

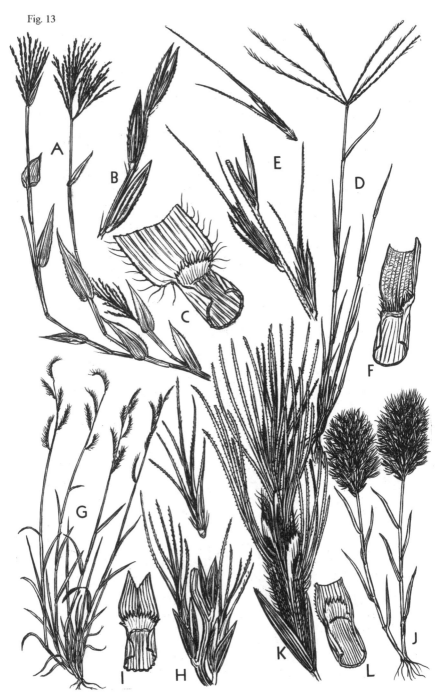

Fig. 13

Fig. 13. **Arthraxon hispidus**, A × 1/3, B × 4, C × 4. **Enteropogon acicularis**, D × 1/3, E × 4, F × 4. **Chondrosum trifidum**, G × 1/2, H × 4, I × 4. **Boissiera squarrosa**, J × 1/3, K × 4, L × 4.

Fig. 14

Fig. 14. **Cortaderia selloana**, A × 1/24, B × 3/2, C × 3/2. **Arundo donax**, D × 1/24, E × 3/2, F × 3/2. **Miscanthus sinensis**, G × 1/24, H × 3/2. **Leptochloa fusca**, I × 1/12, J × 2.

Fig. 15

Fig. 15. **Cynodon incompletus**, A × 1, B × 4, C × 4. **Tragus racemosus**, D × 1, E × 4, F × 4. **Cutandia divaricata**, G × 1, H × 4, I × 4. **Pennisetum clandestinum**, J × 1, K × 4.

Fig. 16

Fig. 16. **Hainardia cylindrica**, A × 1/3, B × 4, C × 4. **Ventenata dubia**, D × 1/3, E × 4, F × 4. **Narduroides salzmannii**, G × 1/3, H × 4, I × 4. **Gaudinia fragilis**, J × 1/3, K × 4, L × 4.

Fig. 17

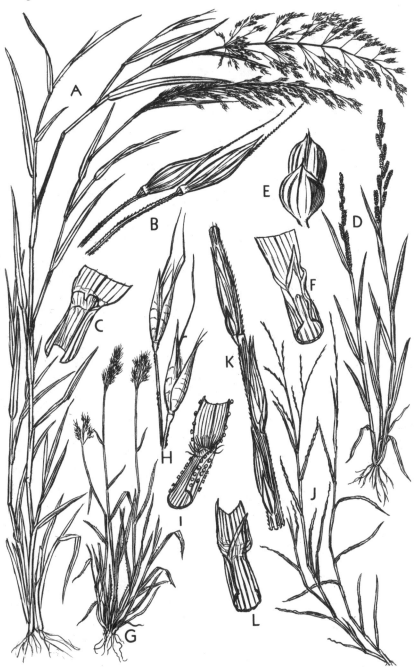

Fig. 17. **Oryzopsis miliacea**, A × 1/5, B × 6, C × 6. **Beckmannia syzigachne**, G × 1/5, E × 6, F × 6. **Pentaschistis airoides**, G1/5, H × 6, I × 6. **Schedonnardus paniculatus**, J × 1/5, K × 6, L × 6.

Fig. 18

Fig. 18. **Eragrostis dielsii**, A × 1/3, B × 4, C × 4. **Eleusine indica**, D × 1/3,
E × 4, F × 4. **Munroa squarrosa**, G × 1/3, H × 4, I × 4. **Harpachne schimperi**,
J × 1/3, K × 4, L × 4.

Fig. 19

Fig. 19. **Paspalum dilatatum**, A × 1/4, B × 4. **Snowdenia polystachya**, C × 1/4, D × 4, E × 4. **Bothriochloa ischaemum**, F × 1/4, G × 4, H × 4. **Dichanthium sericeum**, I × 1/4, J × 4, K × 4.

Fig. 20. **Coix lacryma-jobi**, A × 1/12, B × 2. **Zea mays**, C × 1/12, D × 2, E × 2. **Chasmanthium latifolium**, F × 1/12, G × 2, H × 2. **Sorghum halepense**, I × 1/12, J × 2, K × 2.

Fig. 21

Fig. 21. **Danthonia montevidensis**, A × 1/4, B × 3, C × 3. **Agropyron cristatum**, D × 1/4, E × 3. **Rytidosperma racemosum**, F × 1/4, G × 3. **Aegilops cylindrica**, I × 3, J × 3, K × 3.

Fig. 22

Fig. 22. **Sporobolus africanus**, A × 1/4, B × 8, C × 8. **Tricholaena monachne**, D × 1/4, E × 8. **Eriochloa pseudoacrotricha**, F × 1/4, G × 8, H × 8. **Trisetaria panicea**, I × 1/4, J × 8, K × 8.

Fig. 23. **Chloris truncata**, A × 1/4, B × 4, C × 4. **Crypsis schoenoides**, D × 1/4, E × 4. **Astrebla lappacea**, F × 1/4, G × 4. **Muhlenbergia racemosa**, H × 1/4, I × 4, J × 4.

Fig. 24

Fig. 24. **Eragrostis cilianensis**, A × 1/4, B × 5, C × 5. **Tridens brasiliensis**, D × 1/4, E × 5, F × 5. **Triraphis mollis**, G × 1/4, H × 5, I × 5. **Lagurus ovatus**, J × 1/4, K × 5, L × 5.

Fig. 25

Fig. 25. **Echinochloa crus-galli**, A × 1/4, B × 4. **Panicum capillare**, C × 1/4, D × 4. **Urochloa panicoides**, E × 1/4, F × 4. **Brachiaria platyphylla**, G × 1/4, H × 4.

Fig. 26

Fig. 26. **Pennisetum sphacelatum**, A × 1/5, B × 8, C × 8. **Melinis repens**,
D × 1/5, E × 8, F × 8. **Steinchisma hians**, G × 1/5, H × 8. **Digitaria ternata**,
I × 1/5, J × 8, K × 8.

Fig 27

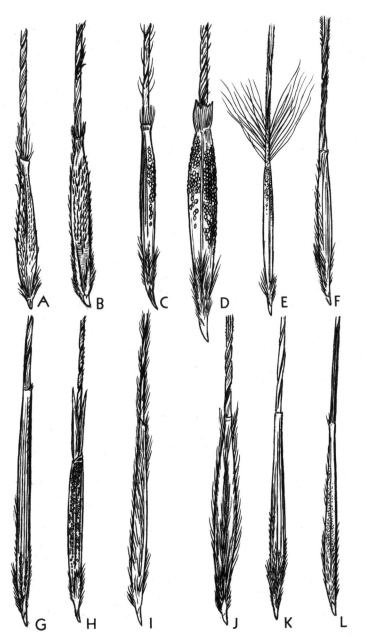

Fig. 27. **Stipa aristiglumis**, A × 6. **S. capensis**, B × 6. **S. filiculmis**, C × 6.
S. neesiana, D × 6 . **S. papposa**, E × 6. **S. variabilis**, F × 6. **S. capillata**, G × 5.
S. charruana, H × 5. **S. tenacissima**, I × 5. **S. gigantea**, J × 3. **S. joannis**, K × 3.
S. pennata, L × 3.

Fig. 28

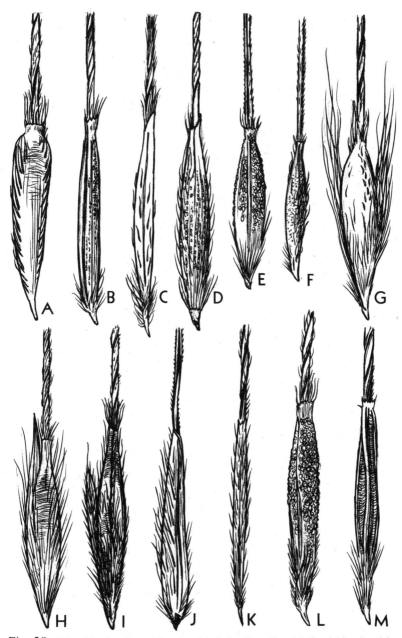

Fig. 28. **Stipa brachychaetoides**, A × 16. **S. hyalina**, B × 16. **S. nitida**, C × 16.
S. philippii, D × 16. **S. tenuissima**, E × 16. **S. verticillata**, F × 16.
S. pampeana, G × 16. **S. ambigua**, H × 10. **S. brachychaeta**, I × 10.
S. dregeana, J × 10. **S. scabra** subsp. **falcata**, K × 10. **S. formicarum**, L × 10.
S. juergensii, M × 10.

Fig. 29

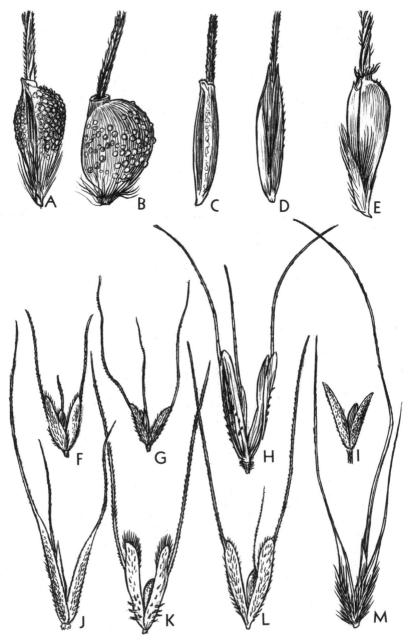

Fig. 29. **Nassella trichotoma**, A × 15. **Piptochaetium montevidense**, B × 15. **Oryzopsis miliacea**, C × 15. **Anemanthele lessoniana**, D × 15. **Piptochaetium bicolor**, E × 8. **Polypogon fugax**, F × 6. **P. australis**, G × 8. **P. linearis**, H × 8. **P. viridis**, I × 8. **P. elongatus**, J × 8. **P. maritimus**, K × 10. **P. monspeliensis**, L × 10. **P. tenellus**, M × 8.

REFERENCES

D1   Tutin, T.G. *et al.*, eds. (1980). *Flora Europaea*, **5**. Cambridge.

D2   Stace, C.A. (1991). *New Flora of the British Isles*. Cambridge.

D3   Hubbard, C.E. (1984). *Grasses*, 3rd ed., rev. Hubbard, J.C.E. London.

D4   Clapham, A.R., Tutin, T.G. & Warburg, E.F. (1962). *Flora of the British Isles*, 2nd ed. Cambridge.

D5   Chippindall, L.K.A. (1955). *Part 1. A guide to the identification of grasses in South Africa*, in Meredith, D., ed. *The grasses and pastures of South Africa*. Cape Town.

D6   Hitchcock, A.S. (1951). *Manual of the grasses of the United States*, 2nd ed., rev. Chase, A. U.S. Dept. of Agriculture Misc. Pub. No. 200.

D7   Simon, B.K. (1993). *A key to Australian grasses*, 2nd ed. Brisbane.

D8   Black, J.M. (1960). *Flora of South Australia*, **1**, 2nd ed. Adelaide.

D9   Gilliland, H.B. *et al.* (1971). *Grasses of Malaya*, in Burkill, H.M., ed. *A revised flora of Malaya*, **3**. Singapore.

D10   Wheeler, D.J.B., Jacobs, S.W.L. & Norton, B.E. (1982). *Grasses of New South Wales*. Armidale.

D11   Judziewicz, E.J. *et al.* (1990). *187. Poaceae (Gramineae)*, in Görts-van Rijn, A.R.A., ed. *Flora of the Guianas*. Koenigstein.

D12   Cabrera, A.L., ed. (1970). *Flora de la provincia de Buenos Aires, Parte 2, Gramineas*. Buenos Aires.

D13   Clayton, W.D., Phillips, S.M. & Renvoize, S.A. *Gramineae (Parts 1-3)*, in Milne-Redhead, E. & Polhill, R.M., eds. (1970-1982). *Flora of tropical East Africa*. London & Tonbridge.

D14   Synge, P.M., ed. (1969). *Supplement to [The Royal Horticultural Society] dictionary of gardening*, 2nd ed. Oxford.

D15   Rosengurtt, B. *et al.* (1970). *Gramineas Uruguayas*. Montevideo.

D16   Tothill, J.C. & Hacker, J.B. (1983). *Grasses of southern Queensland*. St Lucia, Queensland.

D17   Feinbrun-Dothan, N. (1986). *Flora Palaestina*, **4** (text and plates). Jerusalem.

D18   Davis, P.H., ed. (1985). *Flora of Turkey and the East Aegean Islands*, **9**. Edinburgh.

D19   Fitter, R., Fitter, A. & Farrer, A. (1984). *Collins guide to the grasses, sedges, rushes and ferns of Britain and Northern Europe*. London.

D20   Maire, R.[C.J.E.] (1952-1955). *Flore de l'Afrique du Nord*, **1-3**. Paris.

D21   Grounds, R. (1979). *Ornamental grasses*. London.

D21a Grounds, R. (1989). *Ornamental grasses*, [rev.ed.]. London.

D22   Bor, N.L. (1968). *Gramineae*, in Townsend, C.C., Guest, E. & Al-Rawi, A., eds. *Flora of Iraq*, **9**. Baghdad.

D23   Hitchcock, C.L. & Cronquist, A. (1973). *Flora of the Pacific northwest: an illustrated manual*. Seattle & London.

D24   Burbidge, N.T. & Gray, M. (1970). *Flora of the Australian Capital Territory*. Canberra.

D25   Coste, H.[J]. (1906). *Flore descriptive et illustrée de la France, de la Corse et des contrées limitrophes*, **3**. Paris.

D26   Burbidge, N.T. (1984). *Australian Grasses*, rev. Jacobs, S.W.L. London.

D27   Blackall, W.E. & Grieve, B.J. (1974). *How to know Western Australian wildflowers*, parts 1-3, new ed. Perth.

D28   Terrell, E.E. (1968). *A taxonomic revision of the genus Lolium*. Tech. Bull. No. 1392, U.S. Dept. of Agriculture, Washington DC.

D29   Beadle, N.C.W., Evans, O.D. & Carolin, R.C. (1972). *Flora of the Sydney region*. Sydney & London.

D30   Nègre, R. (1961). *Petite flore des régions arides du Maroc occidental*, **1**. Paris.

D31   Quézel, P. & Santa, S. (1962). *Nouvelle flore de l'Algérie et des régions désertiques méridionales*, **1**. Paris.

D32   Host, N.T. (1805). *Icones et descriptiones graminum austriacorum*, **1-4**. Vienna.

D33   Sibthorp, J. & Smith, J.E. (1806-1840). *Flora Graeca*, **1-10**. London.

D34   Dumortier, B.C.J. (1823). *Observations sur les graminées de la flore Belgique*. Tournay.

D35   Ewart, A.J. (1931[1930]). *Flora of Victoria*. Melbourne.

D36   Harker, K.W. & Napper, D. (1960). *An illustrated guide to the grasses of Uganda*. Entebbe.

D37   Fröman, B. & Persson, S. (1974). *An illustrated guide to the grasses of Ethiopia*. Asella.

D38   Willis, J.H. (1970). *A handbook to plants in Victoria*, **1**, 2nd ed. Carlton, Victoria.

D39   Migahid, A.M. (1978). *Migahid and Hammouda's Flora of Saudi Arabia*, **2**, 2nd rev. ed. Riyadh.

D39a Migahid, A.M. & Hammouda, M.A. (1974). *Flora of Saudi Arabia*, **2**. Riyadh.

D40   Britton, N.L. & Brown, A. (1970). *An illustrated flora of the northern United States and adjacent Canada*, **1**, Dover ed. New York.

D41   Gould, F.W. (1975). *The grasses of Texas*. College Station, Texas.

D42   Mohlenbrock, R.H. (1972-1973). *The illustrated flora of Illinois*, **[4-5]** *Grasses: Panicum to Danthonia* and *Grasses: Bromus to Paspalum*. Carbondale & Edwardsville.

D43   Munz, P.A. & Keck, D.D. (1959). *A California flora*. Berkeley & Los Angeles.

D44   Lamp, C.A., Forbes, S.J., & Cade, J.W. (1990). *Grasses of temperate Australia*. Melbourne.

D45   Turner, F. (1895). *Australian grasses*. Sydney.

D46   Gay, C. (1845-1854). *Historia física y política de Chile. Botánica*, **1-8** (text & atlas). Paris & Santiago.

D47   Walters, S.M. *et al.*, eds. (1984). *The European garden flora*, **2** (Monocotyledons). Cambridge.

D48   Bor, N.L. (1970). *Gramineae*, in Rechinger, K.H., ed. *Flora Iranica*, **9**. Graz, Austria.

D49   Rechinger, K.H. (1964). *Flora of lowland Iraq*. Weinheim.

D50   Tchihatcheff, P. de (1860). *Asie mineure, troisième partie: Botanique*, 1-2. Paris.

D51   Cope, T.A. (1982). *No.143. Poaceae*, in Nasir, E. & Ali, S.I., eds. *Flora of Pakistan*. Karachi.

D52   Nicora, E.G. (1978). *Part 3. Gramineae*, in Correa, M.N., ed. *Flora Patagonica (República Argentina)*. Buenos Aires.

D53   Fernald, M.L. (1950). *Gray's manual of botany*, 8th ed. New York.

D54   Synge, P.M., ed. (1956). *The Royal Horticultural Society dictionary of gardening*, 1-4, 2nd ed. Oxford.

D55   Harrison, S.G. *et al.* (1969). *The Oxford book of food plants*. Oxford.

D56   Ohwi, J. (Meyer, G.F. & Walker, E.H., eds.) (1965). *Flora of Japan*, rev. ed. Washington, D.C.

D57   Bailey, F.M. ("1909", 1913). *Comprehensive catalogue of Queensland plants, both indigenous and naturalised*, 2nd ed. Brisbane.

D58   Zotov, V.D. (1963). Synopsis of the grass subfamily Arundinoideae in New Zealand. *New Zealand J. Bot.*, **1**:78-136.

D59   Gardner, C.A. (1952). *Flora of Western Australia*, **1**, part 1 (*Gramineae*). Perth.

D60   Vickery, J.W. (1956). A revision of the Australian species of *Danthonia*. *Contr. New South Wales Natl. Herb.*, **2**:249-325.

D61   Cheeseman, T.F. (1925). *Manual of the New Zealand flora*. Wellington.

D62   Lazarides, M. (1970). *The grasses of Central Australia*. Canberra.

D63   Renvoize, S.A. (1984). *The grasses of Bahia*. Kew.

D64   Breakwell, E. (1923). *The grasses and fodder plants of New South Wales*. Sydney.

D65   Bennett, K.E. (1980). Keys to Zimbabwean grass species. *Kirkia*, **11**:169-286.

D66   Vickery, J.W. (1975). *No.19. Gramineae, part 2*, pp.195-198, in Tindale, M.D., ed. *Flora of New South Wales*. Sydney.

D67   Purseglove, J.W. (1972). *Tropical crops*, **2** (Monocotyledons). London.

D68   Launert, E., Clayton, W.D. *et al.* (1971, 1989). *Gramineae*, in Fernandes, A. *et al.*, eds. *Flora Zambesiaca*, **10**. London.

D69   Bailey, F.M. (1879). *An illustrated monograph of the grasses of Queensland*. Brisbane.

D70   Adams, C.D. (1972). *Flowering plants of Jamaica*. Mona, Jamaica.

D71   Tsvelev [Tzvelev], N.N. (trans. Sharma, R.R.) (1984). *Grasses of the Soviet Union*. Rotterdam.

D72   Zuloaga, F.O. *et al.* (1994). *Catálogo de la familia Poaceae en la República Argentina*. Monographs in systematic botany from the Missouri Botanical Garden, **47**. St. Louis.

D73   Lawson, A.H. (1968). *Bamboos*. London.

D74   Bean, W.J. (1970-1980). *Trees and shrubs hardy in the British Isles*, 1-4, 8th ed. London.

D75   Jansen, P. (1951). *Gramineae*, in Weevers, Th. *et al.*, eds. *Flora Neerlandica*, **1**, part 2. Amsterdam.

D76   McClintock, D. (1957). *Supplement to The pocket guide to wild flowers.* Privately published. Platt, Kent.

D77   Koch, S.D. (1974). *The Eragrostis pectinacea-pilosa complex in North America and Central America (Gramineae: Eragrostideae).* Illinois Biol. Monogr. 48.

D78   Beetle, A.A. (1983-1991). *Las gramíneas de México*, **1-3** (incomplete). Secretaria de Agricultura y recursos hidrraulicos. Mexico City.

D79   Buchanan, J. (1880). *Manual of the indigenous grasses of New Zealand.* Wellington.

D80   Camus, E.G. (1913). *Les bambusées.* Paris.

D81   Institute of Botany, Academia Sinica. (1976). *Iconographia cormophytorum sinicorum*, **5**. Beijing.

D82   Chippindall, L.K.A. & Crook, A.O. (1976). *240 grasses of southern Africa*, **1-3**. Salisbury.

D83   Hay, R. & Synge, P.M. (1969). *The dictionary of garden plants in colour with house and greenhouse plants.* London.

D84   Crouzet, Y. (1981). *Les bambous.* Dargand.

D85   Davidse, G., Pohl, R.W. *et al.* (1994). *Poaceae* in Davidse, G., Sousa, S.M. and Chater, A.O., eds. *Flora Mesoamericana*, **6**. Mexico D.F., St Louis and London.

D86   Edwards, D.C. & Bogdan, A.L. (1951). *Important grassland plants of Kenya.* London.

D87   Gibbs Russell, G.E. *et al.* (Leistner, O.A., ed.) (1991). *Grasses of southern Africa.* Memoirs of the Botanical Survey of South Africa No.58. Pretoria.

D88   Häfliger, E. & Scholz, H. (1980). *Grass weeds 1. Weeds of the subfamily Panicoideae.* Ciba-Geigy Ltd., Basle, Switzerland.

D89   Häfliger, E. & Scholz, H. (1981). *Grass weeds 2. Weeds of the subfamilies Chloridoideae, Pooideae and Oryzyoideae.* Ciba-Geigy Ltd., Basle, Switzerland.

D90   Henrard, J.T. (1950). *Monograph of the genus Digitaria.* Leiden.

D91   Hitchcock, A.S. (1913). Mexican grasses in the United States National Herbarium. *Contr. U.S. Nat. Herb.*, **17**(3):181-390.

D92   Hubbard, C.E. (1934). *Gramineae (continued)*, in Hill, A.W., ed. *Flora of tropical Africa*, **10**(1) (incomplete). Ashford.

D93   Jacobs, S.W.L. *et al.* (1993). *Poaceae*, in Harden, G.J., ed. *Flora of New South Wales*, **4**. Kensington.

D94   Jessop, J.[P.] (1981). *Flora of central Australia.* Sydney.

D95   Kernick, M.D. (1978). *Ecological management of arid and semi-arid rangelands in Africa and the Near and Middle East (Emasar-Phase 2)*, **4**. *Indigenous arid and semi-arid forage plants of North Africa, the Near and Middle East. Technical data.* Rome.

D96   Kitamura, S. & Okamoto, S. (1959). *Coloured illustrations of trees and shrubs of Japan.* Osaka.

D97   Kunth, C.S. (1833). *Enumeratio plantarum*, **1**. Stuttgart.

D98   Lightfoot, C. (1975). *Common veld grasses of Rhodesia*, 2nd ed. Salisbury.

D99   Rivière, A. & Rivière, C. (1878). *Les bambous*. Paris.

D100 Robyns, W. (1955). *Flore des spermatophytes du Parc National Albert*, **3** (Monocotylées). Brussels.

D101 Schreber, J.C.D.[von] (1769-1810). *Beschreibung der gräser*, **1-3**. Leipzig.

D102 Stapf, O. (1897-1900). *Gramineae*, in Thistleton-Dyer, W.T., ed. *Flora Capensis*, **7**. Ashford.

D103 Stapf, O. & Hubbard, C.E. (1917-1934). *Gramineae (Maydeae-Paniceae)*, in Prain, D., ed. *Flora of tropical Africa*, **9**. Ashford.

D104 Vasey, G. (1890-1893). *Illustrations of North American grasses*, **1-2**. Washington DC.

D105 Webster, R.D. (1987). *The Australian Paniceae (Poaceae)*. Berlin.

D106 Volk, O.H. (1974). *Gräser des Farmgebietes von Südwestafrika*. Wissenschaftliche Forschung in Südwestafrika No.13. Windhoek.

D107 Suzuki, S. (1978). *Index to Japanese Bambusaceae*. Tokyo.

D108 Wilson, H.D. (1978). *Wild plants of Mount Cook National Park*. Christchurch.

D109 Zizka, G. (1988). Revision der Melinideae Hitchcock (Poaceae, Panicoideae). *Biblioth. Bot.*, **138**:1-150.

D110 Zángheri, P. (1976). *Flora Italica*, **1-2**. Padova.

D111 Makino, T. (1961). *Makino's new illustrated flora of Japan*, 3rd ed., rev. Maekawa, F., Hara, H. & Tuyama, T. Tokyo.

D112 Polunin, O. & Everard, B. (1976). *Trees and bushes of Europe*. London.

D113 Wilson, H.D. (1978). *Wild plants of Mount Cook National Park*. Christchurch.

D114 Kitamura, S. & Murata, G. (1977). *Coloured illustrations of the woody plants of Japan*. Osaka.

D115 Pignatti, S. (1982). *Flora d'Italia*, **3**. Bologna.

D116 Wagner, W.L., Herbst, D.R. & Sohmer, S.H. (1990). *Manual of the flowering plants of Hawai'i*, **2**. Honolulu.

D117 Valdés, B., Talavera, S. & Fernández-Galiano, E. (1987). *Flora vascular de Andalucia occidental*, **3**. Barcelona.

D118 Hickman, J.C., ed. (1993). *The Jepson manual. Higher plants of California*. Berkeley.

D119 Ozenda, P. (1977). *Flora du Sahara*, 2nd ed. Paris.

D120 Polunin, O. & Huxley, A. (1965). *Flowers of the Mediterranean*. London.

D121 Desfontaines, R.L. (1798-1799). *Flore du Sahara*, **1-2**. Paris.

D122 Täckholm, V. (1974). *Student's flora of Egypt*, 2nd ed. Beirut.

D123 Boissier, [P.]E. (1839-1845). *Voyage botanique dans le midi de l'Espagne pendant l'année 1837*, **1-2**. Paris.

D124 Hsu Kuo-Shih. (1978). *Gramineae (Poaceae)*, in Li Hui-Lin et al., eds. *Flora of Taiwan*, **5**:373-783. Taipei.

D125 Boissier, [P.]E. (1867-1888). *Flora Orientalis*, **1-5**. Basle & Geneva.

D126   Komarov, V.L. *et al.*, eds. (1934). *Flora SSSR [Flora URSS]*, **2**. Moscow & Leningrad. Also as English transl., Jerusalem, 1963.

D127   Cope, T.A. (1994). *Gramineae*, in Press, J.R. & Short, M.J., eds. (1994). *Flora of Madeira*. London.

D128   Thellung, A. (1912). *La flore adventice de Montpellier*. Cherbourg.

D129   Trinius, C.B. (1828-1836). *Species graminum iconibus et descriptionibus illustravit*, **1-2**. St. Petersburg. Also as reprint, Lehre, 1970.

D130   Stace, C.A., ed. (1975). *Hybridization and the flora of the British Isles*. London.

D131   De Visiani, R. (1842). *Flora Dalmatica*, **1**. Lipsiae.

D132   Bor, N.L. & Cope, T.A. (1985). *Gramineae*, in Meikle, R.D., ed. *Flora of Cyprus*, **2**. Kew.

D133   van Slageren, M.W. (1994). *Wild wheats; a monograph of Aegilops L. and Amblopyrum (Jaub. & Spach) Eig (Poaceae)*. Wageningen Agricultural University papers No.94-7. Wageningen, Holland.

D134   Henderson, M. & Anderson, J.G. (1966). *Common weeds in South Africa*. Botanical Survey Memoir No.37. Pretoria.

D135   Bor, N.L. (1960). *Grasses of Burma, Ceylon, India and Pakistan (excluding Bambuseae)*. Oxford.

D136   Koyama, T. (1987). *Grasses of Japan and its neighbouring regions. An identification manual*. Tokyo.

D137   Cavanilles, A.J. (1791-1801). *Icones et descriptiones plantarum*, **1-6**. Madrid.

D138   Willkomm, H.M. & Lange, J.M.C. (1861-1880). *Prodromus florae hispanicae*, **1**. Stuttgart.

D139   Bosser, J. (1969). *Graminées des paturages et des cultures a Madagascar*. Mémoir Orstom No.35. Paris.

D140   Gledhill, E. (1969). *Eastern Cape veld flowers*, 2nd ed. Cape Town.

D141   Radford, A.E., Ahles, H.E. & Bell, C.R. (1968). *Manual of the vascular flora of the Carolinas*. Chapel Hill.

D142   Clayton, W.D. (1972). *Gramineae*, in Hepper, F.N., ed. *Flora of West tropical Africa*, 2nd ed., **3**(2). London.

D143   McVaugh, R. (1983). *Gramineae*, in Anderson, R.W., ed. *Flora Novo-Galiaiana. A descriptive account of the vascular plants of western Mexico*. Ann Arbor, Michigan.

D144   Müller, M.A.N. (1984). *Grasses of South West Africa / Namibia*. Windhoek.

D145   van Oudtshoorn, F.P. (1992). *Guide to grasses of South Africa*. Cape Town.

D146   Launert, E. (1970). *Gramineae*, in Merxmüller, H., ed. *Prodromus einer flora von Südwestafrika*. Lehre, Germany.

D147   Moore, D.M. (1968). *The vascular flora of the Falkland Islands*. British Antarctic Survey scientific reports No. 60. London.

D148   Moore, D.M. (1983). *Flora of Tierra del Fuego*. Oswestry, Shropshire & St Louis, Missouri.

D149   Lee, T.B. (1989). *Illustrated flora of Korea*. Seoul.

D150   van der Zon, A.P.M. (1992). *Graminées du Cameroun*, **1-2**. Wageningen
       Agricultural University papers No. 92-1. Wageningen, Holland.
D151   Smith, L.B., Wasshausen, D.C. & Klein, R.M. (1981-2). *Gramíneas*, **1-3**,
       in Reitz, R., ed. *Flora ilustrada Catarinense*. Itagaí, Santa Catarina,
       Brasil.
D152   Darke, R. & Griffiths, M., eds. (1994). *The new Royal Horticultural
       Society dictionary: manual of grasses*. London & Basingstoke.
D153   Cronquist, A., *et al.* (1977). *Intermountain flora: vascular plants of the
       intermountain west, U.S.A.*, **6** (the monocotyledons). New York.
D154   Kerguélen, M. & Plonka, F. (1989). *Les Festuca de la flore de France*.
       Bulletin de la Société Botanique du Centre-Ouest, nouvelle série
       Numéro Spécial 10-1989. Dignac, France.
D155   Hooker, J.D. ([1852-]1853-1855). *Flora novae-zelandiae*, **1-2**. London.
D156   Stapleton, C.[M.A.] (1994). *Bamboos of Bhutan: an illustrated guide*.
       Kew.
D157   Stapleton, C.[M.A.] (1994). *Bamboos of Nepal: an illustrated guide*. Kew.
D158   Gamble, J.S. (1896). The *Bambuseae* of British India. *Ann. Roy. Bot.
       Gard. (Calcutta)*, **7**:1-133.
D159   Chao, C.S. (1989). *A guide to bamboos grown in Britain*. Kew.
D160   Freeman-Mitford, A.B. (1896). *The bamboo garden*. London.
D161   McClure, F.A. (1966). *The bamboos: a fresh perspective*. Cambridge,
       Mass.
D162   Wang Dajun & Shen Shao-Jin. (1987). *Bamboos of China*. London.
D163   Boom, B.K. (1975). *Flora der gekweekte, kruidachtige gewassen*, 3rd ed.
       Flora der cultuurgewassen van Nederland, **2**. Wageningen.
D164   Jávorka, S. & Casapody, V. (1929-1934). *Iconographia florae hungaricae*.
       Budapest.
D164a Jávorka, S. & Csapody, V. (1979). *Iconographia florae partis austro-
       orientalis Europae centralis / Ikonographie der Flora des Südöstlichen
       Mitteleuropa*. Stuttgart.
D165   Reichenbach, H.G.L. *et al.* (1834-1912). *Icones florae germanicae et
       helveticae*, **1-25**. Leipzig.
D166   Lees, F.A. (1888). *The flora of West Yorkshire*. London.
D167   Wheldon, J.A. (1914). *Some alien plants of the Mersey province*.
       (Reprinted from *Lancashire Naturalist*, **5-6** and *Lancashire & Cheshire
       Naturalist*, **7**).
D168   Allan, H.H. (1936). *An introduction to the grasses of New Zealand*. DSIR
       Bulletin No.49. Wellington.
D169   Henty, E.E. (1969). *A manual of the grasses of New Guinea*. Lae.
D170   Brako, L. & Zarucchi, J.L. (1993). *Catalogue of the flowering plants and
       gymnosperms of Peru*. Monographs in systematic botany from the
       Missouri Botanical Garden, **45**. St. Louis.
D171   Marticorena, C. & Quezada, M. (1985). Catalogo de la flora vascular de
       Chile. *Gayana*, **42**(1&2).
D172   Tovar, O. (1993). Las gramíneas (Poaceae) del Perú. *Ruizia*, **13**:1-474.

D174 Burkart, A. (1969). *Flora ilustrada de Entre Rios (Argentina)*, 2 (Gramíneas). Buenos Aires.

D175 Hitchcock, A.S. (1927). The grasses of Ecuador, Peru, and Bolivia. *Contrib. U.S. Nat. Herbarium*, **24**(8):291-556.

D176 Conzatti, C. (1988). *Flora taxonomica mexicana*, **1**, 3rd ed. México, D.F.

D177 Cope, T.A. & Hosni, H.A. (1991). *A key to Egyptian grasses*. Kew.

D178 Cope, T.A. (1985). *A key to the grasses of the Arabian Peninsular*. Arab Gulf Journal of Scientific Research, Special Publication No.1. Riyadh.

D179 Curtis, W.M. & Morris, D.I. (1994). *The student's flora of Tasmania*, **4B**. Hobart.

D180 Rothmaler, W. (1990-1991). *Exkursionsflora von Deutschland*, **3-4**, 8th ed. Berlin.

D181 Jessop, J.P. & Toelken, H.R., eds. (1986). *Flora of South Australia*, **4**, 4th ed. Adelaide.

D182 Nyárády, E.J. *et al.* (1972). *Gramineae*, in Săvulescu, T. *et al.*, eds. *Flora republicii socialiste România*, **12**. Bucharest.

D183 Jordanov, D. *et al.*, eds. (1963). *Flora reipublicae popularis bulgaricae*, **1**. Sofia.

D184 He Shiyuan *et al.* (1991). *Flora Hebeiensis*, **3**. Hebei.

D185 Nash, G.V. *et al.* (1909-1939). *Poaceae*, in *North American Flora*, **17**:77-638. New York Botanical Garden.

D186 Bonnier, G.E.M. (1911-1935). *Flore complète illustrée en couleurs de France, Suisse et Belgique*, **1-13**. Paris.

D187 Butcher, R.W. (1961). *A new illustrated British flora*, **2**. London.

D188 Wilson, H.D. (1982). *Stewart Island plants*. Christchurch.

D189 Johnson, P.N. (1989). *Wetland plants in New Zealand*. Wellington.

D190 Stanley, T.D. & Ross, E.M. (1989). *Flora of south-eastern Queensland*, **3**. Brisbane.

J1   *Bot. Exch. Club Brit. Isles Rep.* continued as *Bot. Exch. Club Soc. Brit. Isles* and *Bot. Soc. Exch. Club Brit. Isles*

J2   *Trans. & Proc. Bot. Soc. Edinburgh*

J3   *Rep. (Annual) Watson Bot. Exch. Club*

J4   *Gartenflora*

J5   *Trudy Bot. Inst. Akad. Nauk SSSR*, Ser.1, Fl. Sist. Yyssh. Rast.

J6   *Bot. Soc. Brit. Isles Proc.*

J7   *Kew Bull.* preceded by *Bull. Misc. Inform. Kew*

J8   *B.S.B.I. News*

J9   *Irish Naturalists' J.*

J10   *Proc. Bristol Naturalists' Soc.*

J11   *Annual Bull. Soc. Jersiaise*

J12   *J. Gloucestershire Naturalists' Soc.*

J13   *Rev. Hort.*

J14 *Rep. & Trans. Devonshire Assoc. Advancem. Sci.*
J15 *Naturalist (Hull)*
J16 *Welsh Bull. Bot. Soc. Brit. Isles*
J17 *Nat. Cambridgeshire*
J18 *Wild Fl. Mag.*
J19 *Proc. Somersetshire Archaeol. Nat. Hist. Soc.*
J20 *J. Proc. Linn. Soc., Bot.* continued as *J. Linn.Soc., Bot.* and *Bot. J. Linn. Soc.*
J21 *Contr. U.S. Natl. Herb.*
J22 *Darwiniana*
J23 *Watsonia*
J24 *Newslett. Surrey Fl. Committee*
J25 *Wildlife*
J26 *London Naturalist*
J27 *Nat. Wales*
J28 *Glasgow Naturalist*
J29 *Trans. Suffolk Naturalists' Soc.*
J30 *Proc. Dorset Nat. Hist. Antiq. Field Club* continued as *Proc. Dorset Nat. Hist. Archaeol. Soc.*
J31 *Dumortiera*
J32 *Rhodora*
J33 *Bull. Kent Field Club*
J34 *B.S.B.I. Scott. Newslett.*
J35 *Trans. London Nat. Hist. Soc.*
J36 *Ann. Scott. Nat. Hist.*
J37 *Proc. Swansea Sci. Field Naturalists' Soc.*
J38 *Proc. Linn. Soc. London*
J39 *J. Bot.*
J40 *Phytologist*
J41 *Trans. Kent Field Club*
J42 *J. Ecol.*
J43 *Wiltshire Archaeol. & Nat. Hist. Mag.*
J44 *Cytologia*
J45 *J. Jap. Bot.*
J46 *B.S.B.I. Abstr.*
J47 *Bull. Torrey Bot. Club*
J48 *Agric. Gaz. New South Wales*
J49 *Linzer Biol. Beitr.*
J50 *Trans. Edinburgh Field Naturalists' Soc.*
J51 *Göttinger Florist. Rundbr.* continued as *Florist. Rundbr.*
J52 *Taxon*
J53 *Feddes Repert.* preceded by *Feddes Repert. Spec. Nov. Regni Veg.* and *Repert Spec. Nov. Regni Veg.*
J54 *Ann. Roy. Bot. Gard. (Calcutta)*
J55 *Reading Naturalist*
J56 *Sida*

J57	*Acta Horti Gothob.*
J58	*Bull. Soc. Roy. Bot. Belgique*
J59	*Gorteria*
J60	*Candollea*
J61	*Bull. Soc. Bot. France*
J62	*Phytologia*
J63	*New Zealand J. Bot.*
J64	*Collect. Bot. (Barcelona)*
J65	*Bot. Not.*
J66	*Plantsman*
J67	*Bot. Mag.*
J67a	*Bot. Mag. (1995+)*
J68	*Bothalia*
J69	*Arch. Bot. (Forlì)*
J70	*Giorn. Bot. Ital.*
J71	*Webbia*
J72	*Revista Mus. La Plata, secc. Bot.*
J73	*Blumea*
J74	*Anales Inst. Bot. Cavanilles*
J75	*Boissiera*
J76	*Anales Jard. Bot. Madrid*
J77	*Rev. Bot. Appl. Agric. Trop.*
J78	*Monde Pl.*
J79	*Ned. Kruidk. Arch.*
J80	*Hooker's Icon. Pl.*
J81	*Symb. Bot. Upsal.*
J82	*Opera Lilloana*
J83	*Contr. Bolus Herb.*
J84	*J. Roy. Hort. Soc.*
J85	*Bol. Soc. Brot., sér.2*
J86	*Feddes Repert. Spec. Nov. Beih.*
J87	*Bot. Jahrb. Syst.*
J88	*Verh. Schweiz. Naturf. Ges.*
J89	*Madroño*
J90	*Mitt. Bot. Staatssamml. München*
J91	*Il Roso*
J92	*Iowa State J. Sci.*
J93	*J. Agric. Trop. Bot. Appl.*
J94	*Syst. Bot.*
J95	*New Plantsman*
J96	*Kulturpflanze*
J97	*Acta Bot. Neerl.*
J98	*Bamboo Soc. (E.B.S. Gr. Brit.) Newslett.*
J99	*Bot. Cornwall*
J100	*J. Bamboo Soc. Amer.*
J101	*Techn. Bull. U.S.D.A.*

J102 *Blyttia*
J103 *Nordic J. Bot.*
J104 *Brigham Young Univ. Sci. Bull., Biol. Ser.*
J105 *J. Bot. Amer.*
J106 *Kuntziana*
J107 *Bol. Soc. Argent. Bot.*
J108 *Mem. Soc. Brot.*
J109 *Anales Mus. Nac. Montevideo*
J110 *Garden (London 1975+)*
J111 *Preslia*
J112 *Mém. Acad. Sci. Turin, ser.2*
J113 *Revista Argent. Agron.*
J114 *Trudy Glavn. Bot. Sado (= Acta horte petropolitari)*
J115 *Bol. Mus. Nac. Hist. Nat.*
J116 *Bull.Jard. Bot. Belg.* preceded by *Bull. Jard. Bot. État*

R1   Lousley, J.E. (1961). A census list of wool aliens found in Britain, 1946-1960. *Bot. Soc. Brit. Isles Proc.*, **4**:221-247.
R2   Ryves, T.B. (1974). An interim list of the wool-alien grasses from Blackmoor, North Hants, 1969-1972. *Watsonia*, **10**:35-48.
R3   Ryves, T.B. (1988). Supplementary list of wool-alien grasses recorded from Blackmoor, North Hants., 1959-1976. *Watsonia*, **17**:73-79.
R4   Hayward, I.M. & Druce, G.C. (1919). *The adventive flora of Tweedside*. Arbroath.
R5   Webster, M.McCallum. [Card index of alien plant herbarium specimens, coll. MMcCW, 1954-1966, in possession of E.J.Clement.]
R6   Personal communication, Prof C.A.Stace.
R7   Personal communication, D.H.Kent.
R8   Dunn, S.T. (1905). *Alien flora of Britain*. London.
R9   Personal communication, Dr H.J.M.Bowen.
R10 Personal communication, L.J.Margetts.
R11 McClintock, D. (1987). *Supplement to The wild flowers of Guernsey (Collins, 1975)*. St Peter Port.
R12 Crackles, F.E. (1990). *Flora of the East Riding of Yorkshire*. Hull.
R13 Probst, R. (1949). *Wolladventivflora Mitteleuropas*. Solothurn.
R14 Welch, D. (1993). *Flora of North Aberdeenshire*. Privately published. Banchory.
R15 Pankhurst, R.J. & Mullin, J.M. (1991). *Flora of the Outer Hebrides*. London.
R16 Tarpey, T. & Heath, J. (1990). *Wild flowers of north east Essex*. Colchester.

R17   Stewart, O. (1990). *Flowering plants and ferns of Kirkudbrightshire*.
      Dumfries. (Reprinted from *Trans. Dumfriesshire Galloway Nat. Hist.
      Antiq. Soc.*, 3rd ser., **65**.)

R18   Personal communication, Dr T.G.F.Curtis (BSBI Exhib. Meeting
      Nov.1992).

R19   Personal communication, R.M.Payne.

R20   Kent, D.H. & Lousley, J.E. (1956-57). A hand list of the plants of the
      London area. Parts 6-7. Suppls to *London Naturalist*, **35-36.**

R21   Hanson, C.G. & Mason, J.L. (1985). Bird seed aliens in Britain.
      Watsonia, **15**:237-252.

R22   Bonnard, B. (1988). *A new check list of the flowering plants, trees,
      and ferns wild on Alderney, and its off-islets*. Privately published.
      Le Petit Val, Alderney.

R23   Ellis, R.G. (1983). *Flowering plants of Wales*. Cardiff.

R24   Jermyn, S.T. (1975[1974]). *Flora of Essex*. Fingringhoe.

R25   Dony, J.G. & Dony, C.M. (1991). *The wild flowers of Luton*. Luton.

R26   Dickson, J.H. (1991). *Wild plants of Glasgow*. Aberdeen.

R27   Lousley, J.E. (1976). *Flora of Surrey*. Newton Abbot.

R28   Good, R. (1984). *A concise flora of Dorset*. Dorchester.

R29   White, J.W. (1912). *The flora of Bristol*. Bristol.

R30   Rayner, J.F. (1925). A list of the alien plants of Hampshire and the Isle
      of Wight. *Proc. Isle of Wight Nat. Hist. Soc.*, **1**:229-274.

R31   Mill, R.R. (1967). *Flora of Helensburgh and district*. Helensburgh.

R32   Scannell, M.J.P. & Synnott, D.M. (1972). *Census catalogue of the flora
      of Ireland*. Dublin.

R33   Personal communication, A.O.Chater.

R34   Ryves, T.B. (1980). Alien species of *Eragrostis* P.Beauv. in the British
      Isles. *Watsonia*, **13**:111-117.

R35   French, C.N., ed. (1994). *Checklist of the flowering plants and ferns of
      Cornwall and the Isles of Scilly*. Institute of Cornish Studies, Redruth.

R36   Druce, G.C. (1928). *British plant list*. Arbroath.

R37   Personal communication, R.C.Palmer.

R38   Philp, E.G. (1982). *Atlas of the Kent flora*. The Kent Field Club.
      Maidstone.

R39   Bowen, H.J.M. (1968). *The flora of Berkshire*. Oxford.

R40   McClintock, D. (1975). *The wild flowers of Guernsey*. London.

R41   Personal communication, J.R.Palmer.

R42   Le Sueur, F. (1984). *Flora of Jersey*. Jersey.

R43   Lousley, J.E. (1971). *Flora of the Isles of Scilly*. Newton Abbot.

R44   Leslie, A.C. (1987). *Flora of Surrey: supplement and checklist*. Privately
      published. Guildford.

R45   Burton, R.M. (1983). *Flora of the London area*. London Natural History
      Society. London.

R46   Livermore, L.A. & P.D. (1987). *The flowering plants and ferns of North
      Lancashire*. Lancaster.

R47   Dony, J.G. (1969). Additional notes on the flora of Bedfordshire. *Bot. Soc. Brit. Isles Proc.*, 7:523-535.

R48   Dony, J.G. (1986). Further notes on the flora of Bedfordshire. *Watsonia*, 16:163-172.

R49   Gibbons, E.J. (1975). *The flora of Lincolnshire*. Lincoln.

R50   Webster, M.McCallum (1978). *Flora of Moray, Nairn and East Inverness*. Aberdeen.

R51   Corner, R.W.M. (1985). *Flowering plants and ferns of Selkirkshire and Roxburghshire*. Lancaster.

R52   Margetts, L.J. & David, R.W. (1981). *A review of the Cornish flora 1980*. Redruth.

R53   Scott, S. & Palmer, R. (1987). *The flowering plants and ferns of the Shetland Islands*. Lerwick.

R54   Dony, J.G. (1953). *Flora of Bedfordshire*. Luton.

R55   Kent, D.H. (1975). *The historical flora of Middlesex*. London.

R56   Cadbury, D.A., Hawkes, J.G. & Readett, R.C. (1971). *A computer-mapped flora. A study of the county of Warwickshire*. Birmingham.

R57   Dony, J.G. (1967). *Flora of Hertfordshire*. Hitchin.

R58   Petch, C.P. & Swann, E.L. (1968). *Flora of Norfolk*. Norwich.

R59   Swann, E.L. (1975). *Supplement to the Flora of Norfolk*. Norwich.

R60   Graham, G.G., Sayers, C.D. & Gaman, J.H. (1972). *A checklist of the vascular plants of County Durham*. Durham.

R61   Holland, S.C. *et al.* (1986). *Supplement to the Flora of Gloucestershire*. Bristol.

R62   Riddelsdell, H.J., ed. (1948). *Flora of Gloucestershire*. Cheltenham.

R63   Hall, P.C. (1980). *Sussex plant atlas*. Brighton.

R64   Martin, W.Keble & Fraser, G.T., eds. (1939). *Flora of Devon*. Arbroath.

R65   Hanson, C.G. [Checklist of alien grasses, unpublished manuscript (1994) in the possession of T.B.Ryves.

R66   Savidge, J.P. *et al.* (1963). *Travis's flora of South Lancashire*. Liverpool.

R67   Briggs, M. (1990). *Sussex plant atlas: selected supplement*. Brighton.

R68   Simpson, F.W. (1982). *Simpson's flora of Suffolk*. Ipswich.

R69   Good, R. (1948). *A geographical handbook of the Dorset flora*. Dorchester.

R70   Kenworthy, J.B., ed. (1976). *John Anthony's Flora of Sutherland*. Edinburgh.

R71   Perring, F.H., *et al.* (1964). *A flora of Cambridgeshire*. Cambridge.

R72   Edees, E.S. (1972). *Flora of Staffordshire*. Newton Abbot.

R73   Clapham, A.R., ed. (1969). *Flora of Derbyshire*. Derby.

R74   Jermy, A.C. & Crabbe, J.A., eds. (1978). *The island of Mull: a survey of its flora and environment*. London.

R75   An extract from the *Shetland Times*, 1/3/1963.

R76   Messenger, G. (1971). *Flora of Rutland*. Leicester.

R77   Newton, A. (1971). *Flora of Cheshire*. Chester.

R78   Wade, A.E. (1970). *The flora of Monmouthshire*. Cardiff.

R79   Thurston, E. & Vigurs, C.C. (1922). *A supplement to F.Hamilton Davey's Flora of Cornwall*. Truro.

R80   Herbarium specimen annotated by J.E.Lousley.

R81   Whitehead, L.E. (1976). *Plants of Herefordshire*. Hereford.

R82   Leslie, A.C. (1971). A contribution to the alien flora of the Sherborne area. *Proc. Dorset Nat. Hist. Archaeol. Soc.*, **92**:45-47.

R83   Personal communication, G.M.S.Easy.

R84   Grose, [J.]D. (1957). *The flora of Wiltshire*. Devizes.

R85   Stearn, L.F. (1975). *Supplement to The flora of Wiltshire*. Devizes.

R86   Yorkshire Naturalists' Union card index of alien and casual plants (supplied by Dr E.Chicken, 1995).

R87   Frazer, O.H., ed. (1978). *Flora of the Isle of Wight*. Newport.

R88   Roe, R.G.B. (1981). *The flora of Somerset*. Taunton.

R89   Webb, D.A. (1959). *An Irish flora*, 2nd ed. Dundalk.

R90   Personal communication, R.M.Burton.

R91   Hollick, K.M. & Patrick, S.J. (1980). *Supplement to the Flora of Derbyshire 1969: additional records received 1974-1979*. Derby.

R92   Wolley-Dod, A.H. (1937). *Flora of Sussex*. Hastings.

R93   Nelson, G.A., comp. (1965). *Addendum II (1964-1965) to A flora of Leeds and district*. Duplicated manuscript. Leeds.

R94   Personal communication, Dr J.L.Mason.

R95   Primavesi, A.L. & Evans, P.A. (1988). *Flora of Leicestershire*. Leicester.

R96   Salmon, C.E. (1931). *Flora of Surrey*. London.

R97   Hudson, W. (1762). *Flora Anglica*, ed.1. London.

R98   Sibthorp, J. (1794). *Flora Oxoniensis*. Oxford.

R99   Rayner, R.W. (1975). *The natural history of Pagham Harbour*, part 3. Bognor Regis.

R100 Ballantyne, G.H. (1971). Ballast aliens in south Fife, 1820-1919. *Trans. & Proc. Bot. Soc. Edinburgh*, **41**:125-137.

R101 Ingram, R. & Noltie, H.J. (1981). *The flora of Angus (Forfar, v.c. 90)*. Dundee.

R102 Gilbert, J.L. (1965). *Flora of Huntingdonshire: wildflowers*. Peterborough.

R103 Personal communication, J.Martin.

R104 Ivimey-Cook, R.B. (1984). *Atlas of the Devon flora*. Exeter.

R105 Dony, J.G. (1976). *Bedfordshire plant atlas*. Luton.

R106 Brewer, J.A. (1863). *Flora of Surrey*. London.

R107 Watson, H.C. (1868-1870). *A compendium of the Cybele Britannica*, parts 1-3. London.

R108 Mundell, A.R.G. (1991). *Royal Aerospace Establishment conservation group working paper CG 01/91*. Internal report. Farnborough, Hants.

R109 Halliday, G. (1978). *Flowering plants and ferns of Cumbria*. Lancaster.

R110 J.E.Lousley manuscript notes, 1961-1975, in possession of E.J.Clement.

R111 Howitt, R.C.L. & Howitt, B.M. (1963). *A flora of Nottinghamshire*. Newark.

R112 Personal communication, Dr G.Hutchinson.

R113 Personal communication, Mrs S.Reynolds.

R114 Personal communication, W.R.Ingram.
R115 Personal communication, Dr C.M.A.Stapleton.
R116 Personal communication, Dr T.A.Cope.
R117 Personal communication, D.McClintock.
R118 Personal communication, †Mrs C.M.Dony.
R119 Personal communication, Dr R.W.M.Corner.
R120 Personal communication, J.M.Mullin.
R121 Personal communication, B.Wurzell.
R122 Scannell, M.J.P. & Synnott, D.M. (1987). *Census catalogue of the flora of Ireland*, 2nd ed. Stationery Office, Dublin.
R123 Hackney, P. (1992). *Stewart & Corry's flora of the north-east of Ireland*, 3rd ed. Institute of Irish Studies. The Queen's University of Belfast.
R124 Webb, D.A. & Scannell, M.J.P. (1983). *Flora of Connemara and the Burren*. Royal Dublin Society and the Cambridge University Press.
R125 Personal communication, †J.E.Dandy.
R126 Druce, G.C. (1932). *The comital flora of the British Isles*. Arbroath.

S1 Clement, E.J. & Foster, M.C. (1994). *Alien plants of the British Isles*. Botanical Society of the British Isles. London.
S2 Brummitt, R.K. & Powell, C.E., eds. (1992). *Authors of plant names*. Royal Botanic Gardens, Kew.
S3 Lawrence, G.H.M. *et al.*, eds. (1968). *B-P-H Botanico-periodicum-Huntianum*. Pittsburgh.
S4 Bridson, G.D.R. & Smith, E.R., eds. (1991). *B-P-H/S Botanico-Periodicum- Huntianum / Supplementum*. Pittsburgh.
S5 Dandy, J.E. (1969). *Watsonian vice-counties of Great Britain*. Ray Society publication No.146. London.
S6 Scannell, M.J.P. & Synnott, D.M. (1972). *Census catalogue of the flora of Ireland*. Dublin.
S7 Clayton, W.D. & Renvoize, S.A. (1986). *Genera Graminum*. Kew Bulletin additional series No. 13. London.
S8 Kent, D.H. & Allen, D.E. (1984). *British and Irish herbaria*. Botanical Society of the British Isles. London.
S9 Greuter, W., *et al.* (1994). International code of botanical nomenclature (Tokyo code). *Regnum Veg.*, **131**.
S10 Watson, L. & Dallwitz, M.J. (1992). *The grass genera of the world*. CAB International, Wallingford.
S11 Linnaeus, C. (1753). *Species plantarum*. Stockholm.
S12 Chase, A. & Niles, C.D. (1962). *Index to grass species*, **1-3**. Boston, Massachusetts.

INDEX

Compiled by R. Gwynn Ellis
Department of Botany, National Museums and Galleries of
Wales

BSBI PUBLICATIONS

HANDBOOKS

Each handbook deals in depth with one or more difficult groups of British and Irish plants.

No. 1 *SEDGES OF THE BRITISH ISLES*
A.C. Jermy, A.O. Chater and R.W. David. 1982. 268 pages, with a line drawing and distribution map for every species. Paperback. ISBN 0 901158 05 4.

No. 2 *UMBELLIFERS OF THE BRITISH ISLES*
T.G. Tutin. 1980. 197 pages, with a line drawing for each species. Paperback. ISBN 0 901158 02 X. Out of print: new edition in preparation.

No. 3 *DOCKS AND KNOTWEEDS OF THE BRITISH ISLES*
J.E. Lousley and D.H. Kent. 1981. 205 pages, with many line drawings of native and alien taxa. Paperback. ISBN 0 901158 04 6. Out of print: new edition in preparation.

No. 4 *WILLOWS AND POPLARS OF GREAT BRITAIN AND IRELAND*
R.D. Meikle. 1984. 198 pages, with 63 line drawings of all species, subspecies, varieties and hybrids. Paperback. ISBN 0 901158 07 0.

No. 5 *CHAROPHYTES OF GREAT BRITAIN AND IRELAND*
J.A. Moore. 1986. 144 pages with line drawings of 39 species and 17 distribution maps. Paperback. ISBN 0 901158 16 X.

No. 6 *CRUCIFERS OF GREAT BRITAIN AND IRELAND*
T.C.G. Rich. 1991. 336 pages with descriptions of 140 taxa, most illustrated with line drawings and 60 with distribution maps. Paperback. ISBN 0 901158 20 8.

No. 7 *ROSES OF GREAT BRITAIN AND IRELAND*
G.G. Graham and A.L. Primavesi. 1993. 208 pages with descriptions and illustrations of 12 native and eight introduced species, and descriptions of 83 hybrids. Distribution maps are included of 31 selected species and hybrids. Paperback. ISBN 0 901158 22 4.

No. 8 *PONDWEEDS OF GREAT BRITAIN AND IRELAND*
C.D. Preston. 1995. 352 pages. 50 full page illustrations and distribution maps. Paperback. ISBN 0 901158 24 0.

OTHER PUBLICATIONS

LIST OF VASCULAR PLANTS OF THE BRITISH ISLES
D.H. Kent, 1992. 400 pages. Nomenclature and sequence followed by Stace in *New Flora of the British Isles*. Paperback. ISBN 0 901158 21 6.

ATLAS OF THE BRITISH FLORA
F.H. Perring and S.M. Walters, 1990. Reprint of 3rd Edn, 1982. 468 pages. Distribution maps of over 1700 species including updated maps for 321 Red Data Book species. New bibliography of updated distribution maps published elsewhere since 1st Edn, 1962. Paperback. ISBN 0 901158 19 4.

ALIEN PLANTS OF THE BRITISH ISLES
E.J. Clement and M.C. Foster, 1994. xviii + 590 pages. A provisional catalogue of vascular plants (excluding grasses). Paperback. ISBN 0 901158 23 2.

Available from the official agents for BSBI publications:

F.& M. Perring, Green Acre, Wood Lane, Oundle, Peterborough, England PE8 4JQ
Tel.: 01832 273388 Fax: 01832 274568